Interstellar Matter in Galaxies

BENJAMIN BOOKS IN THE
PLANETARY AND EARTH SCIENCES

Alastair G. W. Cameron, Consulting Editor

L. Woltjer (*editor*): INTERSTELLAR MATTER IN GALAXIES—
Proceedings of a conference held at the Institute for Advanced Study,
Princeton, N.J.

H. Y. Chiu and W. F. Hoffmann (*editors*): GRAVITATION AND
RELATIVITY—A volume of lecture notes by J. L. Anderson,
R. H. Dicke, V. W. Hughes, J. Weber, and J. A. Wheeler

A. G. W. Cameron (*editor*): INTERSTELLAR COMMUNICATION
—A collection of reprints and original contributions

The Distribution and Motion of Interstellar Matter in Galaxies

Proceedings of a conference held at
The Institute for Advanced Study
Princeton, New Jersey
April 10 to 20, 1961

Edited by

L. WOLTJER
University of Leiden
The Netherlands

W. A. Benjamin, Inc.   New York   1962

**The Distribution and Motion
of Interstellar Matter in Galaxies**

Library of Congress Catalog Card Number: 62-19891
Manufactured in the United States of America

*The publication of these proceedings was assisted by an Air Force grant,
AF-AFOSR 62-150.*

*The last chapter of manuscript was received on July 19, 1962; this volume
was published on December 20, 1962.*

*The publisher is pleased to acknowledge the assistance of William Prokos,
who designed the cover and the dust jacket.*

W. A. Benjamin, Inc.
2465 Broadway, New York 25, New York

Foreword

In the spring of 1960 I suggested to the Director of the Institute for Advanced Study, Dr. Robert Oppenheimer, and my physicist colleagues at the Institute that a conference on problems of the distribution and motion of interstellar matter in galaxies be held at the Institute for Advanced Study the following year.

The problems in question were at the time under intensive study by a number of astronomers and astrophysicists. New clues, important to the solution of the problem of galactic spiral arms, had been found by J. H. Oort and his collaborators, and this development had already prompted theoretical studies of questions of the large-scale circulation pattern of our galaxy. Extensive observational programs of investigation of interstellar matter, both radioastronomical and optical, were under way in many observatories, and new astrophysically important results regarding cosmic radiation were being obtained. A number of theoretical questions of the dynamics and in particular the magnetohydrodynamics of interstellar matter were pursued. Extensive studies of interstellar matter in other galaxies were also being carried out and had already thrown important light on the problems of evolution of galaxies and questions of their classification.

J. H. Oort, D. Osterbrock, Otto Struve, and L. Woltjer were to be at the Institute for Advanced Study in the spring of 1961. It therefore seemed advantageous to hold the conference at that time. I was happy to receive strong encouragement from Dr. Robert Oppenheimer and my colleagues in physics. The response of a number of astronomers whose advice I sought was also very encouraging, in particular Dr. Lyman Spitzer and Dr. Martin Schwarzschild of the Princeton University Observatory. Financial support of the planned conference was obtained from the Air Force Office of Scientific Research.

The conference was held at the Institute for Advanced Study, April 10 to 20, 1961. Dr. J. H. Oort acted as Chairman of the conference, and Dr. L. Woltjer as Secretary.

During the conference the participants discussed the suggestion that the papers and an extensive summary of the discussions be published in the form of a conference volume. It was agreed that the papers should be published about as presented at the conference rather than in elaborated form, and that it would be of value to include in the conference volume all essential parts of the discussions.

Dr. L. Woltjer agreed to assume the task of editing the conference volume. Additional financial support toward the expenses of preparing the manuscript for the volume was given in the form of a grant by the Air Force Office of Scientific Research. I am very grateful to Mr. Dwight Wennersten and Dr. Gordon Wares of the Air Force Office of Scientific Research for their continued interest in the conference and the present volume.

BENGT STRÖMGREN

Princeton, New Jersey
May 1962

Preface

The papers in this volume were presented at a conference on "Problems of the Distribution and Motion of Interstellar Matter in Galaxies," which took place from April 10 to 20, 1961, at the Institute for Advanced Study, Princeton, New Jersey. The discussions at this conference were recorded stenographically. As given here they have been much abbreviated.

Recently a new system of galactic coordinates has been adopted by the International Astronomical Union. Since this new system presents considerable advantages over the old one, I felt it desirable to use it exclusively. However, in some papers all figures had been drawn on the old system and it was therefore impossible to follow a completely consequent policy. Thus in the papers by Dr. Helfer and Dr. Blaauw coordinates on the old system are used (l^I, b^I), but the coordinates on the new system are also given (l^{II}, b^{II}). In all other papers and in the discussions longitudes and latitudes are on the new system and the superscript II has been dropped.

I am indebted to the University of Chicago Press for permission to reproduce the figure on page 147 from *The Astrophysical Journal*.

I wish to acknowledge a very pleasant collaboration with the publisher in the preparation of this volume.

L. WOLTJER

Leiden, The Netherlands
May 1962

Participants

L. Biermann
Max-Planck-Institut für Physik und Astrophysik, Munich

A. Blaauw
Kapteyn Laboratory, University of Groningen

E. M. Burbidge
University of Chicago: *presently at* University of California at San Diego, La Jolla, Calif.

G. R. Burbidge
University of Chicago: *presently at* University of California at San Diego, La Jolla, Calif.

R. F. Christy
Institute for Advanced Study: *presently at* California Institute of Technology

Freeman J. Dyson
Institute for Advanced Study

G. B. Field
Princeton University Observatory

H. L. Helfer
University of Rochester

S. von Hoerner
Astronomisches Rechen-Institut, Heidelberg

F. D. Kahn
National Radio Astronomical Observatory, Green Bank, West Virginia: *on leave from* University of Manchester

G. Lemaître
Louvain

C. C. Lin
Massachusetts Institute of Technology

P. O. Lindblad
Stockholm Observatory

R. Lüst
Max-Planck-Institut für Physik und Astrophysik, Munich

J. H. Oort
University Observatory, Leiden

R. Oppenheimer
Institute for Advanced Study

D. E. Osterbrock
Institute for Advanced Study: *on leave from* Washburn Observatory,
University of Wisconsin

S. R. Pottasch
Institute for Advanced Study and Princeton University: *presently at*
Indiana University

K. H. Prendergast
Yerkes Observatory, University of Chicago: *presently at* Institute for Space
Studies, New York

M. Schwarzschild
Princeton University Observatory

L. Spitzer
Princeton University Observatory

B. Strömgren
Institute for Advanced Study

O. Struve
National Radio Astronomical Observatory, Green Bank, West Virginia

A. Underhill
Dominion Astrophysical Observatory, Victoria

G. Wares
Air Force Office of Scientific Research

D. Wennensten
Air Force Office of Scientific Research

L. Woltjer
Institute for Advanced Study: *presently at* University Observatory, Leiden

Contents

Contents

Characteristics of interstellar matter in our galaxy

Radio data on the distribution and motion of interstellar gas

J. H. Oort

In this paper I shall try to indicate some of the salient points in what is known about the large-scale distribution and motion of the gas. In this I shall concern myself principally with the results of 21-cm measures. These have given us an over-all picture which was quite impossible by optical means, owing to the strong absorption of light in the galactic layer.

Concentration of Gas to a Disk

The most striking feature is the strong concentration of the gas to a thin layer. The extreme thinness of the layer may be indicated by a few numbers.

From observations of interstellar lines and from color excesses van Rhijn has derived a value of 170 pc for the distance between layers where the average density has fallen to half that near the plane. This value would apply to a region with a radius of about 1 kpc around the sun, which is at about $R = 8$ kpc from the center of the galactic system.

For larger distances from the center the layer becomes somewhat more irregular; no good figures for its thickness are available.* For R between 3.2 and 6.5 kpc Schmidt found the thickness between half-density layers to be 220 pc, with little or no variation over this entire region. In the so-called "3-kpc arm," at about $R = 3$ kpc, it has decreased to roughly 110 pc, whereas within 0.5 kpc from the nucleus it is 80 pc. These thicknesses are of the order of 1 per cent or less of the extent of the layer in the galactic plane.

*Rough estimates by van Woerden indicate that for R between 9 and 13 kpc the layer becomes about twice as thick as in the regions within 8 kpc from the center.

J. H. Oort

 The constancy of the thickness between $R = 3$ and 9 kpc is remarkable in view of the considerable variation of the total mass density over this range. It indicates that between $R = 8$ and 4 kpc the average random motion in the direction perpendicular to the galactic plane (which in the

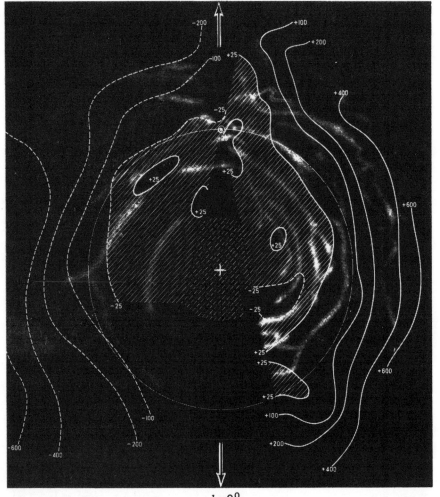

Fig. 1. Deviations of the hydrogen layer from the average galactic plane. The contour levels are in parsecs. In the hatched part the layer deviates less than 25 pc from the average plane. The position of the galactic center is indicated by +, that of the sun by ⊙.

following will be denoted as the direction of z) may vary from about 5 to 13 km/sec. But there is still considerable uncertainty in this. In the nuclear disk within 500 pc of the center, the dispersion in the Z velocities is likely to be considerably larger, possibly as much as 50 km/sec.

The second remarkable point about the layer is its flatness. Within $R = 8$ kpc the average z of the individual regions never deviates more than 75 pc from the mean plane. For R less than 6 kpc these deviations are even less than 30 pc.

In the outer parts the deviations become much greater and they become at the same time systematic. In galactocentric longitude $L = 90°$ (counted from the direction of the center to the sun as zero point) the deviations decrease systematically in the direction of negative z from about -100 pc at $R = 9$ kpc to -600 pc at $R = 14$ kpc, going up to still higher negative values for still larger R. At $L = 270°$ we see the opposite phenomenon, with an average deviation of $+600$ pc at $R = 12.5$ kpc. The phenomenon is illustrated in Fig. 1.

Rotation

The disk of gas is rotating. The angular velocity of rotation increases toward the center. In the part of the disk that is inside the sun's distance from the center (to be denoted by R_0) the velocity of rotation can be determined from observations of the profiles of the 21-cm line. Knowledge of the way in which the angular velocity of rotation varies with R is important for two purposes: (1) for the determination of the average distance at which hydrogen atoms with a given velocity are situated, and (2) for the determination of the gravitational field in the galactic system. Suppose one observes from the sun S in a direction SA making an angle l with the direction to the center C (Fig. 2). If one assumes that in a first approximation the gas is moving in circular paths, the maximum radial velocity observed in the longitude l will be equal to $\Theta_c(R_{min}) - \Theta_0 \sin l$, where $R_{min} = CA$ is the minimum distance from the center, Θ_c is the circular velocity of the gas, and Θ_0 is the circular velocity of the gas near the sun. If Θ_0 and R_0 are known, we can in this same way derive $\omega(R_{min}) - \omega_0$, ω being the angular velocity, while ω_0 refers to the region surrounding the sun.

There are three difficulties: (1) We do not generally hit a spiral arm at the point A of minimum distance to the center. (2) The maximum radial velocity corresponding to the rotational motion is ill-defined, owing to the superimposed random motions of gas clouds. (3) There may be systematic deviations from circular motion, both near the sun and near A.

It is easily possible that the rotation curve which has been adopted for the reduction of the observations made in the Netherlands may have errors of the order of 5 km/sec. This rotation curve is shown in Fig. 3. The inner portion, for $R < 3$ kpc, will be discussed below. For the region between $R = 6$ and 10 kpc, the curve has been partly based on optical velocities (radial as well as transverse) of objects like supergiants and clusters, for which approximate distances are known, while use has also been made of interstellar absorption lines. For distances from the center exceeding 9 or 10 kpc the curve has been derived from a model of the distribution of mass within the galactic system. The model was based on the mass derived from the rotational velocities for $R < 8$ kpc as well as on direct data on stellar densities and on the mass density near the sun as found from motions and density distribution in a direction perpendicular to the galactic plane.

Although systematic *deviations from circular motion* are not so serious for the determination of Θ_c (except for $R_c < 3$), they can be quite serious for the determination of the arrangement of the matter in space. It is therefore important to have some idea of what amount of deviation occurs. Dr. Lindblad will discuss this in more detail. I only wish to point to some evident deviations from circular motions which can be seen in line profiles at $l = 87°3$ and $89°8$ and latitudes between $0°$ and $-5°$ (Fig. 4). In these longitudes the systematic motions should all be negative if we are dealing with pure rotation. Actually, the maximum on the right-hand side lies at about $+6$ or $+7$ km/sec.

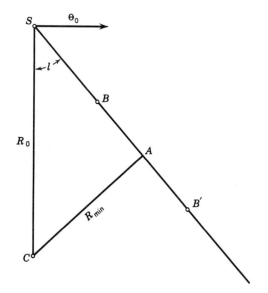

Fig. 2

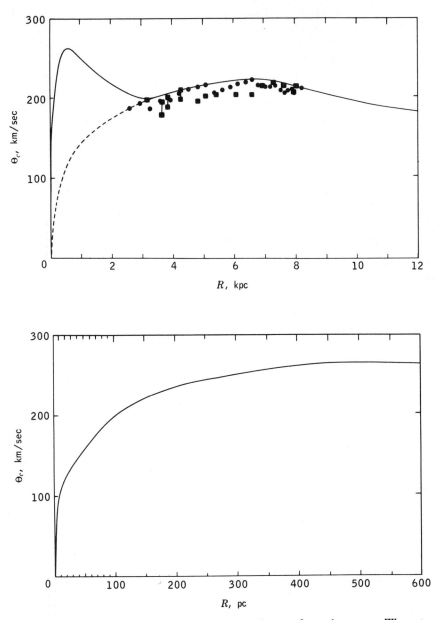

Fig. 3. Variation of circular velocity with distance from the center. The rotation near the center is shown in the lower half on a larger scale. The observed velocities for $R > 3$ kpc are plotted as dots (Leiden) and squares (Sydney). The dashed curve gives the rotation as originally inferred by Kwee, Muller, and Westerhout.

We find deviations of the same order in the anticenter region, where the line profiles indicate systematic motions in radial direction increasing by about 3 km/sec per kpc. The motions are such that the gas at larger R is moving toward the gas in the region directly surrounding the sun.

The evidence we have, although indicating that there are deviations from circular motions, shows on the whole that for $R > 3$ kpc such deviations do not exceed 10 km/sec as an order of size and are therefore not very serious. A special investigation is being made in Leiden in directions near that of the center, in order to fix an upper limit for possible systematic motions in radial direction. The material is not yet complete, but the evidence obtained indicates that systematic radial motions, if present, are probably smaller than 15 km/sec.

Circumstances change radically, however, when we come to values of R of about one-third of R_0. Within this radius, deviations become of the same size as the rotational velocities themselves. I shall discuss this below; now I only want to point to the fact that regular rotation comes back again in the *nuclear* part.

Here we find what looks like a ring of neutral gas with fairly sharp boundaries at 500 and 590 pc and a density of roughly 1 hydrogen atom/cm^3, rotating with a velocity of about 265 km/sec. In addition there is a disk extending from the center to about 300 pc, with gradually decreasing density (at $R = 100$ pc it is approximately 3 atoms/cm^3) and rotational velocities ranging from about 180 km/sec at $R = 70$ pc to about 220 at

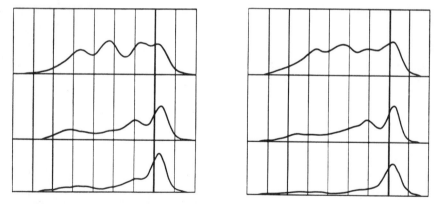

Fig. 4. Some line profiles showing systematic deviation from circular motion. Abscissae are velocities relative to the local standard of rest. The vertical lines are at intervals of 20 km/sec, the heavy line corresponds to zero velocity, positive velocities are to the right. Ordinates are intensities of the hydrogen radiation. The profiles on the left are for galactic longitude $l = 87°3$, those on the right for $l = 89°8$; the latitudes on the new system are $+0°5$ for the upper curves, $-2°0$ for those in the central row, and $-4°5$ for the bottom profiles.

$R = 260$ pc. As has been discovered by Drake, there are within this disk, and particularly very close to its center, some dense regions where the gas has become ionized. There is no evidence of expansion in this ring and disk, so that we believe that in this region we measure again circular velocities. The observational evidence will be given below.

We thus get the rotation curve shown in Fig. 3. Actually, only the parts within $R = 0.6$ kpc and beyond $R = 3$ kpc are known from direct observation. The other parts have been drawn in on the assumption that the structure of the inner parts of the galactic system is analogous to that of the Andromeda nebula* and that the mass-to-light ratio, M/L, is constant in the Andromeda nebula. With this latter assumption we find that the run of Θ_c with R in the Andromeda nebula is remarkably similar to that observed in the gas in the galactic system between $R = 70$ and 600 pc and beyond 3000 pc, except that a factor of 0.79 had to be applied to the M 31 results for the inner parts; the factor decreases slightly when going to 3 kpc. It should be noted that the rotational velocity rises extremely rapidly when going out from the center, reaching 100 km/sec within 10 pc of the center and 200 km/sec at $R = 100$ pc.

There is good reason to believe that the rotations as shown in the full-drawn curve will practically represent the circular motion of the gas except for the interval 0.6 to 3 kpc. It appears likely that, again excepting the region from 0.6 to 3 kpc, hydromagnetic pressures will generally be at least one order smaller than the gravitational force, and that therefore the curve can also give a reasonable approximation of the gravitational force of the galactic system in the plane of the disk.

However, in the region from 0.6 to 3 kpc the magnetic effects are apparently very important. It may be, in fact, that the rotation of the gas in this part has more resemblance to the rotation of a solid body than to that shown by the rotation curve in Fig. 3.

If we assume that the full-drawn curve represents the gravitational field, and if we assume a reasonable value for the axial ratio of the surfaces of equal density (based, for instance, on analogy with population II distribution in other galaxies) we can derive mass densities in the galactic plane. Table 1 summarizes some of the pertinent data derived from this curve. They are compared with results at 3 and 8.2 kpc derived from other data. The mass density is seen to rise to 1000 times that near the sun around $R = 90$ pc. At $R = 10$ pc it runs up to roughly 24,000 times this density. The density is almost entirely due to stars: Within 500 pc of the center

---

* This is not altogether unreasonable. From RR Lyrae variables we get the impression that the concentration of population II toward the center of the galactic system is of the same order as the concentration observed in M 31. Moreover, the population II bulges of all spirals of a class similar to M 31 or to the galactic system show the same type of concentration to the center.

the interstellar hydrogen contributes only about 1/400 to the total mass. The periods of revolution at the various distances considered are shown in the last column of Table 1.

Table 1
Total Mass within R, Densities, and Periods of Revolution for Various Values of R

R, pcs	Mass within R, 10^9 suns	Density			T, 10^6 years
		Stars, 10^{-23} g/cm³	Gas		
			atoms/cm³	10^{-23} g/cm³	
10	0.03	24,000	1,000:	100:	0.5
20	0.07	7,800	100:	10:	1.0
100	0.92	710	3	0.5	3.1
500	8.3	42	1	0.2	12
3,000	16	6.9	0.4	0.1	96
8,200	60	1.0	1	0.2	230

The data on the gas densities near the center are quite uncertain. They are based on the observed thermal radiation. The actual average density depends on how strongly the gas is concentrated into local H II regions. There can be no doubt, however, that the gas density is very much lower than that of the stars. Within $R = 100$ pc the gas density may be of the order of 1/1000 of the density due to stars. The ratio appears to rise to about 1/100 near $R = 1$ kpc. Near the sun it is about 1/5.

From these data we can also obtain an impression about the force K_z in the z direction, and in particular of the value of $\partial K_z / \partial z$ for $z = 0$. Near the sun this derivative is 8.6×10^{-30} sec⁻². At $R = 500$ pc we find 290×10^{-30} sec⁻², or 34 times the value near the sun. To maintain the observed thickness of the layer dynamically against gravitation, the average random motion in the z direction at $R = 500$ pc should be about 15 km/sec; at $R = 100$ pc this might become as high as 50 km/sec. In reality the phenomena may be complicated by hydromagnetic effects.

Distribution in the Disk for $R > 3$ kpc

If the rotation curve and the distance R_0 of the sun from the center are known, we can in principle derive the distribution of the gas in the disk. The gas at B in Fig. 2 will have a radial motion given by

$$R_0[\omega(R) - \omega_0] \sin l$$

If the gas is moving in circular orbits, it can therefore be placed by means of the observed velocity, except for an ambiguity arising from the fact that the gas at a point B', where $B'A = BA$, has the same velocity. These two locations can only be distinguished to a certain extent through a study of the latitude distribution of the gas.

A detailed study of 21-cm line profiles has given the picture shown in Fig. 5. The most striking feature is that the hydrogen is concentrated in long arms which can sometimes be followed more or less continuously over large galactocentric angles. The right-hand part and the upper left-hand corner of the picture are based on observations made in the Netherlands, the other part on observations made in Sydney. The latter were somewhat less detailed and were reduced in a slightly different way. This explains the difference in detail between the two parts. The reduction of

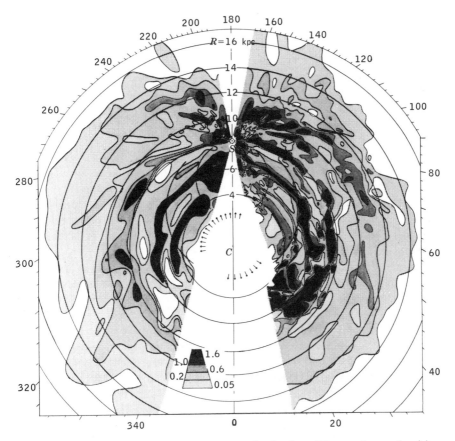

Fig. 5. Distribution of hydrogen in the galactic plane. The maximum densities in the z direction are projected on the galactic plane, and contours are drawn through the points. The density scale indicated is in atoms per cm³.

the Leiden results was made with the aid of the rotation curve shown in Fig. 3. If the Sydney observations for the southern sky are reduced with this same curve we get a rather improbable distribution, with blank spaces in the regions around the points where the lines of sight become tangent to circles around the galactic center, i.e., along a semicircle drawn on the line sun-center as diameter. This indicates that the rotation curve used was too high. The maximum velocities that would correspond to this curve are apparently never reached in the southern part. In the figure the southern observations were therefore reduced with a rotation curve that is about 10 km/sec lower than the one used for the northern part. A difference of about 5 per cent between the rotational velocities on the two sides does not seem too disturbing, if one considers the great irregularities present in all spiral systems of similar type.

An important difficulty in determining the exact shape of the "arms" along which the hydrogen is concentrated is that we do not know whether our supposition that the gas moves in circular orbits around the center is correct. It may be that there are systematic motions in radial direction superimposed on the rotational motions. As has been indicated above there are no signs of *large* radial motions (except for $R < 3$ kpc), but even radial motions of 10 km/sec, if they are systematic, would cause a considerable change in the shape of the "arms" as derived from the 21-cm line profiles.

In a recent investigation Kerr has, indeed, constructed a picture of the hydrogen distribution based on the hypothesis that in addition to rotation the gas has a general motion in radial direction away from the center. On his hypothesis this radial component would be 7 km/sec near the sun and increase as the inverse square of R, reaching a value of 55 km/sec at $R = 3$ kpc. The hypothesis was introduced principally to remove the apparent difference in the rotation curve for the two halves; there is no other direct observational evidence that supports it. In particular, observations of somewhat older stars show no clear evidence that the gas in the region around the sun would have a systematic outward motion.

Other types of systematic radial motions have been proposed by Bertil Lindblad and his co-workers. They pointed out that if in the beginning the gas had had motions deviating systematically from circular motions, the gas and connected stars would, in a coordinate system rotating with a suitably chosen angular velocity, describe elliptical orbits whose centers coincide with the galactic center. These motions would evidently have outward radial components in some parts and inward components in other parts of the galactic system that would rather radically affect the shape of the arms derived from the line profiles.

At the time it is impossible to check any of these hypotheses, and it seems best to accept as a first approximation the picture derived on the supposition of circular motions.

The picture shows a considerable empty sector in the longitudes around the center and a similar sector in the opposite direction. The differential rotations are too small in these directions to resolve the line profiles into distributions in distance. Mainly because of these unexplorable sectors it is still impossible to connect the arms between the two halves of the picture. The blank region within 3.5 kpc of the center will be discussed in detail in the following section.

The full-drawn curve in Fig. 6 shows the way in which the total number of hydrogen atoms in a column of unit cross section perpendicular to the galactic plane varies with the distance from the center. Ordinates give average values of N_H, defined as $\int_{-\infty}^{+\infty} n_H \, dz$, where n_H is the number of hydrogen atoms per cubic centimeter and z is measured in kpc; N_H is thus the density near the center of the layer multiplied by the effective thickness of the layer in kpc. Averages of N_H have been taken over ring sectors extending from 12° to 252° galactic longitude. The data are from a recent investigation by Mr. van Woerden. I am indebted to him for communicating them to me in advance of publication.

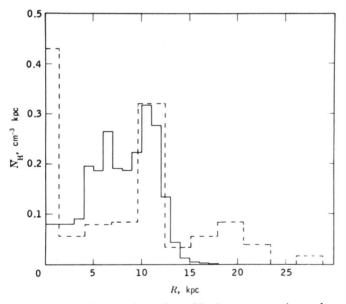

Fig. 6. Variation of the total number of hydrogen atoms in a column of unit cross section perpendicular to the galactic plane with R (from an unpublished investigation by H. van Woerden). The dashed line refers to the Andromeda nebula.

The dashed line in Fig. 6 shows the same quantity $\bar{N}_H$ for the Andromeda nebula. In both cases there is a maximum between 10 and 12 kpc, with a remarkably steep drop toward larger distances. Similar phenomena have been observed in other galaxies. In the earlier-type spiral NGC 4594, for instance, a localized belt of high dust density is found between about 10 and 20 kpc of the center, with maximum density around 13 kpc.

Motion and Distribution in the Central Region

A continuous arm is found in the profiles around the center. It can be followed without interruption from $+3°$ to $-18°$ longitude (the longitudes being counted from the direction to the center) and only vanishes near $-23°$, at about $R = 3\frac{1}{2}$ kpc if at this longitude the arm is assumed to become tangential.

For a spiral arm it is exceptionally homogeneous over the whole length and the variation of its mean velocity with l is remarkably smooth; individual sections of the arm do not deviate by more than 1 km/sec from a straight line. The curious thing is that it has a velocity of 53 km/sec away from the center. The arm can be observed in absorption against the radio source Sagittarius A and lies therefore between the center and the sun. The rotational velocity is presumably about 200 km/sec. Because of its radial motion it stands out beautifully from the material closer to and further from the sun.

The presumable situation of the arm is shown schematically in Fig. 9 (the upper arm). Actually it might spiral in more rapidly and might be closer to the center in the longitudes around that of the center. It is very probable that it continues beyond the point marked a, but the part beyond a cannot be observed because its velocity becomes very nearly perpendicular to the line of sight and it is therefore indistinguishably mingled with the small-velocity gas closer to the sun or at larger distances beyond the center.

This arm, which has been called the "3-kpc arm," has been the subject of an extensive investigation by Mr. Rougoor at Leiden. The arm lies rather accurately in the galactic plane defined by the new system of galactic coordinates. Its thickness between half-density points is $1°.25$, or 110 pc. If gravitation were the only force acting on the gas, this would correspond to an average random velocity of about 9 km/sec. In radial velocity the arm has a half-width of about 17.5 km/sec, which indicates that the random motions in the plane may be about equal to those perpendicular to the plane. However, there is a pronounced variation in the radial-velocity half-width with galactic latitude. At a latitude of $+1°.0$ it is 24.2 km/sec; with decreasing latitude it decreases gradually and becomes 16.5 km/sec at $b = -0°.5$. Where it is seen in absorption against

Sagittarius A it has a half-width of only 11.2 km/sec. All these velocity profiles are extremely smooth and symmetrical. The cause of the systematic variation in width is unknown. The *systematic* motion appears also to vary slightly with latitude: Relative to the center of the arm the part at average distance of 70 pc north of the plane is coming toward us with a velocity of 2.5 km/sec, while the southern half of the arm is moving away with a similar velocity.

Suppose a section through the arm had an axial ratio of 1:3, and therefore a half-width of 330 pc in the galactic plane. The central density would then be 2 atoms/cm³. Between two "vertical" planes with a separation of 1 cm there are 0.8×10^{42} hydrogen atoms. This is comparable to the number in the large outer arms of the galactic system, where this number may be estimated at about 1.6×10^{42}.

When we consider the hydrogen-line profiles around the galactic center it becomes evident that the 3-kpc arm is by no means the only remarkable feature in the central region.

Figure 7 gives a synoptic picture of the line profiles obtained in the true galactic plane. Similar data have been obtained for latitudes $-0°.5$, $+0°.5$, and $+1°.0$. This is the basis for all we know about the neutral hydrogen atoms in the central region. The low-velocity parts, which give a broad central ridge of maximum intensity, have been left out; they are of no importance in the present study.

The 3-kpc arm is shown as a narrow ridge of high intensity extending from $-8°$ to $+4°$ on the negative-velocity side. The interruption of the ridge near the longitude of the center is only apparent, and is due to the absorption caused by the central radio source.

Perhaps the most striking feature of the diagram is the wing of very high negative velocities between $l = -4°$ and $l = 0°$ (the longitude of the center). The circumstance that no such high negative velocities have been observed anywhere else in the region investigated, which extends roughly from $-10°$ to $+20°$ longitude, and the exact coincidence of the upper longitude limit with the direction of the center, suggest strongly that the wing is due to matter situated close to the center.

When we look at the positive velocities, we note that there is a very similar feature at longitudes beyond that of the center. Here, however, it is superimposed upon an extremely irregular background of high-velocity matter making up the very irregular arms shown in Fig. 9. That there is something real superimposed on this background is indicated by the curves in Fig. 8, which were obtained from special measurements of high accuracy made at each quarter of a degree from $-2°$ to $+2°$ longitude. These show that the number of atoms of very high positive velocity drops steeply near the longitude of the center, in very much the same way as at the high negative velocities. Also, the total numbers of atoms in the

J. H. Oort

velocity range considered is almost exactly the same for positive and negative velocities.

The most plausible interpretation of the features just discussed is that they are due to a disk of hydrogen extending to about 600 pc from the center and rotating at high velocity. A more detailed analysis of the line

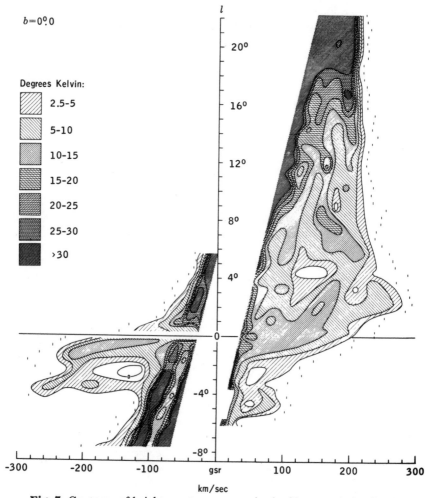

Fig. 7. Contours of brightness temperature in the 21-cm emission line in the central region of the galactic system. The contours are for the plane of maximum hydrogen density. The radial velocities shown are values that have been corrected for the motion of the sun with respect to the galactic center. At the negative velocities the curves have been interrupted over an interval of about 0°5 around the center, because, on the scale of this graph, the steep absorption profiles occurring in this interval could not be drawn adequately.

profiles for the negative velocities—which are uncontaminated by fore-ground or background radiation—indicates that there is a ring of matter with rather sharp inner and outer boundaries at radii R of about 500 and 590 pc. The density in the ring is 1 atom/cm³. There appears to be a practically empty space within the ring, the density only becoming appreciable again at $R = 300$ or 350 pc. It then rises gradually to about 3 atoms/cm³ at $R = 100$ pc. Still further inside the density must increase very strongly. The distribution is shown schematically in Fig. 9. In the innermost region the interpretation of the observations becomes compli-cated because of the absorption phenomena caused by the radio source Sagittarius A. Drake in Green Bank has recently shown that the nucleus of this radio source contains two very dense patches about 15 pc from the galactic center. If one assumes that these are regions of ionized hydrogen, the masses would be of the order of 50,000 solar masses. Smeared out over a sphere of 20-pc radius this would correspond with a density of about 100 protons/cm³.

With the radio telescope used in the present study, which has a beam-width of 0°56, corresponding to 80 pc at the distance of the center, the

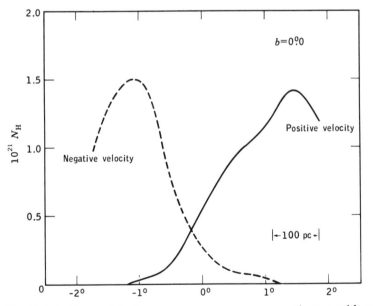

Fig. 8. Numbers of hydrogen atoms per square centimeter with radial velocities between 150 and 210 km/sec (after correction for the motion of the sun relative to the galactic center). The numbers refer to latitude zero on the new system; abscissae are longitudes in the same system. Ordinates are in units of 10²¹ atoms.

J. H. Oort

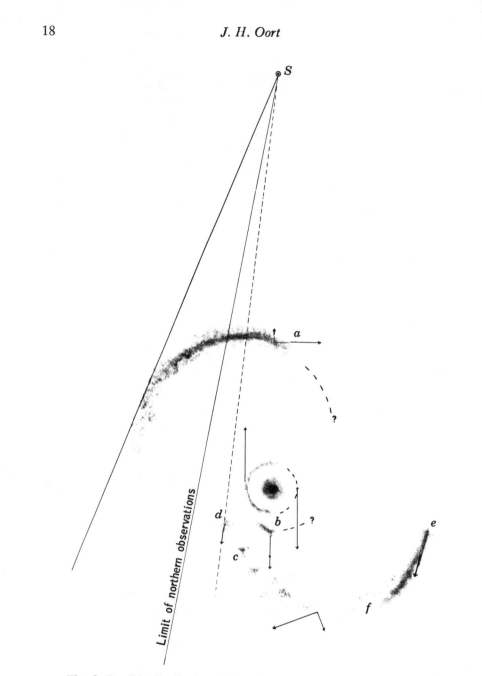

Fig. 9. Possible distribution of hydrogen in the central part of the galactic system. The position of the sun is indicated by *S*. The arm in the upper part is the "3-kpc arm." The ring and disk in the nuclear region do not seem to be expanding.

innermost parts of the rotating disk can be seen in absorption against the wings of Sagittarius A. The absorption has been measured up to velocities of a little over 100 km/sec. It is present at negative as well as at positive velocities.

There is no sign of any expansional motion in this "nuclear" disk and ring, neither in the emission observed at negative velocities nor in the absorption profiles. There appears to be mainly rotation. As has been indicated, the rotational velocities are quite high. In the ring, at 550 pc, it must be roughly 265 km/sec.

We now return to the expanding features. If one observes precisely at the longitude of the center, one finds quite considerable intensities between velocities of $+50$ and $+200$ km/sec. Between $+100$ and $+200$ km/sec there is no appreciable absorption of the radiation of Sagittarius A. This means that the bulk of the gas must lie behind the center and must therefore move away from it with velocities of the order mentioned. This high-velocity feature appears to break off at about $l = -1°5$ (corresponding to 200 pc in lateral direction). The gas concerned is likely to be situated rather close to the center, possibly just outside the rapidly rotating ring. The intensities are considerable (from 15 to 5°K); the total mass of gas involved in the feature may be estimated to be of the order of 10^6 solar masses. In Fig. 9 it has been drawn at b; this is admittedly somewhat arbitrary.

If we next consider somewhat lower longitudes, we find that there is hydrogen moving with radial velocities from $+30$ km/sec up to $+100$ or $+120$ km/sec. The rotation of the system is such that matter observed in longitudes lower than that of the center should approach us if it were moving in circular orbits, and thus have negative velocities. The gas considered must therefore have systematic motion differing radically from the ordinary rotation, especially if the velocity of rotation would be interpolated between that observed in the central disk and the rotations observed for $R > 3$ kpc. There is a sharp drop in the positive-velocity side of Fig. 7 at about $l = -5°5$, and no other positive velocities of any importance have been observed below this limit. If we take this as an indication that the corresponding stretch of gas becomes roughly tangential to the line of sight at $l = -5°5$, the gas might be situated as sketched in Fig. 9 between c and d. If this inference is correct, the gas clouds in this region must have a very high velocity component in the outward radial direction while their transverse velocity must also deviate very greatly from the circular velocities shown in Fig. 3. If the matter near $l = -5°$, having an average radial velocity (corrected for the sun's motion relative to the galactic center) of $+80$ km/sec is put at d (about 1 kpc from the center), and if we would suppose that the outward radial motion should not exceed a value of, say 200 km/sec, the transverse motion must be smaller than 90 km/sec, possibly even considerably smaller. This deviates very strongly from the circular velocity corresponding to the gravitational field, which was estimated to be about 250 km/sec.

At the positive longitudes, structure and motions in the central region cannot be unraveled with any confidence. In these longitudes we observe (Fig. 7) large amounts of gas moving with high positive velocities, much higher in absolute value than the velocities corresponding to the 3-kpc arm at negative longitudes. On the basis of what is observed for the positive velocities at longitudes smaller than that of the center we have assumed as a working hypothesis that this is likewise gas with large velocity components in a radial direction away from the center. Even with this hypothesis there is no way to tell where the gas is located. It is only at about $l = 14°$ that a regular arm appears. From additional data the latter has been inferred to lie around *ef* in Fig. 9. We have tentatively drawn the high-velocity gas observed between the center and $l = 14°$ in such a way that it connects up with this arm. But it should be stressed that this is entirely hypothetical; part of it might well be situated closer to the center.

In the contour diagram (Fig. 7) the great difference between the negative-velocity part at $l < -4°$ and the positive-velocity part for $l > +4°$ is a remarkable feature. It indicates considerable asymmetry in the central part of the galactic system. It should be noted, however, that notwithstanding this difference in character, the total amount of gas having abnormal velocities is almost exactly the same in the two opposite quadrants concerned.

It is of interest to make an estimate of the quantity of gas flowing out of the central region. From the data in Fig. 7 and similar data for other latitudes one can, under certain fairly plausible assumptions, estimate the total number of hydrogen atoms in the central region, this latter being defined roughly as the region within 2.5 or 3 kpc of the center. The total mass of hydrogen atoms in this region is found to be about 3×10^7 times the mass of the sun. If R is assumed to be 3.0 kpc this would give a total average density for a layer of 110-pc thickness of 0.4 atom/cm³. Assuming a radial motion of 50 km/sec, the ring between $R = 1$ and 3 kpc would empty itself in 40 million years and about 0.6 solar masses would flow out per year. Actually the average radial motion is probably higher, and as a rough figure we may accept a mass flow of 1 solar mass per year. This is neutral hydrogen; it is conceivable that there might be an important fraction of ionized hydrogen, although there is no direct observational evidence for this.

The evident question is where the gas can come from. It is conceivable that it could come from evolving stars of population II. According to Table 1 the total mass within $R = 3$ kpc would be about 16×10^9 suns.

If we estimate that about 1/500 of this mass would be transformed into interstellar gas each 10^9 years, then the amount produced would be 0.03 solar masses per year.* This is about 1/30 of what would be needed to counterbalance the observed outflow from the central region.

Although there are considerable uncertainties in both of the above computations, and the possibility cannot therefore be entirely excluded that the two quantities could still balance each other, there is nevertheless some ground to believe that the gas comes from elsewhere. The only other place it could come from is the galactic halo. This possibility might provide information on the structure of the magnetic field and on the ways in which the halo gas condenses into the thin disk.

General References

G. Elwert, *Ergeb. Ekakt. Naturw.*, **32**, 1 (1959).
J. H. Oort, F. J. Kerr, and G. Westerhout, *M.N.R.A.S.*, **118**, 379 (1958).
J. H. Oort and G. W. Rougoor, Distribution and Motion of Interstellar Hydrogen in the Galactic System with Particular Reference to the Region within 3 Kiloparsecs of the Center, Symposium on Radio Astronomy, National Academy of Sciences, 1959, pp. 1–15, reprinted from *Proc. Natl. Acad. Sci.*, **46**, 1 (1960).
Accounts of the observational data and their reduction have been given in *Bull. Astron. Inst. Neth.*, **13**, 151 (1957), by Muller, Ollongren, Raimond, Schmidt, Van de Hulst, and Westerhout, and in *Australian J. Phys.*, **12**, 270 (1959), by Kerr, Hindman, and Gum.

Discussion

Dr. Spitzer: How accurately is the local standard of rest determined for the gas in the solar neighborhood?

Dr. Oort: I would like to define that question a little better. You can of course get a fairly accurate average of all the gas clouds contained, say, within 1 kpc around the sun. But it is not certain that that gives you something you would wish to call a standard of rest, because the whole volume of gas near the sun might have a systematic deviation from circular motion; that is one of the main difficulties. But the internal accuracy is quite good.

---

* A very rough calculation of this quantity was made as follows. The total mass of the stars in a cylinder of 1-pc^2 cross section, perpendicular to the galactic plane and passing through the sun, is approximately 55 solar masses. The cylinder contains 1.2 stars with visual absolute magnitude between $+3.0$ and $+4.0$. If, as a rough estimate, we put the lifetime on the main sequence for stars of $M_V = +3.5$ at 9×10^9 years, and about twice as long for stars of $M_V = +4.5$, roughly 1/9 of the stars in the interval considered would move off the main sequence per 10^9 years. If each of these stars ultimately expels a mass of gas equal to 0.8 solar masses. then the total amount of interstellar gas produced by the stars in the cylinder would be $0.8 \times 1.2/9 = 0.10$ solar masses, or 0.002 times the total stellar mass, in the cylinder. If we assume that in the central region the same fraction of the total stellar mass would be transformed into gas, we arrive at the figure given in the text.

Dr. Spitzer: Better than 1 km/sec probably for that average?

Dr. Oort: Something of that order.

Dr. G. R. Burbidge: What effect would it have if you did not assume that the mass-to-light ratio was constant in your comparison with M 31?

Dr. Oort: In the nucleus we took a value of about 20, corresponding to what had been derived from the outer parts of the Andromeda nebula. If you would put that down to 5 in the central part, the rise in this central part would become a little less steep, of course. You might turn the argument around, perhaps, and conclude from the rotation observed near the nucleus of the galactic system that over the range from about 50 to 500 pc the mass-to-light ratio apparently does not vary too greatly; this is in a range of distance over which the total density varies very greatly, as you can see from the rotation curve and Table 1.

Dr. Christy: If, as you suggested, you drew the 3-kpc arm on our side of the center, spiraling in toward the center, would this make a significant reduction in the estimate of the amount of matter flowing out, since you would then have it at a quite reduced radius?

Dr. Oort: Yes, that is true, but the distance of the arm could not be so very much reduced. It might perhaps be reduced to one-half. So you would have a little less matter streaming out if you drew it that way. But on the other hand the total stellar mass contained within this distance would also be about the same factor smaller. The difficulty of the disparity between the two numbers would therefore not change very much.

Dr. Kahn: Could I ask a question about Kerr's picture? It looks as though the spiral arms on the Australian side were winding the other way from those on the Dutch side.

Dr. Oort: That may very well be due to the expansional motion that was superimposed. This tends to decrease the inclination of the arms.

Dr. Kahn: Wouldn't that rather suggest that the method of reduction Kerr used wasn't quite the proper one?

Dr. Oort: Yes. He concludes that the arms are almost circular. But in a spiral like this, one doesn't usually see circular arms. They usually have an inclination of the order of 5°.

Dr. Woltjer: Is it really plausible to suppose that you can compute the outward flow of gas on the assumption that it is a stationary phenomenon? Even if you grant that the gas could flow continuously out of the halo, does it not seem implausible that you can produce such a regular arm in a time scale of 20×10^6 years? You would have to suppose that the arms as a whole are moving outward, since the gas would tend to spiral inward rather than outward, if it moved along the arm. Is it then not more reasonable to think that it is an intermittent rather than a stationary phenomenon?

Dr. Oort: Perhaps. But you find so much matter also on the other side of the center, which is also streaming outward, but in a rather different way. The total mass of this gas beyond the center is of the same order as that in the 3-kpc arm, so that one would still think that the estimate of the total amount moving out would not be too far wrong. It might be. It is uncertain.

Dr. Biermann: An expansion of 7 km/sec, in the vicinity of the sun—to which mass flow would that correspond? Wouldn't that be quite a similar mass flow to that in the 3-kpc region?

Ed.: In a subsequent discussion this appeared to be the case, because the width of and the density in the gas layer are higher near the sun than at 3 kpc.

Dr. Oort: I do not believe that the agreement is significant.

Evidence for large deviations from the equatorial plane in the neutral hydrogen of the outer parts of the galaxy

A. Blaauw

(on behalf of H. J. Habing and H. van Woerden)

This is a brief report to indicate that, at least in the outer parts of the galaxy, the neutral hydrogen may show large deviations from the galactic plane. In Professor Oort's lecture reference was made to the tilt of the neutral hydrogen layer in the outer parts; in the directions of, roughly, $l^{II} = 30°$ to $120°$ ($l^{I} = 0°$ to $90°$), it tilts toward positive z values by an amount of about 600 pc, whereas in the opposite parts of the galaxy the tilt is downward, i.e., to negative z values. At Groningen, we have found indications of an extension to positive z in the former sector up to several kiloparsec. Our observations provide no information regarding the existence of similar extensions in the opposite sector; this would require southern observations. The indications were found in the course of an intermediate latitude survey meant for the study of the interstellar cloud structure, to be discussed in a later paper.

The profiles at latitude $+10°$ were found to show the following features at the majority of the galactic longitudes in $l^{II} = 30°$ to $130°$ ($l^{I} = 0°$ to $100°$). At low frequencies there is the peak of intensity due to nearby hydrogen. At the somewhat higher frequencies corresponding to the Perseus arm there is very little radiation—which can be explained by the fact that at these latitudes we are traversing the Perseus arm at fairly high z distances. However, at still higher frequencies, corresponding to the outer arm, a small secondary maximum in the profile is noticeable. Its rather regular recurrence at consecutive longitudes was taken as evidence against the possibility that we are dealing here with high-velocity nearby clouds. The preliminary interpretation is that we are observing matter

23

A. Blaauw

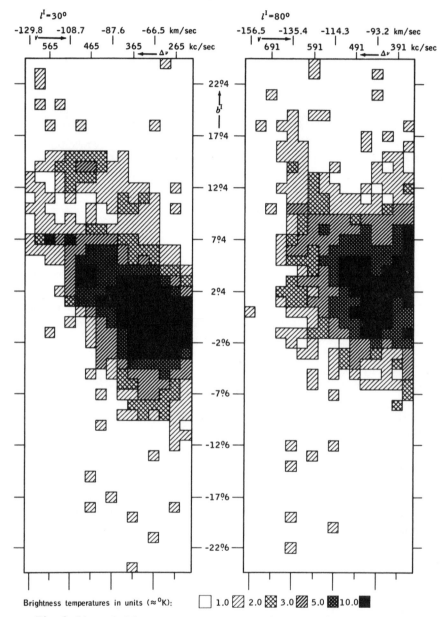

Fig. 1. 21-cm brightness temperatures as a function of radial velocity and galactic latitude (old system) for $l^{I} = 30°$ ($l^{II} = 62°$) and for $l^{I} = 80°$ ($l^{II} = 112°$).

at the distance of the outer arm, but extending up to several kiloparsec above the galactic plane.

If this interpretation is correct, we are, of course, interested also in the intensity of the radiation received from neighboring latitudes and in the run of the hydrogen density with distance from the plane. For that reason, measurements over the whole range of latitudes from the plane up to about $+25°$ have been made at a series of longitudes. Results are shown in Fig. 1 in the form of contour diagrams. Those for the longitude $l^I = 30°$ and $80°$ ($l^{II} = 62°$ and $112°$) are reproduced here as examples. The abscissae are frequency, the ordinates galactic latitude. The intensity of the radiation for a given frequency and latitude is indicated by the degree of shading. The frequency range shown here, at $+250$ kc/sec and higher (with respect to the local standard of rest near the sun), is the one corresponding to the outer arm.

Note the strong asymmetry in latitude of these diagrams. The radiation at these frequencies comes preponderately from the positive latitudes. The already known asymmetry, which was responsible for the tilt of the hydrogen layer, shows in a still more pronounced way, if we include the faint radiation from larger distances from the plane.

If frequencies are converted into distances on the very simple and perhaps not correct basis of the conventional differential galactic rotation picture, it is found that matter extends to z distances of up to $+4$ kpc. The densities are generally quite low compared to that in the arm in the plane; estimates are between 0.02 and 0.1 atom/cm³. The total mass in the high z extension above the outer arm would be of the order of 10^7 solar masses. It must be stressed, however, that these estimates—and the whole interpretation as such—are of a provisional nature.

Discussion

Dr. Strömgren: If one would assume the same ratio between particle density and gas density as in the plane, approximately what would be the optical thickness in the visual for an intermediate latitude ray through those regions?

Dr. Blaauw: It would be very low, of the order of what you would find for the components of the clouds in our neighbourhood. You would have a few of them, and they would give about the same optical thickness.

Dr. Strömgren: Quite. That is not entirely negligible.

Dr. Oort: It would probably be difficult to distinguish from the effects of many nearby clouds?

Dr. Blaauw: Yes.

The kinematics of the local gas system

H. L. Helfer

I should like to present the results of an analysis of the motions of the high-latitude gas $|b| \geqslant 20°$, determined from 21-cm observations. Most of the observations, taken with the Department of Terrestrial Magnetism's multichannel receiver (each channel having a band width of ~ 12 kc/sec) have already been published [A.J., **65**, 1 (1960)]. The line profiles show some minor structure, but generally speaking there is in almost all cases a well-defined main peak, and the peak or median velocity of a profile can be well determined to within ± 1.5 km/sec if the antenna temperature is $\geqslant 10°$K. These peak or median velocities generally change systematically as a function of position on the sky, and consequently an analysis of these peak velocities, assuming that the gas moves in a local velocity field, seems plausible.

Assuming

$$\mathbf{V} = \mathbf{V}_0 + \mathbf{r} \cdot \nabla \mathbf{V} + \cdots \tag{1}$$

we find

$$V_r = A(l^I, b^I) + S((l^I b^I)r + \cdots \tag{2}$$

where

$$A = W_1 \cos l^I \cos b^I + W_2 \sin l^I \cos b^I + W_3 \sin b^I \tag{3}$$

$$S = K + [C + B \sin 2l^I + \gamma)] \cos^2 b^I + A \sin(l^I + \delta) \sin 2b^I \tag{4}$$

are antisymmetric and symmetric, respectively, upon performing the reflection $(l, b) \rightarrow (l + 180°, -b)$. If then we pair up opposite points in

26

the sky, denoting the point in the northern (southern) hemisphere by a $+(-)$ subscript, we find

$$V_{r,+} + V_{r,-} = S(r_+ + r_-) \tag{5}$$

$$V_{r,+} - V_{r,-} = 2A + S(r_+ - r_-) \tag{6}$$

From the pairs of points in the sky for which Eq. (5) = 0, we find the locus $S = 0$, and for these points from Eqs. (6) and (3) we can solve by least squares for W_1, W_2, W_3. The most satisfactory procedure then is to compute A for all points surveyed and subtract it from the observed radial velocity; this corrected radial velocity is plotted in Figs. 1 and 2. Values of $\mathbf{W} = (1.24 \text{ km/sec}, 2.62 \text{ km/sec}, -1.60 \text{ km/sec})$ on the $l^{\mathrm{I}}b^{\mathrm{I}}$ system were used. The velocities have been already corrected for solar motion by the Lund tables. What should be given in the figures then is Sr, and we see that for both hemispheres, plus values are reasonably well separated from minus values and the loci $S = 0$ are fairly well established.

To solve by least squares for the parameters involved in the expression for S seemed treacherous, for five parameters are to be determined (one, e.g., K, may arbitrarily be set equal to 1) in a trigonometric expression, and only a small region of the sky can be used in the solution; the problem of assigning weights to individual points (l, b) appeared extremely difficult. Instead use was made of the fact that for any value of l there theoretically exists either zero or two values, b_1, b_2 of b for which $S = 0$, and these are related by

$$-\tfrac{1}{2}(\tan b_1 + \tan b_2) = A \sin(l + \delta) \tag{7}$$

$$\tan b_1 \tan b_2 - 1 = C + B \sin 2(l + \gamma) \tag{8}$$

From the observations in Figs. 1 and 2, the left-hand sides of Eqs. (7) and (8) may be estimated and plotted as functions of l; then fitting of sine curves give the five constants.

The result gives

$$0 = 1 - [1.1 + \sin 2(l^{\mathrm{I}} + 53°)]\cos^2 b^{\mathrm{I}} + 0.25 \sin(l - 48°) \ \sin 2b^{\mathrm{I}} \tag{9}$$

with bordering extreme solutions:

$$0 = 1 - [0.8 + 1.4 \sin 2(l^{\mathrm{I}} + 55°)] \cos^2 b^{\mathrm{I}} + 0.28 \sin(l^{\mathrm{I}} - 43°) \sin 2b^{\mathrm{I}} \tag{10}$$

$$0 = 1 - [1.2 + 0.9 \sin 2(l^{\mathrm{I}} + 52°)] \cos^2 b^{\mathrm{I}} + 0.20 \sin(l^{\mathrm{I}} - 53°) \sin 2b^{\mathrm{I}} \tag{11}$$

These are plotted in Figs. 1 and 2 as a dotted line, a solid line, and a dashed line, respectively.

These expressions must be multiplied by a scale factor to get the expression for S. The fact that the radial velocities become negative as we go to $|b| = 90°$ informs us that the scale factor must be negative. Crude arguments based upon distance estimates to various gas and dust complexes near us suggest that the magnitude of this scale factor is $\sim 10 \text{ km/sec/kpc}$, with an uncertainty of a factor of 2.

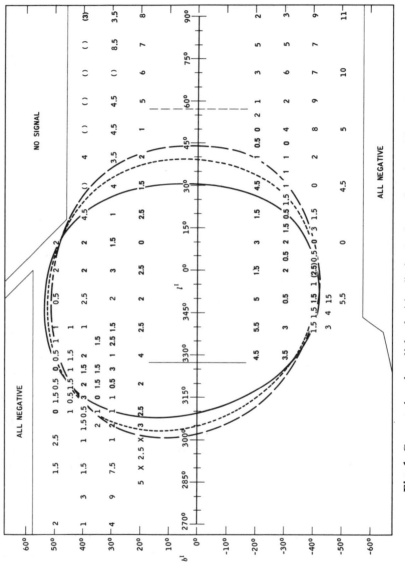

Fig. 1. Corrected peak radial velocities (in km/sec) as a function of l^1 and b^1.

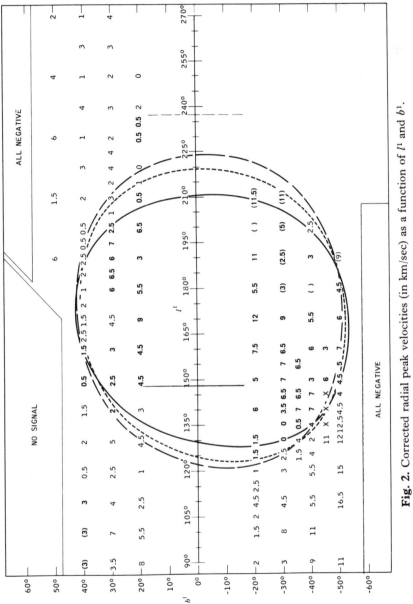

Fig. 2. Corrected radial peak velocities (in km/sec) as a function of l^1 and b^1.

29

A new solution for W_1, W_2, W_3 corresponding to the locus (9) gave values of $+1.34$, $+1.00$, -2.20 km/sec. A term, representing a constant radial velocity shift independent of direction, was carried along and turned out to have a value of -0.6 km/sec; this is comparable with the accuracy of frequency calibration and any expected personal systematic bias in estimating peak velocities.

It therefore appears as if the local gas system is rotating slightly faster than the stars in the solar vicinity, by $\sim 2 \pm 2$ km/sec, and that the gas is moving downward across the plane from $(+b$ to $-b)$ with a velocity of -2.5 ± 1.5 km/sec in the z direction.

The expression for S is quite complicated and differs from the ordinary radial and velocity distance relation used in correcting for galactic rotation effects. The question arises if a simpler expression should not have been used, using simplifying assumptions as to the values of the parameters in the expression for S. The answer appears to be that the observations demand this complicated expression, if one limits oneself to first-order terms in the distance in Eq. (2). The fact that the radial velocities go negative as $|b| \to 90°$ requires $K \neq 0$. The observations $|b| \geqslant 30°$ themselves well determine the angle γ and the sum $B + C$. The term $A \sin(l + \delta)$ represents the slight asymmetry of the $S = 0$ loci; the existence of the asymmetry seems well established, but its precise shape is not well established, hence the larger uncertainty in A and δ.

The possibility of choosing five parameters in the expression for S does not give one extremely wide latitude in choosing the shape of $S = 0$. One can turn the argument presented around and determine the parameters from the locus $S = 0$ of Fig. 1 alone. We then predict the locus $S = 0$ for the opposite hemisphere; Fig. 2 would then represent a comparison between theory (the curves drawn) and observation. The analysis appears successful, and it is reasonable to conclude that the high-latitude gas moves in a velocity field quite different from that observed for the bulk of the gas in the galactic plane, which almost seems to follow Oort's classical velocity–distance relation. There probably is a transition zone between these two velocity fields; velocity observations for $|b| = 10°$, $15°$, and possibly $20°$, should be quite complex, reflecting this superposition of two different velocity fields and gas populations.

The parameters in the expression for S are related to the first-order velocity derivatives of the velocity field in the vicinity of the sun. Imagine a spherical distribution of gas around us. In time, under the action of the velocity field, the gas would distort into an ellipsoid. The parameters determined inform us of the direction of the axes of the ellipsoid and the ratio of the axes; i.e., we determine the amount of contraction or expansion in the three directions. One principal direction is extremely well determined within a few degrees; it is $l^{\mathrm{II}} = 22°$, $b^{\mathrm{II}} = +6°$, with expansion of $+1.1$ times the scale factor ($= 10$ km/sec/kpc?). The other two orthogonal directions are poorly determined; the possibility of the north galactic pole being one of them is excluded, however. Contraction takes place in both directions. Reasonable provisional values are $l^{\mathrm{II}} = 122°$, $b^{\mathrm{II}} = +56°$, with contraction of -1.1 times the scale factor and $l^{\mathrm{II}} = 110°$, $b^{\mathrm{II}} = -33°$, with contraction of -0.8 times the scale factor.

The gas flow is seen to be away from us in the galactic plane (approximately), and toward us in the plane perpendicular to $l^{\mathrm{II}} = 22°$, $b^{\mathrm{II}} = +6°$; since the gas density is extremely low in the direction $l^{\mathrm{II}} = 122°$, $b^{\mathrm{II}} = +56°$, most of the gas flowing in comes from the direction $l^{\mathrm{II}} = 110°$, $b = -33°$ (and its supplement). The numbers give a characteristic time scale for increasing the local gas density by a factor e of $\sim 10^8$ years. Use of the solution for A and S (and our guess as to the scale factor) and the integrated intensity data suggest that the local system has dimensions of $3/2 \times 3/4 \times 1/6$ kpc and a total mass of 2×10^6 to $2 \times 10^7 \, M_\odot$, depending upon the distribution of mass within the system. We note in passing that Heeschen and Lilley have suggested that this local gas system may be connected with Gould's belt. Recent Australian observations tend to discount this view. However, we note if we assume that the local velocity field is characterized by $\partial V_x / \partial z = \partial V_y / \partial z = 0$ that the plane $V_z = $ const. (~ -2 km/sec) intersects the sky along Gould's belt. This again suggests the possibility that the Gould's belt stars are a system of stars moving with $\bar{V}_z \sim -2$ km/sec under the influence of the velocity field of the nearby high-latitude gas.

The entire analysis and discussion will be published shortly [*A.J.*, **66**, 160 (1961)].

Note added in proof. R. X. McGee and J. D. Murray [*Australian J. Phys.*, **14**, 260 (1961)] have published 21-cm observations covering the southern hemisphere. The observations are in reasonable agreement with those discussed here. Their method of analysis is quite different from the one discussed above. However, they come to essentially the same conclusion—that the cold gas is streaming into the solar vicinity from above and below the galactic plane and flowing away from the solar vicinity in the galactic plane. The main area of disagreement is the direction in the galactic plane of the outgoing flow.

Discussion

Dr. Spitzer: You found no radial motion of the gas toward or away from the galactic center?

Dr. Helfer: No. The direction of the gas seems to be within about plus or minus 35° or 30° of the direction of the galactic rotation. All these numbers are crude.

Dr. Spitzer: With respect to what are those velocities given?

Dr. Helfer: With respect to a local standard of rest moving 20 km/sec toward $\alpha = 18^{\mathrm{h}}$, and $\delta = +30°$.

Interstellar gas and young stars near the sun

A. Blaauw

These will be casual remarks, dealing with some aspects of the process of star formation. We consider the stellar associations in the solar neighborhood; this sample may be considered typical for what happens in a section of a spiral arm. Table 1 gives a list of the associations within

Table 1

OB Associations within 800 pc

| | Projected dimensions, pc | Total mass, $10^3 \odot$ | Mean mass density, $\odot/10^3 \text{ pc}^3$ | Age in 10^6 yr | |
				From evolutionary theory	From kinematic data
Scorpio–Centaurus	250 × 30	5.8	9	0–26	<20
II Perseus	50 × 35	1.5	25	0–6	1.5
IC 348	0.5	0.04	640 × 10³		
I Orion	80 × 70	7.6	20	0–15	4:
nebula region only	28 × 17	3.8	475	0–4	
I Lacerta	130 × 70	3.0	4.6	4–12	7
III Cepheus	35 × 15	3.8	480	0–6	
II Monoceros	8 × 4	0.8	6 × 10³	0–3	

800 pc. The first column gives the projected dimensions. These are very different, ranging from several parsec, i.e., clusterlike dimensions, to

32

such large structures as the Scorpio–Centaurus association of about 30×250 pc. The second column gives an estimate of the total mass in the form of stars and protostars; this is based on the known number of massive stars, say O to B5, and an extrapolation by means of the generally adopted initial luminosity function. The third column gives the present mass density in the form of stars and protostars, averaged over the whole volume. We find that the total masses do not greatly vary from one association to the other. The mean densities are small, especially for the largest groups, and of the order of several hundredths of a solar mass per cubic parsec. There are, however, some small groups of much higher density.

The ages of the stars in these groups, as estimated by means of current theories of stellar evolution and by means of kinematic data, are in the last columns. They range from zero to about 26×10^6 years. In one case only—that of the I Lacerta association—is the evidence rather strong that star formation has ceased. All these associations are located within the Gould belt, that is, in the local region of instellar matter situated, quite asymmetrically, south of the galactic equator in the northern sky and north of it in the southern sky.

Do stars always form in groups? Or are there cases where stars seem to have formed in a more or less isolated way? We can say something about this only for the largest stellar masses. It is practically certain that stars of 25 solar masses and more form only in association with other stars. Those in the range of 5 to 25 solar masses form mostly in groups; I should say at least 90 per cent of them. For the smaller masses we have insufficient information. The data on T Tauri stars suggest that here, too, formation in groups is predominant.

Does formation of massive stars always imply the formation of less massive stars? This seems to be so indeed. In cases where O- and B-type stars occur in the association, and where observations extend to faint objects, the presence of low-luminosity stars is established. Examples are the I Orion association, in which Parenago and others have shown stars down to solar masses to occur, and the II Perseus association, which contains both O and B stars and T Tauri variables (around IC 348).

The opposite is not true; we know regions of star formation in which numerous faint T Tauri stars occur, for instance in the Taurus clouds, but where no O and B stars are found. Is this simply a matter of relative frequency of different masses, so that the chances of finding massive stars in the latter cases are too small, as might be predicted on the basis of the luminosity function? This leads us to the question of the uniformity of the initial luminosity function.

There appear to be considerable *differences in the initial luminosity function,* and hence in the initial mass spectrum, if we compare the associations of Table 1. Consider the associations II Per, II Mon, and III

Cep. We count the numbers of stars in the intervals of absolute magnitude -4 to -2, and -2 to -1 for each of them and find: for II Per, 7 and 6; for II Mon, 1 and 4; for III Cep, 23 and 5. We are dealing here with three associations of rather similar size and age. It seems unlikely that in any of these three associations the stars of luminosity -1 would not yet have arrived on the main sequence, except perhaps for a small fraction.

An excess of very luminous stars, say brighter than -4 visual absolute magnitude compared to the less luminous ones, is also found in the h and chi Persei association.

We thus find that large fluctuations exist among the objects in our immediate neighborhood. However, if we add all of them we find good agreement with what is predicted by the initial luminosity function.

How large is a representative volume within which star formation takes place? The projected dimensions of most of the associations of Table 1 cannot be regarded as the typical size of a region of star formation in its earliest stage, because of their expanding motions. To find what may be a typical volume for star formation we have to look at the very youngest objects. Two typical cases, contained within our sample, are the small cluster IC 348 in the association II Per and the Trapezium cluster in Orion. Both have diameters of about $\frac{1}{2}$ pc, i.e., one-tenth of an average open cluster. In both we find the massive B stars as well as much fainter objects, still in the contraction stage. Their mass densities, as far as the stars are concerned, are of the order of 1000 or 10,000 solar masses per cubic parsec.

The sequence of star formation. The small regions just mentioned are parts of larger groups in which different phases of star formation may be recognized. This identification of different phases may be illustrated by means of a few examples. We choose the Scorpio–Centaurus association, the Orion association, and III Cephei. Figure 1 shows, by means of roman numerals, the regions in which star formation must have occurred first (region I), and the subsequent subdivisions (regions II, III, and IV). Region I of Sco–Centaurus (the Centaur region and immediate surroundings) probably was formed about 20 to 30 $\times$ 10^6 years ago. Star formation seems to have terminated in this area. Next in age comes area II in Scorpio and, probably still younger, region III, which is still very heavily immersed in gaseous nebulae. The differences in age between I, II, and III follow from the different positions of the stars in the HR diagram.

The Orion association may be similarly subdivided into the oldest, most northern part, and the younger regions south of it, with the most recent formation of stars in the Trapezium area.

Generally, the consecutive steps in star formation appear to take place according to an asymmetric pattern. We do not find a central

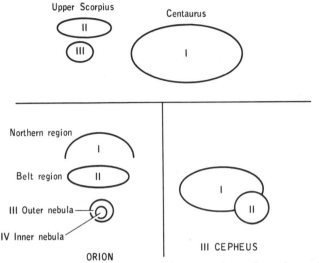

Fig. 1. Schematic representation of some regions of star formation.

region surrounded by a younger or older part; the various stages occur in adjacent areas, giving the impression that the process of formation proceeds in one direction through the original cloud complex.

Association with interstellar matter. The association with the inter-stellar medium appears to vary very much from place to place. Very striking is the fact that the oldest parts sometimes are so very clear of interstellar matter. An example is region I of Scorpio–Centaurus, where interstellar reddening is almost negligible; this region also seems to be void of emission nebulae and neutral hydrogen. This contrasts strongly with region II and even more with region III, which is very heavily involved. Similarly, in Orion and III Cep we find the oldest parts to be least involved in inter-stellar matter.

After a lapse of time of 10 to 20 × 10⁶ years the association seems to have cleared itself of interstellar matter. This also appears in h and chi Persei. I shall comment again in my next paper on the low interstellar-matter content of this latter association.

Delayed formation of heavy stars. In some cases we find that one or more rather massive stars have made their appearance quite late in the history of the association. An example is the star Zeta Ophiuchi. From its motion we find that it must be about 10⁶ years old and must belong to the most recently formed stars in the Scorpio–Centaurus association. Yet it is the earliest type and the most massive star known in the group.

We might have thought that, because of their shorter contraction times, such stars should have made their appearance rather early in the history of the association. It looks as if their formation was somewhat delayed by an unknown process.

The last item connected with the process of star formation which I want to mention concerns the *incidence of double and multiple stars*. The occurrence of double stars must have an important bearing on the theory of the star formation, and one likes to investigate whether different associations show different percentages of double and multiple systems. From a statistical study including both visual and spectroscopic binary data, I have inferred that about 75 per cent of all O to B5 systems are double or multiple. No differences could be detected yet between the different associations, although there is a suggestion that in the outer nebula group in Orion the incidence of duplicity and multiplicity is lower than elsewhere.

Discussion

Dr. Underhill: Didn't Bidelman show that there was a considerable difference in reddening across the field of h and chi Persei?

Dr. Blaauw: I believe that is right. I think this must be due to the foreground material. There is no indication that it is connected with the cluster itself. From the 21-cm measurements you get an idea of where it is. Also, from the emission features you can conclude that there is certainly nothing closely associated with this mass. It would seem that a time of something of the order of 20×10^6 years already suffices for the region to be cleared of interstellar matter.

Dr. Underhill: Is h and chi Persei behind the hydrogen as viewed by us?

Dr. Blaauw: I think this is an unsolved problem, because from the double interstellar lines, as they have been found by Münch, you would think that the double cluster is behind the hydrogen in the Perseus arm. However, photometrically you will find that it is certainly not at the distance of the main part of the Perseus arm but rather in front of it. There is conflicting evidence, and I don't know which one is the right answer. I have a suspicion that the interstellar lines observed by Münch, which give strongly negative velocities, are due to matter which does not move with the mean speed of the Perseus arm, but which is moving toward us.

Dr. G. R. Burbidge: The suggestion that in h and chi Persei there is very little interstellar matter is very striking. It seems to me very difficult to visualize star formation that will really sweep up all the material unless one has relative motions involved. I was wondering if one has some process that forms nuclei; perhaps then do we have a region where a fairly symmetrical accretion may occur. It seems to me this is one mechanism for collecting a large part of the matter.

Dr. Blaauw: I personally would favor the idea that after the initial star formation has taken place you have so many supernova explosions that the rest is swept away.

Dr. Spitzer: Do you need to assume a supernova explosion? Wouldn't one expect that the O stars heat up the interstellar matter, pushing it away at 10 km/sec, which is about the observed velocity of expansion of the H I shells?

Dr. Blaauw: It seems to me unlikely that you have so many O stars and expansion at such high speeds that due to the expansion around the O stars you would be able to remove the matter in sufficient quantities. If you think of the accumulation of mass as it goes outside the area. . . .

Dr. Spitzer: But we know that the expansion velocities are present in the Orion region. It is easy to compute what that region will look like in another few million years.

Dr. Blaauw: That is right. But I suggest we discuss this when we have more complete data on the hydrogen distribution, which I want to present in a later paper.

Dr. von Hoerner: I would like to comment on the massive stars which sometimes appear to have been formed much later, as you said. Some time ago I looked through a large number of HR diagrams of young open clusters and associations, and I was amazed to find such younger stars in about one-third of all cases. You have one, or less frequently two, very young stars well above the breakoff point of the main sequence. But I would not think that this indicates that especially more massive stars are created later on, because if less massive stars had been created later on you couldn't see the difference between these and the older stars.

Dr. Blaauw: I wouldn't want to say that especially massive stars are created later on. But apparently even for massive stars the times at which they are formed in the medium can have quite a range.

Dr. von Hoerner: Yes. The opinion I got is that star formation might have one big wave and maybe later on a smaller wave. So that it just doesn't peter out gradually but more or less in waves.

Dr. Blaauw: A wave in time?

Dr. von Hoerner: Yes.

Dr. Blaauw: A wave in time could correspond to a wave in space, as it has been pictured in the diagram. If you did see this from a large distance you wouldn't be able to distinguish between the different parts.

Dr. Pottasch: When you say there is evidence that star formation is going on at the present time, what other evidence is there besides the presence of O stars?

Dr. Blaauw: I would think in the Taurus star clouds; you have these clumps of T Tauri stars which are evidently associated with the clouds. They have very small relative motions and masses of the order of a solar mass. There is no O star at all in the region, but still there is evidence that these stars are forming.

Photometric studies of the distribution of dust near the sun

B. Strömgren

Photometric studies of the distribution of interstellar dust in our galaxy have been carried out in many investigations during the last 30 years. I should like to report today on some results obtained from a photometric investigation carried out by D. L. Crawford and myself.

Our aim has been to obtain a mapping of the interstellar dust distribution within 200 pc of the sun through determinations of individual distances and color excesses for B8 and B9 stars brighter than apparent visual magnitudes 6^m5. The distances were obtained from visual absolute magnitudes determined from the combination of an H_β index measured through photoelectric photometry with interference filters and the intrinsic color index $(U–B)_0$ found from photoelectric UBV photometry (cf. Strömgren [1] and Crawford [2]). The color excesses E(B–V) and the interstellar visual absorptions A_v were determined from photoelectric UBV photometry according to the method first suggested by W. Becker and further developed into a standard procedure by Johnson and Morgan [3] and Morgan and Harris [4] (cf. also Crawford [2] and Johnson [5]).

The photoelectric H_β and UBV photometry was carried out by Crawford with the 36-inch reflector of the McDonald Observatory and the 16-inch reflector of the Kitt Peak National Observatory. (I should like to mention that Dr. Crawford's work was supported by a grant from the National Science Foundation.) The program consisted of all B8 and B9 stars (Henry Draper classification) in the Bright Star Catalogue that are north of declination $-30°$, and UBV as well as H_β photometry was obtained for the great majority of these stars. Crawford [6] has compiled a photometric catalogue of 501 B8 and B9 stars brighter than visual magnitude $6^{m}5$ which contains the observed values of the H_{β} index β, and of B–V and U–B as well as of E(U–B) and A_{v} derived from the B–V and U–B by the standard procedure just referred to. The probable errors of the catalogue values of the indices B–V, U–B, and β are all approximately $\pm 0^{m}01$. The following discussion is based on the photometry of B8 and B9 stars contained in Crawford's catalogue.

I have already mentioned that the visual absolute magnitudes M_{v} and distances of the B8 and B9 stars were obtained from the indices β and $(U–B)_{0}$. The β–$(U–B)_{0}$ diagram was calibrated in terms of M_{v} for B5–B9 stars of luminosity classes III, IV, and V using M_{v} values of member stars of II Sco, I Per, the Pleiades cluster, and the cluster M 34. The difficulties encountered in such calibration efforts are well known from work on similar photographic–photometric methods (cf. Petrie [7], Kopylov [8], and Sinnerstad [9], also Johnson and Iriarte [10]). Although the difficulties have not yet been completely overcome in the case of the stars in question, i.e., B8 and B9 stars of the main sequence, I believe that the preliminary calibration derived by Crawford and myself is accurate to within a few tenths of a magnitude.

The photometric observational errors give rise to uncertainties in the visual absolute magnitudes measured by an average probable error equal to about $\pm 0^{m}2$. On top of this there are also errors due to the occurrence of binaries among the stars in question, and errors due to the influence of stellar parameters beyond the basic parameters, i.e., stellar mass and stellar age (cosmical scatter). These questions have been recently discussed by, among others, Hardie and Crawford [11] and T. and J. H. Walraven [12] (cf. also Strömgren [13]). The effective probable error of the M_{v} values is presumably about $\pm 0^{m}3$.

Since the average distance of the stars that we are going to consider is about 150 pc, a typical value of the uncertainty of the distance is ± 20 pc. This precision appears adequate in studies of the distribution of the reddening interstellar medium.

It is hardly necessary for me to discuss in detail the general background of the present investigation. Let me just refer to the work of Stebbins, Huffer, and Whitford [14], in which color excesses were determined for O–B5 stars from spectral class and color index, while the individual distances were derived from absolute magnitudes estimated on the basis of the spectral classification. This study provided a most valuable picture of the general distribution of interstellar dust within 1000 pc. However the number of O–B5 stars per cubic parsec is so low that it is impossible to investigate the fine structure of the distribution. Nevertheless, the unevenness of the dust distribution was clearly demonstrated by Stebbins, Huffer, and Whitford.

Through the work of Ambarzumian [15] the importance of the problem of the density variations of the dust component of the interstellar medium, and in particular of the question of the role of discrete clouds, was made clear and new methods of analysis were introduced. This work was followed by a series of investigations by Chandrasekhar and Münch [16], Münch [17], and others. In recent years the role of the spiral arms in connection with the large-scale distribution of the interstellar dust has been more clearly realized.

The program of the B8 and B9 stars brighter than 6^m5 was undertaken for the purpose of studying the fine structure of the dust distribution within 200 pc. For this category of stars the number per cubic parsec is larger than for the O–B5 stars by one order of magnitude. It was therefore expected that new information concerning the distribution could be gained. At the same time it appeared probable that the program would be a first step and that relevant details of the dust distribution could only be studied through a corresponding program of study of a category of stars—F stars— for which the star density is higher by still another order of magnitude. As we shall see, these expectations were confirmed.

In discussing the results of the B8–9 survey, I shall not attempt to make an exhaustive statistical analysis, but I shall try to describe the more important features of the picture that emerges of the dust distribution within 200 pc.

First, let me mention that the material was limited to stars with $(U-B)_0$ between -0^m15 and 0^m70, and not more than about 1^m5 above the age-zero line. The visual absolute magnitudes range from about -2^m to about $+1^m$. Up to a distance of 150 pc the sample is nearly complete, but near the limit of the investigation, 200 pc, only the fraction of the stars which is brighter than 0^m is included. However, the corresponding reduction in the star density is relatively small and does not cause any difficulty in the analysis.

There are 37 program stars with distance modulus $\leq 4^m8$, i.e., within 90 pc. Of these stars 35 have color excesses E(U–B) in the range -0^m03 to $+0^m01$ (the corresponding color index E(B–V) is obtained through multiplication with the factor 1.38, while A_v is larger by a factor 4.2). The average value is -0^m008, and the rms variation around this average value is $\pm 0^m012$. The fact that the average color excess is slightly negative indicates that the effects of interstellar reddening within 90 pc are very small, and furthermore that the adopted procedure of computing E(U–B) from B–V and U–B leads to values that require on the average a small positive correction. For the purpose of the following discussion we have adopted a correction of $+0^m008$ to the E(U–B) values given in Crawford's B8–9 star catalogue.

The rms scatter of the E(U–B) values around the mean is satisfactorily small, and corresponds in fact very closely to the rms scatter computed from the probable error of the photometric observations. This finding increases our confidence in the UBV method of determining color excesses.

From the derived rms of the E(U–B) values for the stars within 90 pc an upper limit to the amount of interstellar reddening present within this volume could be derived. However, the sensitivity of this method is low, because for the stars in question the rms variation of the distances around the mean value (70 pc) is only ± 15 pc.

Two of the stars within 90 pc show appreciable reddening. One is μ Oph with $A_v = 0^m\!.59$; however, the observed distance is 90 pc, and the true location might be well outside the volume considered. The other star is 33LMi, with $A_v = 0.46$ and distance modulus $4^m\!.5$, located at galactic latitude $+59°$. Detailed investigations of areas around these two stars, say through an F-star program, is clearly desirable.

Of the program stars outside 90 pc 24 stars have galactic latitude $|b| \geqq 50°$. Of these, 22 stars are within 200 pc. For the 9 stars in the north galactic cap the average distance is 130 pc, while the average color excess E(U–B), corrected by $+0^m\!.008$ as described, is $+0^m\!.009$. The corresponding numbers for 13 stars in the southern galactic cap are 140 pc and $+0^m\!.006$. Comparison with the stars within 90 pc yields an estimate of interstellar reddening E(U–B) in the galactic caps, namely, $0^m\!.1$ per kiloparsec. This estimate is, of course, uncertain, and all that can be said is that the effects of interstellar reddening are quite small in the galactic caps within 140 parsec. This result is in agreement with that of an investigation by Harris and myself [18] on interstellar reddening in a smaller area near the north galactic pole.

In connection with the discussion of interstellar absorption within 90 pc and in the galactic caps it should be emphasized that the network of the B8–9 program stars is so coarse that existing absorbing clouds might well escape detection. An example is the area in the north galactic cap in which Behr [19] found interstellar polarization for a number of stars to be abnormally large; there is no B8–B9 program star behind this area.

We now pass on to a discussion of the results obtained for the program stars in the distance range 90–200 pc with galactic latitude $|b| < 50°$. The number of these stars is 256, and Table 1 shows their distribution according to distance modulus and interstellar visual absorption A_v.

The group of stars with $A_v \leqq 0^m\!.10$ has color excesses E(B–V) $\leqq$ $0^m\!.03$, and the average value of E(B–V) for the group is E(B–V) = $+0^m\!.001$. In other words, the effects of interstellar reddening are almost negligible for this group of stars considering the probable error of about $\pm 0^m\!.01$ of the catalogue color excesses. About one-half of the stars in the distance range considered, 90–200 pc, belong to this group. The average interstellar absorption coefficient for these stars is about $0^m\!.2$ per kiloparsec.

Along many lines of sight observer-star it is less than $0^m_.1$ per kiloparsec.

Let us consider next the group of 66 stars with $A_v \geq 0^m_.24$, i.e., E(B–V) $\geq 0^m_.08$. The average value of A_v for these stars is $0^m_.41$. Figure 1 shows the distribution of the stars according to galactic longitude l^{II} and latitude b^{II} (new system). The distance modulus is indicated for each star. The distribution indicates the existence of a number of interstellar clouds of relatively heavy absorption. Among these are well-known features such as the absorbing clouds in Ophiuchus, Taurus, and Auriga.

Table 1

Dist. mod.	$A_v \leq 0^m_.10$	$A_v\ 0^m_.11–0^m_.23$	$A_v \geq 0^m_.24$	Total
$4^m_.9–5^m_.1$	17	3	7	27
$5^m_.2–5^m_.4$	27	10	12	49
$5^m_.5–5^m_.7$	21	17	18	56
$5^m_.8–6^m_.0$	18	15	11	44
$6^m_.1–6^m_.3$	20	15	7	42
$6^m_.4–6^m_.5$	17	10	11	38
Total	120	70	66	256

If we would assume that the interstellar absorption were evenly distributed along the lines of sight observer-star for the stars of this group, then we should derive an average interstellar absorption coefficient of about 3^m per kiloparsec. However, the distribution shown in Fig. 1 strongly suggests that the heavy absorption is limited to clouds, with average diameters of the order of 40 pc. The interstellar visual absorption coefficient within a typical cloud of heavy absorption is then seen to be about 10^m per kiloparsec.

Comparison of the results obtained for the two groups of stars with $A_v \leq 0^m_.1$ and $A_v \geq 0^m_.24$, respectively, indicates the very wide range of variation in the density of the reddening medium, by at least two orders of magnitude. Neither case is exceptional, the first group containing about one-half of the stars, the second one-fourth.

In estimating the contribution of the clouds of heavy absorption to the average interstellar absorption coefficient we must not overlook that there is a correlation between the locations of the B8–9 stars and the absorbing clouds. Regions like that of the Scorpius association contain both a concentration of young B8–9 stars and heavily absorbing interstellar matter. A better measure of the contribution of the heavy-absorption

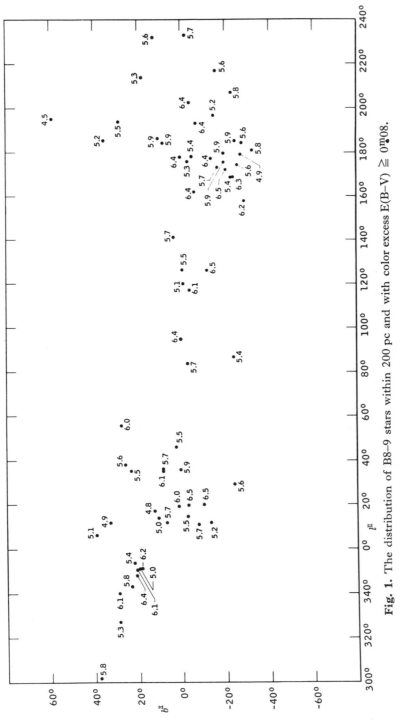

Fig. 1. The distribution of B8–9 stars within 200 pc and with color excess $E(B-V) \geqq 0^{m}.08$.

43

clouds is therefore obtained from the fraction of the area of the sky under investigation which is covered by the clouds in question, rather than from the fraction of B8–9 stars that belong to the group with $A_v \geqq 0\overset{m}{.}24$. The former fraction is found to be about 0.2. In this way it is found that the clouds of heavy absorption contribute more than one-half of the average interstellar absorption coefficient in the volume of space investigated. This estimate is confirmed through a study of the color excesses of 32 B8–9 program stars with values of the distance modulus in the range $7\overset{m}{.}3$ to $7\overset{m}{.}7$. The average interstellar visual absorption coefficient along the lines of sight to these stars is here found to be about $0\overset{m}{.}5$ per kiloparsec.

Our estimate of the relative role of the heavy-absorption clouds in the solar neighborhood agrees fairly well with that made by Greenstein [20] on the basis of the results of studies of dark nebulae by the star-count method (cf. Bok [21]).

The heavy-absorption clouds studied with the help of the stars of the group with $A_v \geqq 0\overset{m}{.}24$ can be investigated through the statistical methods of star counts and in greater detail through the methods developed at the Stockholm, Uppsala, Lund, and Warner and Swasey Observatories, which utilize photographically determined colors and spectral classifications. On the other hand, the spatial distribution of the lighter absorption indicated by the stars of the intermediate group with A_v $0\overset{m}{.}11$ to $0\overset{m}{.}23$ is presumably best determined on the basis of photoelectrically measured color excesses and distances of high precision such as we are considering here.

I should now like to discuss quite briefly some questions concerning the lighter absorption indicated by the color excesses found for the stars of the intermediate group in Table 1. Crawford and I have studied the distribution of these stars in relation to the distribution of the stars of the group of stars with negligible color excesses. We find evidence for the existence of regions of light interstellar absorption, typically about 30 pc in diameter, surrounded by regions of negligible interstellar absorption. The light-absorption clouds thus indicated are comparable in size to the larger regions that Dr. Blaauw described. However, the conclusion is reached that a detailed investigation of this kind of fine structure requires precision color excesses and distance moduli for a category of stars with a space density one order of magnitude higher than that of the B8–9 stars. The group of main-sequence F0–5 stars would be very well suited for the purpose (cf. Strömgren [1]). The results obtained from the B8–9 star survey would serve the purpose of selecting suitable areas in the sky for further study by the F0–5 star approach. In this way the number of stars that would have to be observed photometrically could be considerably reduced.

I would finally like to mention two further investigations planned by

Crawford and myself on which observational work is now under way. The first investigation concerns stars to visual apparent magnitude $8^m.25$ classified in the Henry Draper catalogue as B8 and B9 stars. As was already suspected by Morgan and others, most of these stars upon further investigation turn out to be of earlier type. On the basis of measured color excesses and distance moduli for these stars we hope to study large-scale features of the dust distribution within 700 pc. The second program comprises F5 stars in high galactic latitudes to 12^m. The dust distribution at larger distances from the galactic plane will be investigated through the method of photoelectrically determined color excesses and distances. Through this study we hope to gain information pertaining to the question of the total optical thickness of our galaxy. Dr. Oort has recently emphasized again the importance of obtaining new information on this question.

References

[1] B. Strömgren, in D. J. K. O'Connell (ed.), "Le Problème des populations stellaires" (Pont. Ac. Sc., p. 385, 1958).

[2] D. L. Crawford, *Ap. J.*, **128**, 185 (1958).

[3] H. L. Johnson and W. W. Morgan, *Ap. J.*, **117**, 313 (1953).

[4] W. W. Morgan and D. L. Harris, in A. Beer (ed.), "Vistas in Astronomy," Vol. 2, p. 1124, 1956.

[5] H. L. Johnson, *Lowell Obs. Bull. 90*, 1958.

[6] D. L. Crawford, Kitt Peak Natl. Obs. Contrib. and McDonald Obs. Contrib., to be published.

[7] R. M. Petrie, in A. Beer (ed.), "Vistas in Astronomy," Vol. 2, p. 1346, 1956.

[8] I. M. Kopylov, *Commun. Ap. Obs. Crimea*, **20**, 156 (1958).

[9] U. Sinnerstad, *Stockholm Obs. Ann.*, **21**, No. 6; **22**, No. 2.

[10] H. L. Johnson and B. Iriarte, *Lowell Obs. Bull. 91*, 1958.

[11] R. H. Hardie and D. L. Crawford, *Ap. J.*, **133**, 843 (1961).

[12] T. and J. H. Walraven, *B.A.N.*, **15**, 67 (1960).

[13] B. Strömgren, I.A.U. Symposium No. 10 [The Hertzsprung–Russell Diagram, J. L. Greenstein (ed.)], *Ann. Ap.*, Suppl. No. 8, p. 59 (1959).

[14] J. Stebbins, C. M. Huffer, and A. E. Whitford, *Ap. J.*, **90**, 209 (1939); **91**, 20 (1940).

[15] V. A. Ambarzumian, *Abastumani Obs. Bull. 4*, 7 (1940); also V. A. Ambarzumian and S. G. Gordeladse, *Abastumani Obs. Bull. 2*, p. 37, 1938; *Trans. I.A.U.*, **7**, 452 (1950).

[16] S. Chandrasekhar and G. Münch, *Ap. J.*, **112**, 380, 393 (1950); **114**, 110 (1951); **115**, 94 (1952).

[17] G. Münch, *Ap. J.*, **116**, 575 (1952); **121**, 291 (1955).

[18] Cf. *A.J.*, **58**, 276 (1953).

[19] A. Behr, *Veroeffentl. Sternwarte Göttingen*, **126**, 1959.

[20] J. L. Greenstein, *Harvard Circ. 422*, 1937.

[21] B. Bok, "Distribution of the Stars in Space," University of Chicago Press, Chicago, 1937.

Discussion

Dr. Spitzer: Is it conceivable that one could compute the autocorrelation coefficient of the color excess from your present data and get information on the cloud sizes?

Dr. Strömgren: The first thing you do naturally is to look at the pictures, but the data that we have are quite well suited for this sort of analysis. The individual distances and color excesses being known have some advantages in comparison with earlier discussions. On the other hand, it remains a handicap with a study of the grains that we have only one quantity, the absorption, not the velocity.

Dr. Spitzer: It would certainly be true that with ten times as many stars you would get a very detailed picture. However, your present data are so much more complete than anything we have had before that they should yield important new information on the spatial distribution of the obscuring clouds.

Dr. Struve: Has Dr. Strömgren seen the recent atlas by Khartasi? Mr. Khartasi is a member of the staff of the Mount Abastumani Observatory in Armenia. It is a very interesting atlas because it is pictorial. It is presented in the form of charts in which he has plotted the absorption clouds in the Milky Way, somewhat along the line of the early days. He gives the numbers, which as I remember range from 1 to a little over 700. But of course the numbers are very indefinite because they merge together. It would be extremely interesting, I think, to correlate these results with the results of the atlas. I might add that Mrs. Lynds is preparing another atlas which is based on the Palomar sky survey.

Dr. Strömgren: This would of course be extremely interesting. I think that the large majority of these features are further away and can only be correlated with the extended program. But what I would be particularly interested in would be to see if there are features corresponding to the fairly strong nearby absorption other than the well-known features.

Dr. Struve: The atlas by Khartasi shows an enormous amount of absorbing material that is quite different from Barnard's data. Barnard concentrated on the very opaque objects. But this, in the galactic plane, shows an almost continuous sort of absorption layer. There are regions in Sagittarius and Scorpio where there is a tremendous extent in galactic latitude, but there are other galactic latitudes where it is tremendously spotty, and in other regions it is very narrow, confined to the galactic equator.

Dr. Blaauw: In the lower picture you have quite an asymmetric distribution of stars in latitude for the middle longitudes. They are all in the lower part of the picture. This is, of course, the Gould belt. But is it really so—that at the positive latitudes there are so few B8–B9 stars?

Dr. Strömgren: The material is so nearly complete to magnitude 6.5 that in this range, where we are not concerned with the limitation to declinations north of $-20°$, it should give the true distribution of what the Harvard classification calls B8–B9.

Dr. Blaauw: It is not a selection effect that there might be such terrific absorption at the positive latitudes that you simply don't have any stars?

Dr. Strömgren: No, I don't think so. I would like to make one further comment in connection with your question. We are using this material also for another purpose. We are computing the galactic rectangular coordinates, and then using the distances with the proper motions and radial velocities to give space velocities; the H_β and UBV photometry give the age. On the basis of that material we want to study the present distribution and the distribution of the points of the formation of these stars.

Dr. Blaauw: Can you state what the range of age is that you find for these stars?

Dr. Strömgren: Yes. When you look at the whole rectangle here it is from zero to one hundred million. With the H_β and UBV photometry we can single out the stars that are younger than 20×10^6 years.

Dr. Blaauw: This would mean that in Gould's belt one finds a range of ages up to 10^8 years.

Dr. Strömgren: Yes, I should qualify this though, because the distribution that you would find if you separated it according to the youngest and the oldest stars hasn't been investigated yet.

Radio data on gas clouds at intermediate latitudes

A. Blaauw
(mostly on behalf of K. Takakubo
and H. van Woerden)

This paper deals with 21-cm data on the detailed structure of the interstellar medium, especially in connection with results obtained recently at Groningen and based on observations made at Dwingeloo. Previous 21-cm studies in Holland, which revealed the spiral structure in the galaxy, were confined to the low latitudes. In that work the individual clouds entered only when their random motions were discussed; the velocity distribution of the clouds affected the shape of the profiles for the individual spiral arms. This led to a statistical correction to obtain the profile free of the widening caused by cloud motions.

The Groningen work started from the idea that at certain intermediate latitudes it should be possible to have in the beam only a limited number of clouds (say, 3 to 8) which should then be recognizable as individual peaks in the profile. By separating these out we might obtain material to study the individual clouds. The work at Groningen was done by Dr. van Woerden (who is mainly responsible for the observational part of it) and Dr. Takakubo from Sendai, Japan, who spent 2 years with us to analyze the data. Table 1 gives some data on the interstellar cloud model as it has been derived from the optical work. In considering this, it has to be kept in mind that actually the interstellar clouds are very irregularly shaped bodies—that it is very hard to define exactly what a cloud is. This is immediately apparent from the photographs of emission and absorption nebulae. Yet it has proved useful to have a simplified model for reference. We shall not discuss the sources of the data in Table 1; a summary of some of them was given by Van de Hulst in the Cambridge Symposium on interstellar matter. To the data of Table 1 we may add that the

Table 1

Elements for Description of the Interstellar Clouds from Optical Observations

a_0	= radius of cloud	5–20 pc
n_0	= density inside cloud	10 atoms/cm³
$\mathcal{N}(0)$	= number density of cloud centers at $z = 0$	10–100 × 10³ per kpc³
$\bar{n}$	= over-all particle density	1 atom/cm³
K	= number of clouds traversed by line of sight	5–10 per kpc
F	= fraction of space occupied by clouds	10%

distribution of the clouds perpendicular to the galactic plane is usually described by an exponential function that can be characterized by the scale height z_0, i.e., the mean distance from the plane.

For the 21-cm program we decided to make observations at latitudes $\pm 10°$, $\pm 15°$, $\pm 20°$, $+25°$, and over the widest possible range of galactic longitudes. The grid was chosen so as to coincide with the areas in which Hubble has made his nebular counts, so that it would eventually be possible to compare total absorption with total amount of hydrogen. The beam width used is $0°.56$ between half-power points, and the band width for most of the observations is 8 kc/sec, i.e., 1.7 km/sec. For some we used only 0.9 km/sec.

Figures 1, 2 and 3 show some of the profiles, chosen from the $+25°$ zone. Optical depth is plotted against frequency. Optical depth is simply defined by the formula $\tau = -\ln(1 - T_{obs}/125°)$, which is correct if the temperature of the interstellar matter is supposed to be $125°$, the standard value usually adopted in the Dutch radio work.

Inspection of about 200 profiles reveals the following principal features:

1. There are almost always strong indications of several peaks in the profile; and even if no secondary maxima show, the shape suggests that the profile is a superposition of different components.

2. The extensions of the profiles at the higher frequencies are always in the direction in which one would expect to find them according to the differential galactic rotation.

Property 1 is what we had more or less expected. We are inclined to identify the different components with the individual interstellar clouds— similar to the identification of different components of optical interstellar absorption lines with different interstellar clouds. The natural procedure therefore is to resolve the profiles into these components and study the latter's properties statistically. In our analysis, this resolution has been based on the assumption that the individual components are gaussian-shaped; this proves to give a very satisfactory representation of the profiles

A. Blaauw

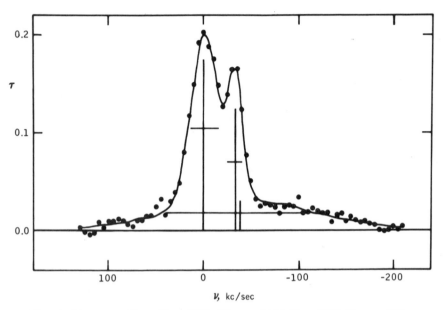

Fig. 1. 21-cm profile at $l^{\mathrm{II}} = 22°3$, $b^{\mathrm{II}} = +26°5$ ($l^{\mathrm{I}} = 350°$, $b^{\mathrm{I}} = +25°$).

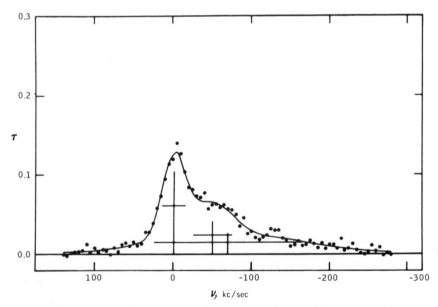

Fig. 2. 21-cm profile at $l^{\mathrm{II}} = 42°6$, $b^{\mathrm{II}} = +26°4$ ($l^{\mathrm{I}} = 10°$, $b^{\mathrm{I}} = +25°$).

even with a small number of components. Each component is character-ized by its mean velocity (or frequency), its velocity dispersion σ, and its central optical depth, τ_0. These three parameters are indicated in Figs. 1 to 3 by the crosslike features. The smooth lines represent the computed profiles based on the superposition of the gaussian components; it will be seen that they follow the observations very well.

Altogether the survey produces about 600 gaussian components. It is realized that the material of observed components must be affected by blends (limited resolving power of the method) and incompleteness of the recognition of the weak components. These deficiencies are taken into account in the analysis.

The velocities of the components range usually between -30 and $+30$ km/sec. The central optical depths τ_0 are generally quite small and seldom exceed 0.4. The velocity dispersions σ range from 1.1 to 15 km/sec. About 10 per cent of them are between 1 and 2 km/sec; these narrow components are, on the whole, the ones that can be most easily separated.

The analysis carried out so far, which is meant to check the identifica-tion of the gaussian components with the interstellar clouds, is based

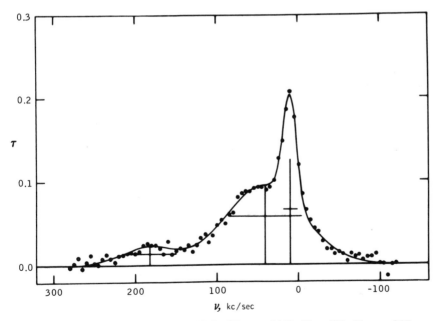

Fig. 3. 21-cm profile at $l^{11} = 123°0$, $b^{11} = +24°7$ ($l^{1} = 90°$, $b^{1} = +25°$).

primarily on the statistics of the quantity $\tau_0\sigma$. This is a measure of the mean total number of atoms per square centimeter per cloud as projected on the sky, averaged over the whole beam. This total number may be denoted by N_H. We thus have a statistic of N_H. In addition to this, use is made of the velocities of the components, particularly the differential galactic rotation shown by them.

The basic quantity, the statistics of the numbers N_H, we shall denote by $\psi(N_H)$. The cloud model is to be chosen so that it fits the observed $\psi(N_H)$. What quantities determine this fit? To identify these we start from the assumption that all clouds are identical spherical bodies with radius a_0 and density n_0. We assume their centers to have the exponential space distribution perpendicular to the galactic plane characterized by the scale height z_0. Their number density may be represented by $\mathscr{N}(z) \sim \mathscr{N}(0) \exp(-|z|/z_0)$. This distribution, as "seen" by the beam, is illustrated in Fig. 4.

It is easily found that the following quantities enter into the explanation of the observed statistics $\psi(N_H)$: (1) the ratio a_0/z_0, (2) the product $a_0 n_0$, and (3) the product $\mathscr{N}(0)z_0^3$.

Of these, the ratio a_0/z_0 determines the *shape* of $\psi(N_H)$. As long as this ratio remains the same, the cloud distribution in the beam as seen by the telescope does not differ; the distribution of the fractions of the clouds lying inside the beam remains the same and hence also the shape of $\psi(N_H)$. If, for constant a_0/z_0 we increase $a_0 n_0$, then the values of N_H are increased proportionately; hence the quantity $a_0 n_0$ determines the horizontal scale of the curve $\psi(N_H)$. Further, if, for constant a_0/z_0, the product $\mathscr{N}(0)z_0^3$ increases, the total number of clouds producing a given N_H increases proportionately. Hence the quantity $\mathscr{N}(0)z_0^3$ determines the vertical scale of the curve $\psi(N_H)$.

In addition to the quantities a_0/z_0, $a_0 n_0$, and $\mathscr{N}(0)z_0^3$ we can also directly determine z_0. By measuring the amplitude of the differential

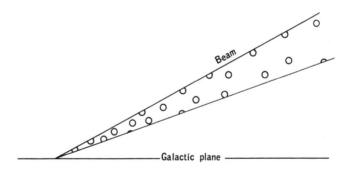

Fig. 4. Distribution of clouds in the beam.

galactic rotation in the velocities of the components, we can determine their mean distance from the sun and hence their mean distance from the plane. Combining this with the assumed density distribution perpendicular to the galactic plane we find z_0.

In actual practice, Takakubo's analysis was based only on the best established data for the gaussian components. Thus, he has limited himself to the highest latitude zones and to the directions of largest differential galactic rotation in order to reduce the influence of blending of components. Moreover, only the components with dispersions below 7 km/sec (the ones best recognized) were used. Naturally, appropriate completeness factors had to be applied for this in the statistics.

In a second approximation the assumption of uniform cloud densities n_0 and radii a_0 was dropped. Instead, all values of the sizes and densities are allowed, but the following restrictions are supposed to hold:

1. The radii are distributed according to $\exp(-a/\bar{a})$, where $\bar{a}$ is the mean radius.

2. The product $n_0 a$ is the same for all clouds, n_0 being the internal density.

The first assumption is inspired by results derived by Cederblad (*Medd. Lunds Astronomical Obs.*, [II] 12, No. 119, 1946) for diffuse nebulae; the second by a study by Ter Haar [*Z. Ap.*, **32**, 251 (1953)].

Again, the observed statistics of $\psi(N_H)$ is reproduced by a suitable choice of the parameters $\bar{a}/z_0$, $a n_0$, and $\mathcal{N}(0)z_0^3$.

The provisional results of this analysis based on part of the observational material are given in Table 2. A scale height $z_0 = 130$ pc was used.

Table 2

Provisional Elements of a Cloud Model Derived from 21-cm Observations

First approximation: all clouds equal a_0 and n_0; scale height $z_0 = 130$ pc	Second approximation: distribution of radii $e^{-a/\bar{a}}$, and $a n_0 = $ constant; scale height $= 130$ pc
$a_0 = 2.8$ pc	$\bar{a} = 1.2$ pc
$n_0 = 20$ atoms/cm^3	$n(\bar{a}) = 47$ atoms/cm^3
$\mathcal{N}(0) = 7.5 \times 10^5$ per kpc^3	$\mathcal{N}(0) = 13 \times 10^5$ per kpc^3
$\bar{n} = 1.4$ atoms/cm^3	$\bar{n} = 0.7$ atom/cm^3
$K = 10$ per kpc	$K = 19$ per kpc
$F = 7\%$	$F = 11\%$
Mass of cloud: 46 ◯ masses	

The conversion from the observed mean distance of the components (derived from differential rotation) to the scale height is not a straightforward one, owing to the incompleteness of the most distant, weak, clouds in our material. The adopted value $z_0 = 130$ pc satisfies both the differential rotation and the optical data.

Comparing Tables 1 and 2, the optical and the radio results, the general impression is that the gaussian components are probably to be identified with the optical clouds; we probably are dealing in the two observational approaches with the same structures. The very idealized nature of the cloud picture as it has been used here precludes the derivation of more detailed conclusions concerning the cloud properties.

Apart from these results of a statistical nature, there are a number of interesting features derived from the velocity distribution of the components. First of all, I want to point out that the effect of differential galactic rotation is shown with remarkable regularity, notwithstanding the fact that we are dealing here with objects at fairly small distances. This is illustrated by Figs. 5 and 6. They refer to the zones $+25°$ and $+20°$, respectively, and for each zone they show, for each longitude of observation, the various components into which the profile has been resolved. For instance, for $b^I = +25°$, $l^I = 90°$, the four components have velocities of about -3, -10, -38, and -73 km/sec. Their velocity dispersions σ are represented by the half-length of the horizontal sides of the rectangles. The vertical dimension of these is a measure of τ_0.

We notice first of all the presence of the well-defined double sine curve in the mean velocities of the components as a function of longitude. The semiamplitude is only about 10 km/sec, corresponding to a distance of approximately 500 pc. It seems to me that the differential rotation is exhibited by the nearby interstellar matter in a remarkably regular way, more regularly than we observe it for stellar objects at such small distances.

Another important feature is the excess of fairly large negative components in the range of longitudes 100° to 180° ($l^I = 70°$ to 150°). and of positive components around longitude 0° ($l^I = 330°$). At first sight, the former might be interpreted as being due to differential galactic rotation; we should then be dealing with matter at the distance of the Perseus arm. However, this seems rather unlikely, for the following reasons.

The latitude at which these high-velocity components are observed, up to 25°, would require them to be at distances between 500 and 1000 pc above the galactic plane. This is somewhat unlikely from what we know of the galactic concentration of matter on that side of the Perseus arm. Moreover there are strong indications that similar high-velocity objects occur at even higher latitudes. We do not yet possess 21-cm observations at these latitudes, but there is interesting evidence in optical observations. Recently, Münch and Zirin [*Ap. J.*, **133**, 11 (1961)] have published a list of high-velocity interstellar K-line components in 24 stars above 20° latitude. We represent, in Fig. 7, the velocities of these components in a way

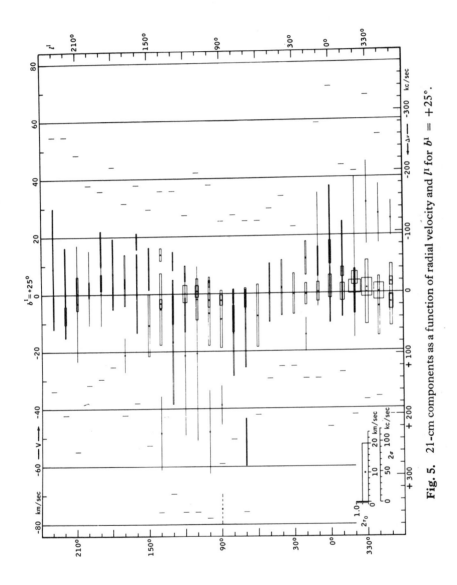

Fig. 5. 21-cm components as a function of radial velocity and l^I for $b^I = +25°$.

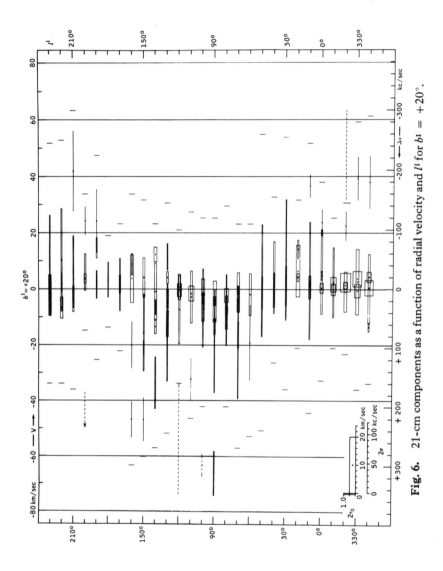

Fig. 6. 21-cm components as a function of radial velocity and l^{I} for $b^{I} = +20°$.

similar to Figs. 5 and 6; the velocities are plotted against the longitude of the star. We note that unfortunately Münch and Zirin have no stars in the longitude interval between 90° and 180° ($l^I = 60°$ and 150°). However, there seem to be indications that at the adjacent longitudes high negative velocities occur very similar to those noted for these longitudes in Figs. 5 and 6. But these velocities occur in stars at +62° latitude ($b^I = +64°$) (HD 93521) and −37° latitude (HD 215733). These velocities cannot be interpreted as being due to differential galactic rotation in distant objects.

This fact, together with the occurrence in the 21-cm measures of high positive velocities around longitude 0° ($l^I = 330°$), where differential rotation cannot explain them either, suggests that we are dealing with a new, unexpected phenomenon. This seems to have the character of a general flow of interstellar clouds toward the solar neighborhood, coming from the direction of galactic longitude around 140° ($l^I = 110°$). If such a flow exists it will reveal itself by negative velocity components in a fairly wide range of longitude around the central direction, as is observed. I tentatively would like to suggest that we are dealing indeed with such a

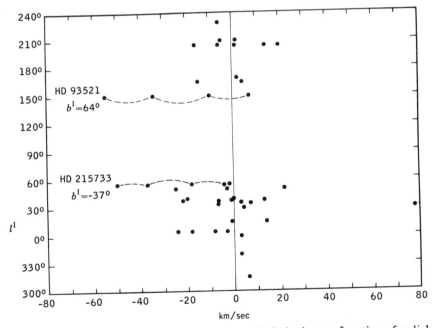

Fig. 7. K-line components in stars above 20° latitude as a function of radial velocity and l^I.

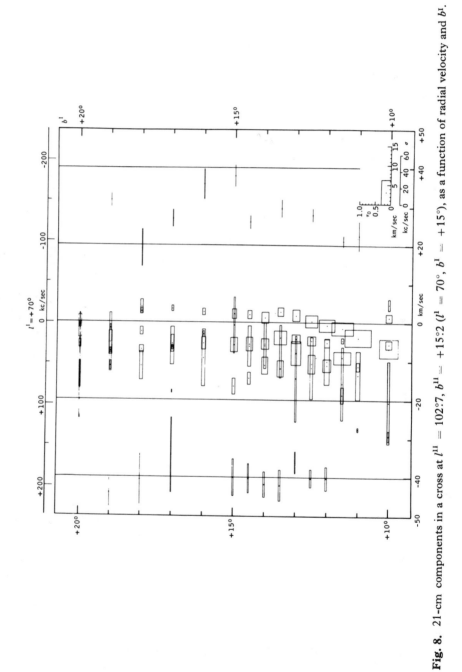

Fig. 8. 21-cm components in a cross at $l^{II} = 102°7$, $b^{II} = +15°2$ ($l^{I} = 70°$, $b^{I} = +15°$), as a function of radial velocity and b^{I}.

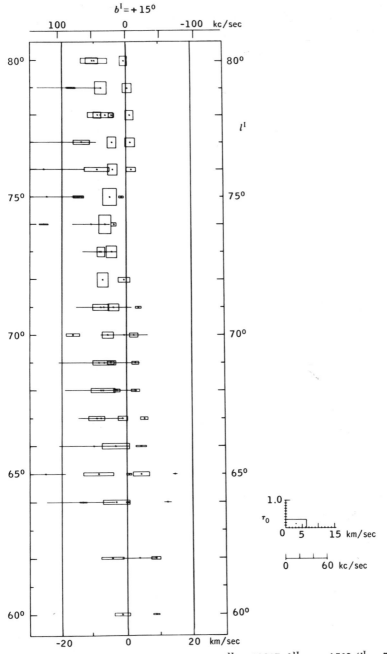

Fig. 9. 21-cm components in a cross at $l^{II} = 102°7$, $b^{II} = +15°2$ ($l^{I} = 70°$, $b^{I} = +15°$), as a function of radial velocity and l^{I}.

flow of matter; it must then be coming from the direction of the Perseus arm. Perhaps the excess of positive velocities observed around longitude $0°$ ($l^I = 330°$) corresponds to the same flow observed in the receding direction. There are some interesting phenomena observed in the direction of the Perseus arm which will be discussed in a later paper and which may have a common origin with the phenomenon just described.

Plots such as those of Figs. 5 and 6 provide a means for charting the contours on the sky for clouds whose velocities are well separated from other clouds, provided the observed points are chosen closer together in the sky. The method may be illustrated by means of Figs. 8 and 9. These are arranged similarly to Figs. 5 and 6, but the observed positions are now chosen along the two legs of a "cross" centered on $l^I = 70°$, $b^I = +15°$ ($l^{II} = 102°.7$, $b^{II} = +15°.2$). Data referring to the leg at constant longitude are given in Fig. 8, at intervals $\Delta b = 1°$ or $0°.5$. Figure 9 refers to the leg at constant latitude, with observations at intervals $\Delta l = 1°$. We note that, for instance in Fig. 8, a rather isolated component with small velocity dispersion occurs around zero velocity which can be traced from $b = +11°$ to $+15°$ and perhaps even up to $+18°$. This same component is also recognized in Fig. 9 at longitudes l^I of $70°$ ($l^{II} = 103°$) and lower. Another component can be traced in Fig. 9 at zero velocity from longitude $l^I = 76°$ ($l^{II} = 109°$) upward.

Plots such as these, when covering a fine grid over an extended part of the sky, will provide data on the shapes of interstellar clouds. Work along these lines is in progress.

Discussion

Dr. Oort: You will have noticed how much the detailed data on the emission at 21 cm can teach about the fine structure of the interstellar medium, just because of the ease with which the necessary observations can be made, and the fact that you don't need stars, as in the optical case, to see the gas in absorption against the light of the stars.

Ed.: A lengthy discussion followed on the effects of the beam width. For clouds that fill the beam completely, $\sigma\tau$ as determined at Groningen is proportional to the number of hydrogen atoms per square centimeter along the line of sight. For clouds that fill the beam only partially it is less than that. In fact it is then proportional to the number of hydrogen atoms per square centimeter along the line of sight in the cloud multiplied by the fraction of the beam that is filled.

Dr. Schwarzschild: Are you putting in your statistics the actual antenna pattern?

Dr. Blaauw: No, in the statistics a sharp cutoff has been used. As long as you are using the idealized picture of clouds of uniform density there is not much point in going to the refinement of the beam unless you also take into consideration the density distribution in the cloud.

Dr. Christy: Is it possible that this technique is less sensitive on clouds that are small compared to beam width, and that therefore the mean cloud size you find is in part determined by the beam width?

Dr. Blaauw: Yes. Actually the distant clouds are not very well represented in the beam width because they tend to give profiles that are very low. It is the mean value of the number of atoms per square centimeter over the whole area of the beam which counts in detecting the components, and the more distant the cloud is, the lower this quantity becomes. The most distant clouds tend to be not observed unless their σ values are very small.

Dr. Biermann: Are there any early-type stars behind these fast clouds that are moving toward us?

Dr. Blaauw: There may be. We don't know what the distances of these high-velocity clouds are. A remarkable thing is that they all have large values of σ.

Dr. Schwarzschild: If I understand correctly you had essentially two ways of getting at the scales of these clouds: One was looking at one place and making the statistics of the $\sigma\tau$ values. That method relied on a sort of resolution of the size of the clouds. If the clouds were all very small compared to your beam width you wouldn't get their diameter. If the clouds were very big compared to the beam width, you wouldn't get anything. With an unknown profile of a typical cloud, and the profile of the beam not being taken into account, how sensitive really is the shape of your statistics and therefore how much weight should one give to these numbers of the order of 2 pc? The other method, which you followed at the end, which I appreciate means a terrific amount of work, really uses the resolution of the beam explicitly, and therefore I am not sure that I wouldn't like to trust these results rather than the preceding ones.

Dr. Blaauw: It certainly is true that the second method should be taken also. I think one should not take these figures too seriously, except that they give a picture similar to the optical one. If we now talk about the clouds in the 21-cm profile and in the optical profile, it gives confidence that we are talking about the same things. However, from then on I quite agree that if you want to have individual data on the clouds you should go by these "crosses," or rather by a grid which fills a certain part of the sky.

Dr. Strömgren: In that connection, if one takes the somewhat larger areas that are outlined by the method of following the components with the radial velocities, one could perhaps look at the small value that follows from the intensity variations as the fine structure within the larger region. You must, of course, in some way or other simplify the description and have a cloud picture, but could one say something beyond that about the contrast that is necessary between the clouds and the space in-between? Would you be able to reproduce your intensity results if you have a picture in which there were density fluctuations, perhaps 3 to 1 between the small structure clouds and the space in-between, or must you assume a bigger contrast?

Dr. Blaauw: I presume we have to assume a bigger contrast.

Dr. Strömgren: The path through the cloud is so small compared to the path through what is in-between that for the cloud to be effective the contrast must be rather big. This small structure then would be rather pronounced. Is that correct?

Dr. Blaauw: I think it would be.

Dr. Spitzer: If I understand correctly the physical basis for these small radii, it is the plot of the frequency of $\sigma\tau$ against different values of $\sigma\tau$. The analysis you have described assumes that τ, the optical thickness through the middle of the cloud, is the same for all clouds. I think it is clear that it would be entirely possible to explain your results with any assumption about the radius if you were willing to make a suitable assumption for the distribution of the optical thicknesses of the clouds. And since we don't really have any a priori information on the distribution of τ, isn't it clear that we could explain the observed results with any radius?

Dr. Strömgren: You have already commented on the comparison between the optical and the radio data. May I just return to one comparison, the number of clouds in the line of sight. Is it correct to say that the value 19 follows rather directly from your seeing the number of resolved components and the estimated line of sight, and that the correction for overlap is not large?

Dr. Blaauw: Indeed, I believe if one considers what are the sources of uncertainty of various quantities determined, this quantity K is one of the best determined.

Dr. Helfer: I want to make two points. The direction of streaming in here agrees pretty much with the main direction of contraction that was found in the analysis I reported on earlier. I talked in terms of expansion and contraction but the phenomena are exactly equivalent to this sort of thing. This is your preferred direction. However, when you go to very large negative latitudes, around $-60°$ or so, and again just look at the crude median velocity data without looking at individual clouds, you find the median velocities are quite highly negative, -10 or -15 km/sec all around the sky. The Australian results also seem to show this.

The other point is on your scale-factor argument. Particularly in the direction of l equals $120°$ ($l^{\mathrm{I}} = 90°$)—there is much more material beneath than above the plane. From b equals $-30°$ to $-50°$ and in fact right down to the south galactic pole, there is an enormous amount of material. This is well beyond the Gould belt. It is very hard to avoid the impression that the gas in that vicinity is located in some sort of a system which is well beneath us and that we are looking down into it essentially in the southern part; and we just see slight fringes above us when we look in the northern part of the galaxy. That means that the zero point of your scale height would be changed.

Dr. Blaauw: This should come out in a separate discussion of the northern and southern latitudes.

Dr. Helfer: Yes. I hope that the southern region with all this gas will be very quickly investigated, because it is quite different from the northern hemisphere. A third point is that the region of the Pleiades seems to show some extended clouds, which are perhaps $3°$ or so across. This is based on the DTM radio observations, which have a very crude beam resolution ($3°5$) and a band width of about 12 kc. But there are certainly two clouds, perhaps three or four. These things are above the limit of resolution of the DTM equipment, both in beam width and in frequency. It would be most interesting if these could be observed, too, to enable us to discuss the controversy regarding the presence of hydrogen in the Pleiades cluster itself.

Dr. Oort: I should like to say that we have in Leiden initiated a program on high-velocity clouds in quite high latitudes. We had tried this before in a very provisional manner but the results were not certain enough.

Large-scale structure in the region around h and chi Persei

A. Blaauw
(mostly on behalf of Mrs. M. Hack
and H. van Woerden)

This paper concerns some features in the cloud structure observed in the direction around $l^{II} = 132°$ ($l^I = 100°$), which were discovered in the course of the intermediate latitude survey and which appeared to deserve special attention. When observations for the large survey were made at longitude $134°5$ ($l^I = 102°5$), latitude $-10°6$ ($b^I = -10°$), a very sharp and intense peak was observed at the frequency corresponding to a velocity of about -50 km/sec. This indicated that there was either an isolated high-density cloud with high negative velocity in the solar neighborhood, or a large cloud complex at a distance of about 2000 pc. Our principal aim was to outline the shape of the cloud and to find its mass and possibly other features.

Profiles were determined for a fine grid of points in the region $l^{II} = 126°$ to $142°$ ($l^I = 94°$ to $110°$), $b^{II} = -6°6$ to $-18°6$ ($b^I = -6°$ to $-18°$). By means of these, contour diagrams were made similar to the one described in my first paper in this volume. Thus, for each galactic longitude, a plot is made with frequency as an abscissa and latitude as an ordinate, and the intensity of the radiation received is indicated by the degree of shading. Three examples, for $l^{II} = 133°$, $134°$, and $135°$ ($l^I = 101°$, $102°$, and $103°$) are given in Fig. 1. These examples, and similarly the contour diagrams for adjacent longitudes, show the following features:

1. They reveal the isolated area of high intensity of radiation around frequency $+225$ kc/sec (velocity -48 km/sec) and between latitudes $-9°$ to $-14°$, which led us to explore this region of the sky; this I shall refer to as feature 1.

64 *A. Blaauw*

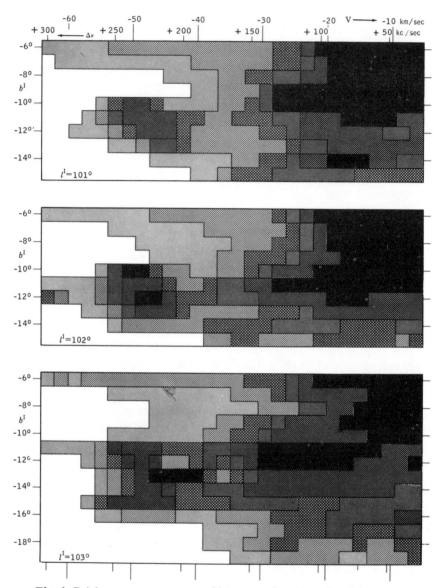

Fig. 1. Brightness temperature at 21 cm as a function of radial velocity and galactic latitude (old system) for $l^{II} = 133°$ ($l^I = 101°$), $l^{II} = 134°$ ($l^I = 102°$) and $l^{II} = 135°$ ($l^I = 103°$).

2. There appears to be a less clearly separated second feature at about frequency $+125$ kc/sec (-26 km/sec) and at about the same latitudes. This will be referred to as feature 2.

To study feature 1 we now separate out the frequency range 210 to 250 kc/sec (-45 to -53 km/sec), and we plot the intensity of the radiation in this interval as a function of longitude and latitude. These intensities are subsequently converted into total numbers of hydrogen atoms per square centimeter integrated along the line of sight; these numbers are represented by N_H as before. The result is shown in Fig. 2; the various degrees of shading indicate the integrated numbers N_H in units of 10^{20} atoms. The figure shows the shape of the cloud in projection against the sky.

A similar plot was obtained for feature 2; this is shown in Fig. 3. Other plots (not reproduced here) show the mean frequency of this radiation as a function of l^I and b^I. From these it appears that the variation of the mean velocity over the two features is very small, of the order of 1 or 2 km/sec only. It was further found that the internal velocity dispersion in both features is of the order of 4 km/sec only.

For further interpretation of these results, for instance for the mass estimates, we require to know the distances of these gas complexes. We have no direct means yet to determine these. We shall consider two

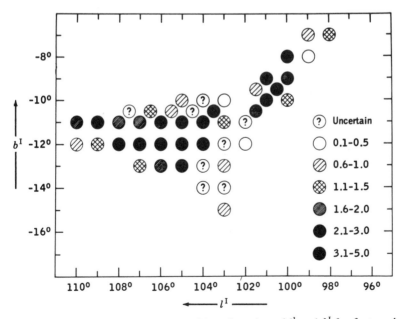

Fig. 2. N_H in units of 10^{20} atoms/cm^2 as a function of l^I and b^I for feature 1.

possibilities. Either we put them at 220 pc, that is, in the immediate neighborhood of the sun, or we put them at about 2200 pc, for the reason mentioned below. If we do the first, we obtain the masses and densities (using assumed depths) given in the middle division of Table 1. We then

Table 1
Properties of the Two Features

	Feature 1	Feature 2
Mean frequency	+225 kc/sec	+125 kc/sec
Mean velocity	−48 km/sec	−26 km/sec
Projected area	28 square degrees	39 square degrees
Assumed distance 220 pc		
Total mass	450 ⊙	1400 ⊙
Projected area	410 pc²	560 pc²
Assumed depth	10 pc	10 pc
Density	4.4 atoms/cm³	10 atoms/cm³
Assumed distance 2200 pc		
Total mass	45,000 ⊙	140,000 ⊙
Projected area	41,000 pc²	56,000 pc²
Assumed depth	200 pc	200 pc
Density	0.22 atom/cm	0.50 atom/cm³

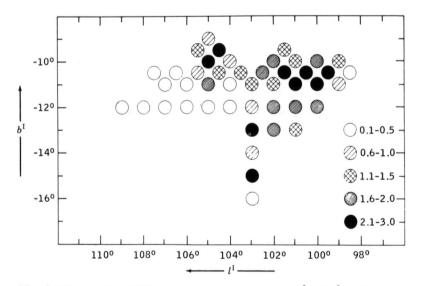

Fig. 3. N_H in units of 10^{20} atoms/cm² as a function of l^I and b^I for feature 2.

find two clouds which, although perhaps rather massive, may still be reckoned to belong to the category of individual clouds of which we described the statistical properties in the preceding paper. The dimensions are about 10 by 50 pc and the densities several atoms per cubic centimeter. However, this interpretation does not appear quite satisfactory. It seems somewhat hard to understand how these fast-moving clouds (fast with respect to the local standard of rest) could have preserved their very small internal velocity dispersion and the very small

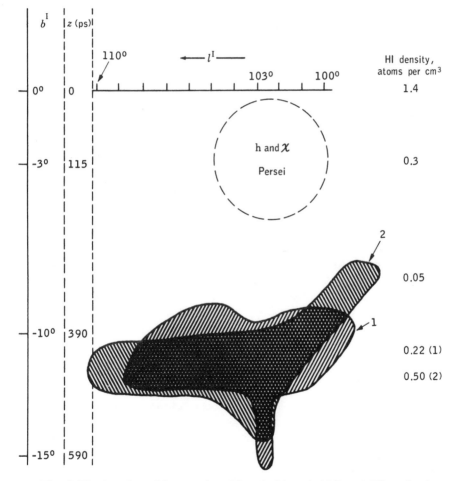

Fig. 4. The location of features 1 and 2 and of h and chi Persei. The galactic coordinates are on the old system.

relative velocity of different parts notwithstanding the frequent encounters
with other clouds which they must have experienced in the past.

The main reason for seriously considering the alternative interpreta-
tation with a tenfold larger distance may be explained by means of Fig. 4.
In it we have plotted the areas of the sky covered by the two features.
We notice that they occur just a few degrees below the large association
h and chi Persei, the center of which is at about $l^{II} = 134°7$, $b^{II} = -3°6$
($l^{I} = 102°5$, $b^{I} = -3°$). The dotted circle roughly outlines the
region of the association. We should like to consider the possibility
that the two features have a physical relation with the association. For that
reason we used as the alternative distance that of the association, which is
about 2200 pc. The corresponding masses and densities are in the bottom
division of Table 1. We are now dealing with large bodies, which we would
rather describe as cloud complexes, similar in mass to, for instance, the
Orion complex. The radial velocity of h and chi Persei is -38 km/sec,
which is just in between the values for the two features.

The densities obtained in this case—with an assumed depth of
200 pc—are a few tenths of an atom per cubic centimeter. It is interesting
to compare these with estimates for the surroundings. These are indicated
on the right-hand side of the figure; the left side shows the latitudes, and
the distances from the galactic plane corresponding with a distance from
the sun of 2200 pc. The association h and chi Persei appears to be situated
in a region of rather low density—a fact that has been noticed before.

The presence of these large cloud complexes at a distance of about
400 pc from the galactic plane presents an interesting problem as to the
stability of the configurations. The situation must be one of a temporary
character because the gravitational attraction of the mass in the galactic
plane must be pulling the two clouds back into it. This would happen in
the course of 20 million years or so. The inference is that the situation as
it is observed must have come about quite recently; it may not be older
than a similar lapse of time.

We should like to suggest that it has been caused by a general pushing
away of the interstellar matter from the region of the double cluster. We
might think of the thermal expansion, which according to the Oort–
Spitzer theory occurs in the ionized regions around associations in general.
Another possibility is that we are dealing with a more violent explosion,
as would be the case if h and chi Persei would have been the scene of a
large number of supernova explosions. We observe an exceptionally large
number of supergiants in the association, which implies that a very large
number of massive stars are present. This suggests that if supernovae
of type II are due to the most massive stars, the conditions for the occurrence of a large number of supernovae of type II must have been quite
favorable in this region.

Discussion

Dr. Schwarzschild: On the observational side, how does this region look, both as to galaxy counts and as to possible interstellar lines of very distant stars?

Dr. Blaauw: This is just at the limit of the normal zone of avoidance; moreover Hubble's counts were made only every 10° in longitude and so do not contain sufficient information. As to the stars and interstellar lines, you do find of course that there are a number of faint B-type stars in the area. Nothing is known about them except the very poorly determined spectral type. All the work on classification and polarization ends at −6° latitude.

Dr. Strömgren: If you take the normal ratio of interstellar absorption and the number of H atoms in the line of sight, what does the absorption effect come out to be, approximately?

Dr. Blaauw: I believe if you take an average of 2 times 10^{20} for the projected density, you must have something of the order of a few tenths of extinction.

Dr. Oort: That would be difficult to see in the galaxy counts, I am afraid, because they are so irregular.

Dr. Blaauw: This is what we predict. Maybe it is more. It is certainly worthwhile to check this. Although, of course, you must not forget that there is foreground matter. This has been separated in the 21-cm velocities, but it does contribute to the absorption.

Dr. Biermann: If we try to connect this with what we discussed yesterday, then a possible picture would be that we have between these two clouds either an expanding H II region or a supernova, as you say. When we compare the energies concerned, the total kinetic energy would be approximately that of a supernova of type II, but then we would run into the difficulty that the disparity of initial velocities might make it less likely. On the other hand, if we say it is an expanding H II region, this would match the velocity of about 12 km with respect to the center of the mass very well, and also the work of Goldsworthy. If we say the acceleration took place over a few million years and after this the exciting star just burned out, then the picture seems to come out quite satisfactorily. I think the process would require something of the order of 10 per cent or so of the available energy.

Dr. Oort: It is an enormous mass. Moreover, it would have had to be pushed away from the galactic plane also at a very high velocity.

Dr. Blaauw: There must be something between 40 and 80 supergiants associated with h and chi; if they have all been O-type stars a very strong expanding force would have occurred. From the luminosity data, the age of the double cluster must be of the order of 20×10^6 years. That is the time scale that would correspond to pushing the clouds away from the galactic plane with such a velocity that it would now have approximately zero velocity. I should have mentioned also that there is a difference in the interstellar line velocity and the star velocity of Münch of the order of 12 km/sec. It is a remarkable thing that the interstellar velocity that Münch measures is practically the same as the velocity of the first feature. So perhaps there is in the line of sight also quite an amount of mass which has the same relative velocity with respect to h and chi as the clouds I have discussed. Such a relative velocity in the time scale that we are talking about corresponds to something of the order of 250 pc.

Dr. Oort: Isn't that very large? There would have been much initial interstellar matter, I suppose.

Ed.: A somewhat inconclusive discussion followed on whether either O stars or supernovae would really provide enough energy. It appeared that a geometric

A. Blaauw

factor, accounting for the fact that the present clouds cover only a fraction of the area of a sphere around h and chi Persei, should also be included.

Dr. Christy: If there were a magnetic field strong enough to organize the motion and you pushed the magnetic field away, would this help account for the small internal velocity dispersion?

Dr. Blaauw: You would think of something organizing the orientation also, because the main body of both these clouds is nearly parallel to the plane.

Some remarks on the transition region between disk and halo

J. H. Oort

I shall make only a few remarks, because this is a report on an investigation that has not been completed. The program was started with the idea of getting some information on the region outside the expanding 3-kpc arm, to see whether any signs of radial or other abnormal motions would be found. Since this program has not yet been completed, I shall report only on the matter that is found at somewhat larger distances from the galactic plane outside the actual disk.

If you observe matter with a velocity that corresponds to the maximum rotational velocity in a given direction, you can determine with reasonable confidence its distance from the sun and thus also its distance from the plane. The present observations went out to latitudes of about 6°.

The kind of thing that has been produced so far are diagrams like Fig. 1. The most important fact for our present purpose is that there are still quite considerable intensities at distances of the order of 500 pc from the galactic plane, intensities that are perhaps between 5 and 10 per cent of the intensities one observes in the plane. Thus, well outside the real disk one still finds neutral hydrogen with an average density of between 5 and 10 per cent of the density in the plane. That is not entirely new. It had been noted by Dr. Schmidt in his investigation of the general structure of the inner parts of the galactic system, made with a telescope of much larger beam width. The investigation I am discussing now is being done by Whitney Shane at Leiden. The beam width used is $0°.56$. There is not much more that I can say about it at present except that these outer contours do not follow any of the spiral structures. What one is seeing here looks like a somewhat regular envelope surrounding the disk.

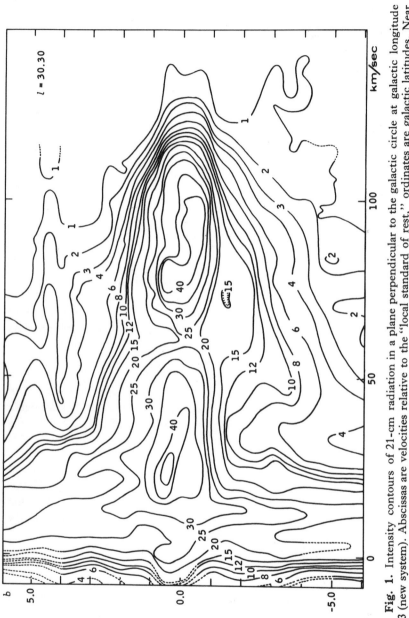

Fig. 1. Intensity contours of 21-cm radiation in a plane perpendicular to the galactic circle at galactic longitude 30°.3 (new system). Abscissas are velocities relative to the "local standard of rest," ordinates are galactic latitudes. Near the "tangential point," 1° in latitude corresponds with $z = 123$ pc. The numbers attached to the contours are in units of 2°K.

72

Another remark on the same subject deals with the possible presence of *dust* at greater distances from the galactic plane. The only reliable data on color excesses and absorptions that we dispose of refer to the thin disk where B-type stars have been observed. These, as well as the interstellar matter itself, are distributed extremely irregularly, as Dr. Strömgren pointed out earlier, and we are likely to find enormous differences from one longitude to another. The irregularities are found not only in the galactic equator; the nearby cloud complexes also produce great differences in the higher latitudes.

Another way in which we can observe the average absorption in directions away from the galactic plane is by counts of faint galaxies. Such counts were made a long time ago by Dr. Hubble and later by Dr. C. D. Shane and his co-workers at the Lick Observatory. It would be interesting to see whether the total absorption one finds from these nebular counts can be accounted for by matter close to the galactic plane, or whether part of the matter must be at greater distances.

From Hubble's nebular counts one finds an optical thickness of about $0\overset{m}{.}3$ in the direction of the galactic pole. This was derived from counts made at different latitudes and therefore refers to the average density over quite a large region.

There is one way (even with the present data) one can investigate whether all of this absorption takes place quite close to the galactic plane or not. That is by considering general star counts in different galactic latitudes. If one confines oneself to longitudes near the directions that differ 90° from the direction to the center, one can expect that the stellar density would not vary too greatly in planes parallel to the galactic plane. From the actual star counts in such directions one might get at least a rough estimate of the absorption.

One can, for instance, compare the counts of stars at a given apparent magnitude m_{90} at the pole with stars of corresponding apparent magnitude m_b at a latitude b, where m_b would be chosen in such a way that it corresponds to stars at the same distance from the galactic plane and with the same absolute magnitude as the stars of magnitude m_{90} near the poles. Thus

$$m_b = m_{90} - 5 \log \sin b + \Delta A$$

where ΔA is the difference in absorption in front of stars at latitudes 90° and b, respectively.

If we now consider the number of stars per square degree, $N(m_b)$, of magnitude m_b at lattitude b and the corresponding number at magnitude m_{90} near the pole, and if we assume that there is no change in star density parallel to the plane, we should have

$$N(m_b) = N(m_{90})/\sin^3 b$$

J. H. Oort

if the absorptions applied are correct. If one does this and assumes that all the absorption derived from the galaxy counts is in front of the stars considered, one gets the results shown in Table 1. Here $|\bar{z}|$ is the logarithmic mean distance in parsecs from the galactic plane which would correspond to the value of m_{90} given in the first column; $\Delta \log N(m)$ is the average difference between the values of $\log N(m)$ that are observed in the latitudes indicated in the third column and $\log N(m)$ as computed from the above equations. The probable errors were derived from the differences between the individual areas used. The star counts used are from the "Mt. Wilson Catalogue of Selected Areas" (tabulated by van Rhijn in Groningen Publications No. 43). The fainter magnitudes have been corrected for systematic error as determined by Baum (unpublished).

The large values of $\Delta \log N(m)$ are apparent. It is, of course, possible that this is a real phenomenon and that the star density in the region around the sun is a factor of 2 or more lower than the average density on either side of it. But it may also be due to our having made a wrong assumption, and that not all the absorption is in front of these stars.

Table 1

Differences between Observed and Computed Star Densities

m_{90}	$|\bar{z}|$	$|b|$	ΔA	$\Delta \log N(m)$	$A(90°)$	$\Delta \log N(m)$
10	173	7–20°	1^{m}20	0.221 ± 0.023	0^{m}13	−0.03
12	316	12–33	0^{m}66	0.160 ± 0.017	0^{m}15	0.05
14	574	21–50	0^{m}27	0.048 ± 0.015	0^{m}17	0.02

To investigate this possibility I have indicated as an example a possible distribution of absorbing matter in the fifth column of the table, where $A(90°)$ denotes the absorption in the direction of the galactic poles, between the sun and a point at a height $|\bar{z}|$ above the plane. The last column gives the $\Delta \log N(m)$ computed from this distribution. It is seen that the residuals are now quite satisfactory. In this case one-half of the absorbing matter indicated by the counts of galaxies would lie beyond 300 pc from the plane.

At 300 pc from the plane the density of the absorbing matter will be at most about 10 per cent of that in the plane. We can see that from color excesses of B stars and also from 21-cm measurements. This matter would have to extend, then, to distances of several kiloparsecs from the plane to produce the rest of the absorption found from the galaxy counts.

I should stress that this is a possible but by no means certain interpretation of the data. As Dr. Strömgren has pointed out, observations are now in progress which will certainly give the information required.

Let me add that the question came up also in connection with the observations made by Dr. van Houten, who found that in a number of galaxies, like NGC 4594, where you have heavy absorption in the equatorial plane, the color becomes gradually bluer when you go out from the nucleus along the minor axis. This might be explained by assuming that in addition to the absorbing matter contained in the disk there would be an appreciable amount extending up to, say, 2 kpc from the equatorial plane. Of course, in this case there are other possible explanations as well.

Discussion

Dr. Schwarzschild: Could we ask Dr. Strömgren whether his program will tell us anything about absorption at 300 pc or more above or below the plane, just so that we don't miss another twenty years?

Dr. Strömgren: The present mapping goes to about 170 pc. In going beyond that, we will, of course, now have the advantage that for any line of sight we can correct for the absorption within 170 pc. The next step, going to about 500 pc, will, I think, not be too difficult.

Dr. Schwarzschild: Do you have enough early-type stars at that distance?

Dr. Strömgren: No. The first step with the B8 and B9 only goes to 170 pc. The next step will go to 500 pc and requires of course photometry of other stars. In the course of investigations in the galactic polar caps that are made for other purposes, I expect to get an inventory of F stars to the twelfth magnitude. That should take us out to about 400 pc. However, the F's I am sure will be thinning out. It is a question whether the F's are present in sufficient numbers. If this fails, then we know that the weak-line K giants will be suitable. In investigations that Mr. Gyldenkerne and I carried out some ten years ago we found that from measures of the break at the G band, which are insensitive to interstellar reddening, we can predict the intrinsic colors to an accuracy of about one to two hundredths. Dr. Crawford is now engaged in preparations for a program of these K giants that goes to the twelfth magnitude and which may go even beyond that. I think that should solve the problem.

There are, of course, difficulties in connection with the third parameter in this region of the Hertzsprung–Russell diagram, and they have recently been emphasized by the Cambridge, England, work. However, from what I have seen of further work done by Mr. Gyldenkerne and Dr. Crawford, it is clear that if the wavelengths are chosen much as they were before (however, measuring the indices with somewhat narrower bands), and if this is supplemented by a measure of what I call the metallic index, then a very cleancut three-dimensional classification is obtained. In particular, Mr. Gyldenkerne finds that he can reproduce with fair accuracy—that is, with probable errors of three or four tenths—Wilson's absolute magnitudes based on the K emission line. Also, it is possible to obtain a rather clean separation into intermediate- and low-velocity stars.

I think one can be fairly confident that the K-star program in the galactic cap will tell us something out to about 1000 parsec. Beyond that I think we have real difficulties. Nothing is planned, but it might be a very good idea to give some thought to this. The difficulty is that methods of predicting intrinsic colors have not been developed to the same extent for the halo stars; and if you look at, say, the halo stars of type F, as you have in Miss Roman's list of high-velocity stars for which the spectra have been observed, then the situation is very much more difficult than for the population I F stars. The spectral features are so much weaker. For one thing, the hydrogen lines correspond, of course, to G-type stars, and they are quite weak. On the other hand, measures with narrow filters might be all that is necessary here, because the other difficulty that is encountered when you try to use the H_β index for the G stars, namely, a contamination from metal lines, is absent for the population II stars. So possibly if one uses a fairly big telescope, one can still use a hydrogen criterion. The metal-line criteria would of course be difficult to use in this kind of work.

Dr. Oort: You might also compare, if you can go faint enough, K-type giants in the direction of the pole and at, say, 20° latitude at the same height above the plane. Then you would have stars comparable in absolute magnitude and probably in all other characteristics. In this case the line of sight would pass through a much larger part of the layer than in the case where you look only at the pole. The differential effect might teach you what you want to know about absorption in this region with considerable accuracy. Then you would be free of all the other complications. But, of course, it means going to two or three times larger distances.

Dr. Strömgren: I take it that going to at least two times larger distances would be important in any case, so that one doesn't restrict it to some spot that might not be typical. It is certainly an advantage, as you point out, that we gain this factor. If you want to go to those large distances, if there are enough of the ordinary disk population K giants present, then I don't think there are difficulties. If you have to take halo stars, I still think that means of predicting the intrinsic colors are not yet sufficiently developed. But, as you point out, with effects of this magnitude it looks quite promising.

Dr. Oort: The comparison with the galaxy counts will be quite difficult, because they are so irregular. In order to do anything at all you must even out over very large regions of the sky. But if you have enough data, that also can be done, of course.

Dr. Lüst: May I ask another question about the 21-cm line at higher latitudes? Is there any connection between the features that you see at the 21-cm line and, for instance, the features one sees in the continuous spectrum?

Dr. Oort: There is no connection whatsoever, as far as we can make out. This spur that sticks up at about 30° longitude, which is so very prominent in the continuum measurements, does not show up in the 21-cm results, in any case not conspicuously.

Dr. Helfer: What longitude range did you use in averaging for your star counts?

Dr. Oort: About a quadrant 90° away from the center, so as to take out any gradients of density.

Dr. Helfer: This is the direction where in the northern hemisphere the 21-cm profiles are quite compressed toward the plane?

Dr. Oort: Yes, although the region is so large that I think that averages out. But again let me make this very clear—that I don't want at all to imply that there *is* this absorption far away. It is just a possibility and one might explain these results in a nice way if one did assume it.

Dr. G. R. Burbidge: Did you see in the light of Mr. Shane's work any possi bility that you could get a reasonable signal further above the plane than about 500 pc?

Dr. Oort: Yes, I think so, with some trouble. We want to extend the program in that direction. But you must make longer integrations. One would have to make special observations.

Measurement of polarization of the continuous radiation at 75-cm wavelength

J. H. Oort

Summary

Measures of linear polarization have been made recently with the Dwingeloo 25-m telescope, equipped with a feed and receiver specially designed for this purpose by C. L. Seeger. The observations were made by Seeger and Westerhout; Brouw and Tinbergen participated in the reductions and discussion. The observations were mainly concentrated in three fairly extended zones. In many places some polarization is indicated; in some regions it is as large as 10 per cent. At the conference the view was put forward that the polarized radiation observed from the direction of the large "spur" extending from the galactic plane toward the north galactic pole at 30° new galactic longitude would be connected with this spur. Subsequent discussion has shown that only some regions in the spur show polarization and that this may have no direct relation to the spur itself. At low latitudes radiation coming from distances larger than about 200 pc may mostly be depolarized by Faraday effects. A rather large region of strong polarization has been found around $l = 140°$, $b = +8°$. The polarization in this region is variable in direction in a rather systematic way. The region has an angular diameter of the order of 20°. Apparently the Faraday rotation in this direction cannot be very large. The average electron density in front of such regions must be quite small, probably not larger than 10^{-3} cm^{-3}. The observations cannot as yet furnish an estimate of the strength of the magnetic field.

The polarization measures will be continued and it is hoped that in the near future direct observations of the Faraday rotation can be made.

One of the most important things would evidently be to obtain polarization data for more distant regions. This, however, requires observations at much shorter wavelength.

References

Gart Westerhout, C. L. Seeger, W. N. Brouw, and J. Tinbergen, *Bull. Astr. Inst. Neth.*, **16,** 187 (1962).

W. N. Brouw, C. A. Muller, and J. Tinbergen, *Bull. Astr. Inst. Neth.*, **16,** 213 (1962).

Discussion

Dr. Woltjer: I certainly would be surprised if, with the halo consisting of all kinds of irregular supernova shells and things of that kind, one could ever get such large polarizations.

Dr. Spitzer: If one did take the low field model seriously, I would presume that it would predict agreement between the optical and radio observations and no Faraday effect. One would presumably assume a jumbled field. The polarization would represent the direction in which the mean-square field is greater; that is, it would represent the major axis of the ellipsoidal distribution of fields; so you would get the same direction both for the optical and the radio polarizations. The scale of the field might be too small to produce a systematic Faraday effect. These considerations suggest that looking at the change of the polarization angle with frequency might be quite a critical test for this model. I believe on the basis of the model that you have presented that you would definitely expect a rotation of the plane of polarization as the frequency increased from 400 Mc/sec to say 450 or so. If you find no such rotation, I think you have no alternative but to assume that the field is very small in scale.

Dr. Woltjer: I don't think you would have agreement between radio and optical results because in your model of the halo you have to suppose that the main part of the synchrotron radiation arises in supernova shells and things of that kind, since your interstellar field is too weak to produce any synchrotron radiation with the known relativistic electron density.

Dr. Spitzer: What happens if you assume enough high-energy particles, I don't know.

Dr. Oort: But you cannot, because we don't see them near the earth. So you are strictly limited there, I think. Following Dr. Woltjer's question I would also like to ask whether you would picture that this feature at 140° longitude, where we observe the high polarization, is part of a supernova shell and has therefore high magnetic fields. Then there would be no reason to find any parallelism with the optical polarization. As to the Faraday effect, maybe the electron density is low.

Dr. Prendergast: I am a little worried about Dr. Spitzer's mechanism. You were suggesting that perhaps these directions are simply the preferred directions for some ellipsoidal distribution. But you have to line up the axes of the ellipsoids in various parts of the sky and you have no such mechanism as galactic rotation available in the spur.

Dr. Spitzer: There are stretching phenomena. Your point is perhaps a more general one, namely, how do you get coordinated dynamical phenomena over a fairly large region without a systematic magnetic field? One has to be able to do that. If one can't do it without a magnetic field, one has to have a magnetic field. The spiral structure, the spur, and a number of other things all give the same indication.

Cosmic rays near the sun

R. Lüst

About five to eight years ago the main interest in cosmic rays was the study of elementary particles and high-energy physics. In the meantime large accelerators have become available which make it possible to investigate those particles under much more favorable conditions. Through this, the emphasis on cosmic rays has changed considerably during the last years mainly to two other problems of general interest. The first problem is the detailed study of the primary component of cosmic radiation, and with more detailed information about this the second problem is the question about the origin and the propagation of cosmic rays through space. Therefore the object of cosmic radiation is becoming more and more a subject of astrophysics. For astrophysical research cosmic radiation has two aspects. The first aspect is that broader knowledge of the primary component gives us additional information about different regions in the cosmos from where the cosmic rays come and through which they propagate, for instance, the nearest neighborhood of the earth, interplanetary space, the sun, and interstellar space. The second aspect is that we can understand the cosmic rays and their origin only if we use other astronomical observations and knowledge. Furthermore, a certain theory of the origin of cosmic rays will also influence our picture of other astrophysical problems, such as the problems of our symposium.

Today I should like to discuss the properties of cosmic rays near the sun. For this purpose we may distinguish two groups of cosmic-ray particles: (1) those not coming from the sun and (2) those coming from the sun. One should keep in mind that this already implies a certain theoretical picture, namely, that not all cosmic rays are produced by the sun. I shall not go into the details of this theory, since I think there is now more or less general agreement that such a theory must be rejected for several reasons. I shall start with a discussion of the first-mentioned group of particles, but at the end I shall also discuss the second group since, in connection with the topic of our symposium, this information might be quite useful with respect to other stars.

Cosmic Rays Not Originating at the Sun

Mass spectrum. The main part of the primary component of cosmic rays are protons and α particles, while the nucleons of other elements contribute only less than 1 per cent to the total flux. But especially the abundance of heavier elements may give us important indications about the origin and also about possible storage in the interstellar space. The fragmentation of heavier nuclei in interstellar space may provide evidence for the path length which the cosmic rays have travelled, and hence evidence of their age. This might be of importance in connection with the energy balance of interstellar matter.

The difficulties in obtaining reliable numbers for the mass spectrum are twofold, since in the earth's atmosphere a certain amount of fragmentation takes place and since it is in no way simple to identify the various nuclei. During the last years very high balloon flights with large emulsion stakes have reduced these uncertainties considerably. The approximate values are given in Table 1.

One can see from Table 1 that carbon, nitrogen, and oxygen are more abundant from all the heavier nuclei, but the extraordinary overabundance of lithium, beryllium, and boron compared to the cosmical abundance

Table 1
Abundances in Cosmic Rays

	H	He	Light nuclei L (Li, Be, B)	Medium nuclei M (C, N, O, F)	Heavy nuclei H "Fe" $Z \geqslant 10$	$23 < Z \leqslant 30$	Very heavy nuclei VH $Z > 30$
Relative abundance in cosmic rays	100	15.5	0.24	1.20	0.4	0.1	$< 10^{-4}$
"Universal abundances" of Suess and Urey	100	7.7	$\sim 10^{-6}$	0.20	0.03	0.003	$\approx 10^{-6}$

is of special importance. The ratio N_L/N_M is about 1/3. Also the other groups of heavier elements are more abundant than in the cosmos. This progressive overabundance goes roughly $Z^{1/2}$ as the atomic number increases. Comparing the ratio of the very heavy group with the medium group one can see that cosmic radiation contains about two times as many heavy elements as is normal in the cosmos. I should mention that these abundances have been determined only in the energy range of about 5 to 50 Bev/nucleon. Nothing is really known about the very low energies, where the sun and the interplanetary medium will have some influence, nor is anything known about the high-energy part of the spectrum.

So far I have talked only about the positively charged particles. Apparently the electrons contribute only very little to the total flux of cosmic radiation, but, owing to the observations of radiofrequency radiation, where a part has to be interpreted as synchrotron radiation, the exact figures for the electron flux are very important.

The old observations by Critchfield and Cowachers during 1948–1950 using Wilson chambers in a balloon indicate that the electron flux would be less than 1 per cent of the total flux. They obtained an upper limit of "soft" primary radiation at high altitudes (18 mb, 55° geomagnetic latitude) of 1.3×10^{-3} particle/cm²/sec/steradian with an energy larger than 1.1 Bev. (The flux of the protons will be given below.) Just recently Meyer and Vogt have published preliminary results for the electron flux obtained during 1960 with normal Geiger counters and scintillation counters in a balloon. They give an upper limit of 8×10^{-3}/cm²/sec/steradian with energies larger than 1.3 Bev. They also give some limits for other energies, which are shown in Table 2.

Table 2

Flux of Vertically Incident Electrons per cm²/sec/steradian

	$25 < E < 100$, Mev	$100 < E < 1300$, Mev	$E > 1300$, Mev
Lower limit	28×10^{-3}	3.5×10^{-3}	0
Upper limit	31×10^{-3}	11×10^{-3}	8×10^{-3}

Very recently, in 1960, Earl (Minnesota) determined the electron flux at balloon altitudes with a cloud chamber. Although no evidence for primary cosmic-ray electrons could be obtained by Critchfield, improvements in cloud-chamber techniques and higher balloon altitudes made it possible to demonstrate the existence of a small flux of primary electrons (electrons all together). After reducing the data, Earl found a flux of $3.2(\pm 1) \times 10^{-3}$ electron/cm²/sec/steradian with $E > 0.5$ Bev (no more than 13 ± 10 per cent of the flux is due to secondaries). With a proton flux of 1.1×10^{-1} proton/cm²/sec/steradian, this would give 6 per cent of the proton flux. The reasons for this higher value are: (1) minimum energy lower, (2) proton flux higher in 1949 (2.2×10^{-1} proton/cm²/sec/ steradian) than in 1960, and (3) thickness of the air above the balloon was less in the present experiments. These upper limits for the electron flux might be compared with the estimates one gets from the radio observations. Biermann and Davis concluded that with a magnetic field of 5×10^{-6} gauss in the halo and 2×10^{-5} gauss in the disk, the observed radio-frequency radiation can be explained as synchrotron radiation only if there exists an electron flux 3 to 5 times larger than the upper limit given by Critchfield. An electron flux equal to the upper limit given by Meyer and Vogt now would be just sufficient.

Energy spectrum. In discussing the energy spectrum of cosmic-ray particles one may divide them into two classes: the low- and the high-energy range. One reason for this is the experimental techniques used to study cosmic rays. In the low-energy range (below 10 Bev for protons) the earth's magnetic field acts as a spectrometer, since there exists a certain cutoff energy for a given geomagnetic latitude. The particles of highest energy can be studied only by indirect effects, namely, by the air showers which those particles produce in the earth's atmosphere. The other reason for such a distinction is that the particles of lowest energy (around and below 1 Bev) are strongly influenced by solar activity. During the time of high solar activity we see fewer particles entering the top of the earth's atmosphere than during the time of low activity, which is probably due to a screening effect of the interplanetary medium. In 1958, at the time of sunspot maximum, Neher gives a value of 4.7×10^{-2} particles/ cm²/sec/steradian for the total flux with a mean energy of about 5 Bev, whereas for the time of the sunspot minimum in 1954 he derived a value of 2.7×10^{-1} particles/cm²/sec/steradian. The additional particles entering the earth's atmosphere had an energy of about 0.5 Bev.

The integral energy spectrum can be well described by

$$N(\geqslant E) \sim E_t^{-\gamma}$$

where E_t is the total energy per nucleon. The exponent γ is about 1.1 for protons in the Bev range. For the other nuclei, the spectrum is similar but somewhat steeper, and the exponent γ is of the order of 1.3 and increases with Z up to about 2 for the heaviest nuclei. The shape of the low-energy end of the spectrum (around and below 1 Bev) is strongly influenced by solar activity.

The integrated energy spectrum at the higher energy range has a simple power-law form:

$$N(\geqslant E) \propto E^{-\gamma}$$

where E is the kinetic energy. Up to about 10^6 Bev γ is almost independent of the energy and seems to increase slightly at the highest energies observed. In this range the information about the relative abundances of the other elements is very scanty. For the exponent γ the following values are given:

$$\gamma = 1.64 \pm 0.04 \quad \text{for} \quad 1.4 \times 10^{10} \text{ ev} < E < 1.4 \times 10^{15} \text{ ev}$$

$$\gamma = 1.74 \pm 0.09 + (0.09 \pm 0.02) \log_{10}(E/10^6 \text{ Bev})$$

$$\text{for} \quad 10^{15} \text{ ev} < E < 10^{17} \text{ ev}$$

Some air showers have been observed with primary energies up to 10^{17} ev, which indicates that even in this region of the spectrum γ shows no large variation. Davis and Peters made the suggestion that the largest air showers (with energies above 10^{16} ev) are mainly due to heavy nuclei, but more recent discussions do not seem to support this.

Isotropy. Finally, a last observational fact, relevant to our discussion, must be discussed. This is the problem of the degree of isotropy of cosmic radiation. Elaborate experimental work has been done to search for a possible point source of cosmic radiation or at least to establish some kind of anisotropy. During the years an anisotropy has at times been reported, but the measurements of a longer period showed that it was statistically not meaningful. According to Greisen's review of the situation, there is no established anisotropy in any energy range. If we measure the degree of isotropy by

$$\delta = \frac{\Delta F}{F}$$

where $F =$ flux in a certain direction, $\Delta F = F_{\max} - F_{\min}$. We have

$$\delta \approx 10^{-3.5} \qquad E \leqslant 10^{13} \text{ ev}$$

$$\delta \approx 10^{-2.5} \qquad E \leqslant 10^{15} \text{ ev}$$

$$\delta \approx 10^{-1} \qquad E < 10^{17} \text{ ev}$$

In all cases the statistical errors are still so large that the true anisotropy could be zero. Anyhow, it seems reasonable to assume that the anisotropy is really very small and that it has to be taken seriously in any theory one tries to develop for cosmic rays.

Cosmic-Ray Particles of Solar Origin

Let me now discuss very briefly those cosmic-ray particles which originate from the sun. This may give us some indication of the production of cosmic-ray particles on stars in general. It is now well established that the sun produces cosmic rays—that means relativistic particles. As early as 1941 the first increase of cosmic radiation in connection with a large solar flare had been observed, where particles in the range 1 to 10 Bev had been produced. Observations during recent years show that more often the sun produces protons with smaller energies (about 100 Mev) in connection with somewhat smaller flares and even during small flares (at higher rates) relativistic electrons in the Mev range.

Equipment capable of observing relativistic protons, protons above about 1 Bev—where this limit is given due to the absorption in the earth's atmosphere—has been in operation since 1937, operating continuously. Since then nine cosmic-ray increases with relativistic protons have been observed associated with solar flares. The dates are: Feb. 1942, March 1942, July 1946, Nov. 1949, Feb. 1956, July 1959, May 1960, 12 Nov. 1960, and 15 Nov. 1960.

In all cases the increase in the intensity of cosmic radiation has been so large that the only possible explanation is that these particles have been produced at the sun. The energies of the particles must have been between 1 and 10 Bev and, at least for the event of February 23, 1956, even somewhat higher, up to about 50 Bev. For this largest event so far observed, the flux above 3 Bev was about 300 times the normal cosmic-ray intensity. In this case the energy that went into cosmic radiation was quite high compared with the total energy output, where the spectroscopic evidence gave a value of 10^{33} ergs, while the energy of cosmic rays amounted to about 10^{31} ergs.

But observations during recent years show that much more frequently there are flare events in which intense bursts of particles have been produced which do not attain relativistic energies. The evidence for these events during the past two or three years has come about partially due to improved techniques and to the increased total amount of time available to observe at very high altitudes, since particles below relativistic energy do not penetrate deep into the atmosphere even through their secondary production; hence they are not observable at fixed stations on the surface of the earth. These increases of cosmic-ray intensity at lower energies have been observed by two methods. One method is the use of balloons at very high altitudes; the other technique is the observation of the change of absorption of the cosmical radio noise. This change in absorption is due to the arrival of protons in the energy range 10 to 100 Mev. All these events are connected with solar flares of strength 3 at least, and more than 20 of these events have been observed during the period of high solar activity of 1957 to 1959. Since there is a preference to observe more events originating on the western hemisphere of the sun, the actual rate must be even higher. The proton fluxes are of the order of 10^2 protons/cm^2/sec, but a number of them have even reached 10^4 protons/cm^2/sec.

The events mentioned so far refer to protons, but there are a number of other events where there is evidence that relativistic electrons have also been produced. These are some of the so-called radio bursts, which are strong increases of the radiofrequency radiation. They are of shorter duration, but during active periods of the sun they are quite frequent. The first of this type of burst is the so-called type IV burst, which is caused by synchrotron radiation of relativistic electrons in local magnetic fields. In the meantime, γ rays due to Bremsstrahlung of these electrons have been observed also. But very recent observations by Wild show that the so-called type III bursts are also due to relativistic electrons since Wild was able to measure the velocity of the sources through the solar atmosphere by using an interferometer, and this velocity is approximately the velocity of light. A study by Rabben showed that these events are very frequent during periods of high activity and that they are even connected with very small flares. During high activity we may observe a group of bursts, several single bursts about every 100 minutes; optical flares occurred about three times as often. Furthermore, the flares connected with these radio bursts always belong to the same active region; the other ones originate in other regions.

Summarizing, relativistic electrons with energies of about 1 Mev are produced on the sun during periods of high activity about every hour, protons with energies of the order of 10 to 100 Mev are produced about every 3 or 4 weeks, and relativistic protons are produced much less frequently.

General References

C. L. Critchfield, E. P. Ney, and S. Oleska, *Phys. Rev.*, **85,** 461 (1952).
J. A. Earl, *Phys. Rev. Letters*, **6,** 125 (1961).
K. Greisen, in "Progress in Elementary Particle and Cosmic Ray Physics," Vol. 3, New York, Interscience, 1956.
F. S. Johnson, "Satellites Environment Handbook," Stanford University Press, Stanford, Calif., 1961.
P. Meyer and R. Vogt, *Phys. Rev. Letters*, **6,** 193 (1961).
H. V. Neher, *Ann. Rev. Nucl. Sci.*, **8,** 217 (1958).
E. P. Ney, *Ap. J. (Suppl.)*, **4,** 371 (1960).
J. A. Simpson, *Ap. J. (Suppl.)*, **4,** 378 (1960).

Discussion

Dr. Woltjer: What is the highest energy in cosmic rays about which you can really be sure if you take into account all questions—such as the altitude in the atmosphere of the first interaction?

Dr. Oppenheimer: 5×10^{19} ev.

Dr. Helfer: M. V. K. Appa Rao, working with M. F. Kaplon at the University of Rochester, has found from an emulsion stack He^3/total helium = 0.4 ± 0.1 for the energy range 200 to 400 Mev per nucleon and 0.3 ± 0.1 for the magnetic rigidity range 1.3 to 1.6 Bev. No solar activity was observed in a reasonable time period before the stack was flown.

Dr. Strömgren: In connection with the emission of relativistic electrons during bursts of type III that go on during high solar activity, has the average energy output in the form of these relativistic electrons during the period of high activity been computed?

Dr. Lüst: I think that it might be of the order of 1 per cent of the solar constant.

Dr. Biermann: Radio data, especially on bursts of type III, lead to the conclusion that the electrons are accelerated to relativistic energies on the sun more often than was realized before. Even flares which optically can hardly be detected may be accompanied by a burst of type III resp. a group of several such bursts. But the figure for the total amount of energy going into that of relativistic particles does not appear to have changed in its order of magnitude, although it certainly increased substantially.

Dr. G. R. Burbidge: Could I ask one more question on that? Can you make any estimates of the number of relativistic electrons which actually escaped from the sun? You are detecting the radiation. Are the electrons all accelerated, radiate, and remain trapped in the sun, or do some escape?

Dr. Biermann: My guess is that a fraction could escape. What is observed is that the relativistic electrons travel far out into the solar corona, and since they reach levels of fairly low density I don't see any reason why they should not escape. It is difficult to be more definite than that. It looks as if the sensitivity of radiofrequency measurement might be higher than that of optical observation because the smallest events have been below the general lower limit of the flare classification. If one compares Rabben's statistics (*Z. Ap.*, 1959) with those of others, one finds that he has relatively more events of lowest energy. The fraction that is accompanied by type III bursts is roughly the same as for the events of higher energy. So it may well be that one could still increase the sensitivity of the radio measurements. As to the optical method, it might be difficult to get down to lower energies.

Galactic magnetic fields and the equilibrium of interstellar clouds

L. Woltjer

Already a number of years ago Ginzburg (e.g., [6]) has shown that the density of cosmic-ray electrons in interstellar space can be estimated— if the magnetic field intensity is known—from the intensity of the galactic nonthermal radio radiation. Recently Biermann and Davis [1] and Woltjer [12] have used this fact to obtain a minimum estimate for the value of the magnetic field intensity B on the basis of an upper limit on the density of cosmic-ray electrons obtained by Critchfield, Ney, and Oleska [3]. These estimates can be somewhat improved because cosmic-ray electrons now appear to have been actually observed (Earl [5]). Earl observed 11 electrons only, with energies above 0.5 Bev; one or two of these are estimated to have been produced in the earth's atmosphere. It is not very well possible to estimate the flux outside the solar system from data obtained near the earth for energies below 1 or 2 Bev, because of solar effects. Earl found only one electron above 2 Bev, corresponding to an integral flux of $F(>2) = 4.5 \times 10^{-4}$ cgs units, if a correction factor 1.5 is applied to account for solar effects. Five electrons with energies in excess of 1 Bev were observed; with an uncertain correction factor 2 we find $F(>1) = 26 \times 10^{-4}$ cgs. Representing the differential energy spectrum of the cosmic-ray electrons by

$$n(E) = kE^{-\beta} \qquad \text{cm}^{-3}/\text{Bev} \tag{1}$$

and taking $\beta = 2.4$, the two flux estimates lead to $k = 0.7 \times 10^{-12}$ and $k = 1.5 \times 10^{-12}$; of course, these values are extremely uncertain. The radiation produced by an isotropic distribution of electrons given by Eq. (1) in a magnetic field B with random directions is

$$J(\nu) = 10^{-22}k(10^{-13}\nu)^{-\frac{1}{2}(\beta-1)}B^{\frac{1}{2}(\beta+1)}S(\beta) \tag{2}$$

where $S(2) = 2.23$ and $S(3) = 2.02$. From the somewhat uncertain spectral index of 0.7 for the nonthermal radio radiation (recent data may indicate a somewhat smaller value, like 0.5 or so for the lower frequencies) we have $\beta = 2.4$. From Mills [7] data $J(85 \text{ Mc/sec})$ is known roughly throughout the galaxy. Since in a steady state with an isotropic momentum distribution of the particles in the regions where the magnetic field is weak, k is constant in all accessible regions of the galaxy, we assume k to be given by its value near the earth. Then B can be found. Denoting the field in the spiral arms near the sun by B_0 we find for the two values of k obtained above, $B_0 = 4\gamma$ and $B_0 = 2.8\gamma$ ($1\gamma = 10^{-5}$ gauss). In view of the poor statistics used in the determination of k, the result is of course somewhat uncertain, but a value as small as 1γ seems excluded. We shall adopt $B_0 = 3\gamma$, in qualitative agreement with certain results concerning dynamic phenomena and perhaps the regularity of the interstellar polarization. This is the field in the spiral arms near the sun. In between the arms it may be only half that value, but this is uncertain. In the central regions of the halo, B would be 0.8γ, and in the halo, say, 500 pc above the sun, 0.6γ. Let us pause briefly now to examine the various assumptions that have been made in this analysis.

1. We have assumed that a general distribution of nonthermal radio radiation does exist, i.e., that the radio radiation does not originate in localized sources. The halo certainly shows some quite irregular features, but variations in magnetic field strength as a function of position in a continuous halo can very well account for this. Mills has indicated that the spiral arms can be seen in the continuous nonthermal radio radiation, but the poor fit with the northern results makes this somewhat uncertain. If the field were uniform in intensity in the disk, this would not affect the above analysis very much. The average field strength in the disk would then be about three-quarters of the value for B_0 given above, but real uniformity certainly does not prevail. The width of the radio disk is of the order of 500 pc, much larger than the width of the interstellar gas layer. This also shows that it would be difficult to interpret the radiation in terms of a large number of sources, e.g., supernova remnants: Typical population I objects would not have such a wide distribution, but population II or disk population I objects would not show anything like spiral structure.

2. We have assumed that the cosmic-ray electrons can travel more or less freely through most of the galaxy and that the electrons near the earth are thus a representative sample of the galactic electrons. As long as we do not have a better knowledge of the structure of the magnetic field, it is not very possible to make a theoretical estimate of how good this assumption is, although one can perhaps argue from cosmic-ray composition that cosmic rays are not confined in a spiral arm for a very long time.

The cosmic-ray data also indicate that an isotropic momentum distribution is probable.

Observationally this point as well as the preceding one may be analyzed by looking for variations in the spectra of different regions of the halo and the disk. Not much variation is expected between regions in which there is a free interchange of particles, at least if the exponent of the energy spectrum is not a function of energy. In the part of the spectrum where β changes with energy there would be a relation between the local field strength and the spectral index of the radiation. Experiments on the identity of the spectra of the halo electrons and the ones observed near the earth would be even more crucial. Finally, it can be shown that due to the energy loss by electrons of high energy, a "knee" should be present in the electron energy spectrum, where the spectrum would change from one characterized by an exponent β to one with exponent $\beta + 1$. The position of the knee depends on the mean-square magnetic field along the electron trajectory and on the time that the electron spends in the galaxy. Assuming that the average cosmic-ray particle traverses 3 g/cm^2 of interstellar matter, we find that the "knee" should occur around 8 Bev, if our estimate of the field is correct and if the particles are not accelerated very much in the halo. None of these observations would prove, per se, the correctness of the analysis we have made, but they could at least give a valuable consistency check on our picture of the propagation of the relativistic electrons through the galaxy.

At first sight there seems to be a serious conflict between the field intensity derived here and the upper limit of about 0.5γ which R. D. Davis et al. [4] have obtained from the Zeeman effect in the 21-cm absorption line in some dense clouds of neutral hydrogen. This apparent conflict leads to some interesting consequences. First, we note that by the techniques used, only the mean value of the field component along the line of sight is measured. The three clouds for which Davis et al. obtained their results are all extremely dense. Thus two explanations are possible: either the field intensity in the clouds is indeed so low and the clouds are essentially diamagnetic bodies situated in a strong field, or the field intensity is not small, but the field directions are variable on a rather small scale so that the mean field is much smaller than the root-mean-square field.

In the first alternative the pressure in the cloud is equal to $B^2/8\pi$. Thus in the cloud we have $NT = 2.6 \times 10^5$ for $B = 3\gamma$. Eventual non-thermal mass motions are included in the definition of T. From the width of the line profiles in the three clouds [8] we have $T = 250°$ on the average. Thus $N = 1 \times 10^3$ cm^{-3}, a very high density indeed, but not impossible. The observations show that in such a cloud there are of the order of 2×10^{21} neutral hydrogen atoms/cm^2 along the line of sight if the true temperature is 125°. The number varies as T^{-1}. The diameter of the cloud would thus be less than 1 parsec along the line of sight. One of the clouds in front of the Cas A source lies in the Perseus arm at a distance not much smaller than Cas A itself. Thus unless the cloud were very anisotropic it would, as has been pointed out to me by Dr. R. D. Davis, be much too small to cover the source, which has a diameter of about 7 pc. Of course one could save the situation by supposing that the cloud does not cover the source completely. Then the optical depth in front of the covered portions could be arbitrarily large. Or one could suppose—which is more plausible—that the volume of the cloud is only partly filled with matter. However, this gives rise to some difficulties with the diffusion time of the magnetic field, which we shall now consider.

How long the cloud may remain a diamagnetic body, i.e., how long it will take the surrounding field to diffuse inward, depends upon the electrical conductivity. It is well known that the conductivity of interstellar matter is extremely high if only the ionized particles are taken into account. It has been pointed out by Biermann and Schlüter [2] however, that collisions between the plasma component and the neutral gas can enhance the dissipative phenomena by a very large factor. This is especially so in the present case: The magnetic field pushes the charged particles slowly through the neutral cloud and thus the field lines diffuse inward (ambipolar diffusion) at a rate determined by the frequency of collisions between ions and neutrals. The velocity at which the ions move through the neutral gas is easily seen to be given approximately by

$$v_D = \frac{B^2}{8\pi L n_i n_{\mathrm{H}} \langle \sigma v_t \rangle m_{\mathrm{H}}} \tag{3}$$

where L represents a characteristic length for the field structure, v_t is the mean thermal velocity, and m_{H} is the mass of the hydrogen atoms. In a neutral cloud we have $n_i = 5 \times 10^{-4} n_{\mathrm{H}}$. From Osterbrock's [10] calculations the effective value of $\langle \sigma v_t \rangle$ per hydrogen atom is about 3×10^{-9} cm³/sec. Expressing L in parsec we find

$$v_D = 5 \times 10^{15} \frac{B^2}{L_{\mathrm{pc}} n_{\mathrm{H}}^2} \qquad \text{cm/sec} \tag{4}$$

The time scale in which the field can diffuse inward is

$$t_D = \frac{L}{v_D} = 2 \times 10^{-5} \frac{L_{\mathrm{pc}}^2 n_{\mathrm{H}}^2}{B^2} \qquad \text{year} \tag{5}$$

and with $L = 3$ pc, $n_{\mathrm{H}} = 10^3$, and $B = 3\gamma$, we have $t_D = 2 \times 10^{11}$ years. Thus once a diamagnetic cloud with these parameters has been formed, it remains so for a time long compared to the age of the galaxy. However, if the cloud is thought to consist of a large number of filaments, the situation is different. With a radius of 0.1 pc the field would penetrate in 2×10^8 years.

Of course the most serious difficulty in the strictly diamagnetic model is that there is nothing to prevent the cloud from expanding along the lines of force. With the high pressures in the cloud we can hardly assume that the gas in the cloud is in pressure equilibrium with an intercloud medium. It also is unclear how such clouds can be formed.

Let us therefore turn to the second alternative, in which a somewhat irregular field in the cloud is nearly in equilibrium with a systematic spiral-arm field. Since the average thermal energy in the cloud may be much less than the average magnetic energy, the field will be largely force free. At first, one would be inclined to think that such a field would be incompatible with interstellar polarization, and for a strictly random field this is of course true. Spitzer [11] has already indicated that interstellar polarization could be explained by assuming a random field which has been drawn out by differential rotation: The mean field would vanish but the mean-square field parallel to the fluid velocity would be much larger than perpendicular to this direction. A similar situation may occur in the magnetic clouds, since the field is compressed in the direction perpendicular to the arm.

Let us now examine how the magnetic cloud picture we have given here compares with the usual hydrodynamic picture. In the usual theory of interstellar clouds the cloud equilibrium presents difficulties. An isolated cloud will expand with a velocity equal to a few times the velocity of sound. A typical interstellar cloud would double its radius in a few million years. It is difficult to see how collisions between clouds could completely remedy the situation. For clouds in the halo, where collisions are even less important, the situation is even worse. For this reason Spitzer introduced a hot tenuous halo gas ($n_e = 5 \times 10^{-4}\,\mathrm{cm}^{-3}$, $T = 10^6$) which could be in pressure equilibrium with the clouds in the halo. But in the disk, clouds of very different pressures may well occur and it would seem improbable that they can all be in equilibrium with an intercloud medium. Let us consider the picture of cool dense clouds in the halo in somewhat more detail.

Some observational evidence concerning these clouds has been given by Münch and Zirin [9]. They give some reasons to believe that the observed clouds should be H II regions; if the clouds were H I regions they could not radiate the energy which flows in from the halo by heat conduction. Let us accept their data and let us suppose that the typical halo cloud has a mass somewhat smaller than the disk clouds, about $100\,M_\odot$. Then the radius of the cloud is about 30 pc. We now ask the following question: If somewhat different accelerations are experienced by different parts of the cloud, could it remain a coherent unit? More specifically, let us for a moment consider the cloud to consist of two spherical clouds of mass $\frac{1}{2}M$ and with their centers distance R apart. Let us assume that the acceleration perpendicular to the galactic plane is not quite the same at the two centers but differs by ΔK_z. Clearly if $\frac{1}{2}M \, \Delta K_z$ exceeds the gravitational attraction between the two clouds $(1/4 GM^2/R^2)$ they will be torn apart, since the equilibrium with the halo gas is neutral with respect to fragmentation. With the parameters given above, the condition is $\Delta K_z > 5 \times 10^{-13}$ cm²/sec. For comparison, near the sun, at 300 pc above the plane, K_z itself is 10^4 times larger. At this height we find for the smoothed galactic force field $\partial K_z/\partial \varpi = 3 \times 10^{-12}$ cm²/sec/pc and for the irregularities due to spiral arms something of the same order or slightly larger. Since $R = 30$ pc the effect is strong enough to produce a relative displacement of 150 pc in 10^8 years. This example shows quite explicitly the general difficulty in these cloud models—that there is nothing to give the cloud coherence.

The situation is quite different when the clouds have internal magnetic fields. The cloud fields that are confined by the spiral-arm fields prevent the gas in the clouds from expanding. As long as the gas pressure is much smaller than the magnetic stresses, the cloud equilibrium depends very little on this pressure; clouds of densities smaller than about 10^3 cm⁻³ all may be in equilibrium. A cloud with a density of about 10 atoms/cm³ could even be ionized, without expanding very much. The difference between the halo clouds and the disk clouds is apparent: since the field in the halo is estimated to be a factor 5 smaller than the field in the spiral arms, and since the fields in the clouds should decrease by the same factor, the radius of the cloud should increase by a factor $\sqrt{5}$. Then the density in the cloud decreases by a factor 10.

The typical disk cloud (typical here means essentially the one with the parameters of Spitzer's [11] table 2) has a radius of 7 pc and a density of about 10 atoms/cm³. In the halo these parameters would become $R = 15$ pc and $n = 1$ cm⁻³. If we assume that the clouds which move into the halo have masses somewhat smaller than the average disk cloud, the density might be somewhat smaller. Münch and Zirin show that a mass of about 100 $M_\odot$ for their clouds would lead to $R = 15$ pc and $n_H = 0.3$ cm⁻³, if the clouds are an H I region. This is not unlikely, since the heat conduction from the hot halo gas is no longer important. Also, Blaauw's data may be an observational indication that these clouds are in fact neutral. Thus the magnetic cloud picture seems to be consistent with these data. Of course if this picture is accepted, the parameters of the halo gas become completely undetermined and might be rather different from the ones derived by Spitzer. The present picture would also be consistent with the indications that there are more clouds far above the plane than would be expected from the z-velocity distribution in the plane.

Let us finally turn to some speculations on the origin of these clouds. A large part of the interstellar matter now seen in the galaxy has been once or a number of times part of a stellar envelope. We do not yet know how the gas is ejected from the stars. In the case of the sun, which is of course a very inefficient contributor to the interstellar medium, it is thought that many of the gas clouds that are expelled carry magnetic fields. In view of the ubiquity of stellar magnetic fields, it is not implausible to assume that this is also the case in the ejecta of other stars. We also know that appreciable magnetic fields are present in the shells of supernovae. Thus on the whole it is reasonable to suppose that most of the gas that is added to the interstellar medium carried rather-small-scale magnetic fields. These fields will prevent the general galactic field from diffusing in the clouds.

Let us now see what happens when two clouds collide. If the field vectors are parallel, the collision may be largely elastic. But if the field vectors are antiparallel, a highly compressed layer of gas could arise in the neutral plane between the two clouds, and dissipation there will be high. From our estimates in connection with the diffusion time in diamagnetic bodies, it seems that the field lines in the outer regions of the clouds could well annihilate each other over a region of some width around the interface. Then the field lines in the two clouds could be reconnected and might unify the two clouds. It thus seems that the growth of the clouds could perhaps be understood. The clouds so formed will still have a quite irregular field. This field will gradually be dissipated, the smallest-scale components disappearing first. It is difficult to estimate the time scale for this; instabilities will also play an important role. But the figures given above for the diamagnetic clouds show that these time scales need not be very long compared with the galactic time scale. If the field is partly dissipated, the cloud will be compressed by the outer field and thus the density will increase. If the density becomes large enough, star formation seems likely to occur. Thus magnetic fields of the type discussed here do not necessarily impede star formation, in contrast with the situation in which a systematic large-scale field pervades the whole cloud.

The present discussion is very incomplete, and it would seem that a thorough discussion of the dynamics and decay of a gas cloud with irregular fields which is almost completely neutral is much needed. Also the phenomena occurring near young hot stars (like elephant trunks, etc.) would have to be discussed from the point of view of the present picture. On the other hand, some significant advantages of the magnetic model have been discussed. And if the conflict between magnetic field intensities derived from nonthermal radio emission and the Zeeman effect persists, the present picture seems about the only way to resolve it.

References

[1] L. Biermann and L. Davis, *Z. Astrophys.*, **51**, 19 (1960).
[2] L. Biermann and A. Schlüter, *Z. Naturforsch.*, **5a**, 237 (1950).
[3] C. L. Critchfield, E. P. Ney, and S. Oleska, *Phys. Rev.*, **85**, 461 (1952).
[4] R. D. Davis, C. H. Slater, W. L. H. Shuter, and P. A. T. Wild, *Nature*, **187**, 1088 (1960).
[5] J. A. Earl, *Phys. Rev. Letters*, **6**, 125 (1961).
[6] V. L. Ginzburg, *Izv. Akad. Nauk. USSR, Ser. Fiz.-Mat.*, **20**, 5 (1956).
[7] B. Y. Mills in R. N. Bracewell (ed.) "Paris Symposium on Radio Astronomy," Stanford University Press, Stanford, Calif., 1959, p. 431.
[8] C. A. Muller in R. N. Bracewell (ed.), "Paris Symposium on Radio Astronomy," Stanford University Press, Stanford, Calif., 1959, p. 465.
[9] G. Münch and H. Zirin. *Ap. J.*, **133**, 11 (1961).
[10] D. E. Osterbrock, *Ap. J.*, **134**, 270 (1961).
[11] L. Spitzer, "Compendium of Astronomy and Astrophysics," Vol. 7, University of Chicago Press, Chicago, 1962, Chap. 9.
[12] L. Woltjer, *Ap. J.*, **133**, 352 (1961).

Discussion

Dr. Blaauw: In discussing the effect of the variations in the force K_z, you spoke about a time of 10^8 years. That is quite long compared to half the oscillation times with which we are concerned. If you have velocities of the order of 20 km/sec or so, I think it wouldn't take more than 5×10^7 years for it to be back. So your estimate of 100-pc disruption would be quite high.

Dr. Woltjer: This is only an estimate of the effects of the general gradient of K_z. There may be much stronger irregularities in the neighborhood of spiral structure.

Dr. Blaauw: On the other hand, if you are far away from the plane these irregularities are less important.

Dr. Woltjer: Essentially I would only consider this as an example of the kind of trouble one runs into if one doesn't have a binding element in the clouds.

Dr. Blaauw: It is nice to see that this mechanism would sort of stretch them out.

Dr. Field: How would you explain interstellar polarization?

Dr. Woltjer: I think in the same way, although with different interpretation, as Dr. Spitzer did it with his more irregular fields. One could, for example, consider the situation in which one starts out with a spherical cloud in which there are irregular magnetic fields. If one would compress this by a parallel field, there would be a tendency to get the mean-square magnetic field much larger along the direction of the impressed field than perpendicular to it. In general, I think that if one has a cloud with such an irregular field it would tend to acquire, at least in the mean square, a magnetic field much stronger parallel than perpendicular to the external field.

Dr. Prendergast: Isn't it true that any magnetic mechanisms which allow you to make one cloud out of two—you mention the neutral-point mechanism—would work equally well to join the general field to the internal field?

Dr. Woltjer: This is to a certain extent true.

Ed.: Dr. Kahn brought up the behavior of doughnut-shaped clouds; the somewhat confused discussion that followed is omitted here.

Dr. Oort: How does one know that polarization occurs in these dense clouds? It may well be that most of the polarization phenomena are due to less-dense spaces in between the clouds.

Dr. Spitzer: Don't you get into some difficulty forming these cloud fields out of stellar materials, because the flux is so small per unit mass? That is, the ratio of B to ρ is so much smaller in a star than it is in interstellar material. I would expect that if you took material from the sun and expanded it, the resulting field would be negligible.

Dr. Woltjer: If you expanded the whole sun, that is quite correct. But on the other hand one sees, both in the supernovae and perhaps also in the solar atmosphere, but certainly in the supernovae, that apparently the magnetic field per unit mass, when it has been expelled, is much larger than it was in the original object.

Dr. Spitzer: Don't you find that rather an unpalatable conclusion?

Dr. Woltjer: Yes, but if you look at the Crab, is there any other conclusion possible?

Dr. Spitzer: Van Wyck has suggested that the field in the Crab is due to the compression of the interstellar field by the material from the supernova.

Dr. Woltjer: It is extremely hard to interpret the detailed field distribution in the Crab with its strong central concentration in that way.

Dr. Spitzer: If the flux on a large scale has really been increased by that much there is certainly something that we don't understand going on in that object. That need not surprise us, but it is such a flagrant violation of all the theoretical ideas that form the basis of this subject as we know it!

Dr. Woltjer: This is something that in general applies to many of the non-thermal radio sources for which one does not yet have a solution.

Dr. Kahn: How easily can we move the clouds through the general field? Would you not have to hold back a little bit so that the gravitational attraction of the galaxy on the gas can retain the field?

Dr. Woltjer: That depends very much on the detailed phenomena in the boundary between the clouds and the general galactic field. At the moment about the only thing one can specify to a certain degree is how much slip one needs. It is very difficult to specify how much slip one should expect.

Dr. Kahn: But if you actually have friction, wouldn't you again have the trouble arising with the neutral atoms?

Dr. Woltjer: Putting in some numbers, I do not think this gives trouble.

Dr. Blaauw: How narrow a component do you need to do the Zeeman experiment?

Dr. Woltjer: The components used had widths of the order of 2 km/sec. Of course it would be very interesting to also do the experiment for much smaller clouds, that is, for much less deep absorption lines, where the possible diamagnetic effects are completely irrelevant.

Dr. Blaauw: You would expect such clouds to occur in not too small numbers from the emission profiles.

Dr. Woltjer: Yes, it is fairly difficult to measure them.

Dr. von Hoerner: Have you considered the question of what would happen to the structure of a cloud when it goes high up from the galactic plane, where it is in a relatively quiet surrounding and doesn't get pushed—so that the inner turbulence might slow down and it might attain some kind of a regular shape?

Dr. Woltjer: Within the halo the cloud would presumably adjust itself so that its internal field would again make equilibrium with the external halo field. This irregular internal field is not a field that arises out of some turbulence. I suppose one has to consider it as the field that is being brought in the interstellar gas during the production of the interstellar gas.

Dr. von Hoerner: Hasn't each magnetic field, if you start with a random field, the tendency to get more and more regular?

Dr. Woltjer: Yes. So one would indeed suppose that a field gradually tends to straighten itself out. Of course the time scale for this is connected with the time scale on which you can get significant dissipation.

Dr. Biermann: Perhaps it is worth mentioning that in the laboratory experiments the plasma is almost always crossing containing magnetic fields much faster than one expects it to on theoretical grounds. The reason for this situation is highly obscure.

Dr. Woltjer: That is just the point which gives me some confidence that coagulation of clouds could occur, but it is very difficult to make reasonable estimates.

Dr. Schwarzschild: Do I get this straight, that the energy of the internal motions, macroscopic or thermal, is small compared to the energy of the internal or external fields, so that the internal field has to be essentially force-free?

Dr. Woltjer: It has to be essentially force-free except that there may be localized regions in the cloud where the density is higher. But these will of course gradually dissipate.

Dr. Schwarzschild: But then there are sort of two stages of the internal field wanting to straighten itself out. The first is on some kind of a dynamical time scale. It finds the cleanest force-free field that its initial topology—whatever this may mean—permits.

Dr. Woltjer: Yes, but it is not at all obvious that the initial topology admits any very regular force-free field. With infinite conductivity you can never make a very clean force-free field out of an irregular field.

Star formation and magnetic fields

L. Spitzer

I wish to present some suggestions about the galactic magnetic field which are by no means new but on which some recent work has been done [11]. The point of view that I am taking this afternoon is to explore an alternative possibility for the galactic magnetic field.

The leading contender for the galactic magnetic field has for some time been a uniform magnetic field with an intensity in the neighborhood of 2×10^{-5} gauss. This value has interesting historical antecedents. A uniform field along a spiral arm was first suggested by Chandrasekhar and Fermi [5], and a value for the intensity was derived from the directions of the polarization observed in distant stars; the small deviations from parallelism give a relatively high field strength. If one employs the most recent values of the relevant parameters, one obtains a value of 2×10^{-5} gauss for B.

It is also possible, as Tukey and I suggested [12] quite some years ago, to achieve somewhat the same results with a very much weaker field. The value that I will discuss this afternoon is about 2×10^{-6} gauss, less by an order of magnitude than the conventional value, corresponding to an energy density less by two orders of magnitude.

Why should we doubt this higher field? A number of questions are raised by the higher intensity. One of the big theoretical problems, which I give greater weight to than perhaps others might, is the difficulty of explaining how a field of this sort ever originated, unless one assumes that it was essentially primitive.

Perhaps there is no good reason why we shouldn't assume that creation was a vector event, in addition to a scalar event, and that a magnetic field was present when the galaxy was formed. On the other hand, we should not take this as a basic assumption until we have at least examined other alternatives. To me, at least, this argument provides one reason for exploring the possibility that the magnetic field in the galaxy is actually considerably less than is generally supposed.

A field of order 2×10^{-5} gauss dominates interstellar motions. That is, the kinetic energy of the interstellar clouds is less than the magnetic energy density of this field by perhaps an order of magnitude. Hence, the lines of force stay predominantly parallel despite the motions of interstellar gas clouds.

If one goes to a field of order 2×10^{-6} gauss one reaches the other extreme, where the energy density of the magnetic field is less than the energy density of interstellar clouds. With a uniform field of this magnitude, magnetic forces would certainly not dominate the motions of interstellar clouds. In fact with such a field one can assume that the motions of interstellar clouds are in the first approximation unaffected by the magnetic field. In this case one can then apply the theorems developed by Batchelor [1] and by Biermann and Schlüter [2] for the amplification of the magnetic field by twisting the lines of force. In fact, it is not too difficult to visualize that a magnetic field of this order of magnitude could be entirely built up from a small "seed field" by this mechanism.

In other words, a magnetic field of strength 2×10^{-6} gauss could grow from a small field by stretching and tangling of the lines of force, whereas I think it is very difficult to see how a uniform field some 10 times greater could grow from this mechanism, since the energy density of this field considerably exceeds the energy of the motions of interstellar clouds.

One might raise the question: With this field, how is the polarization explained? The answer [12] to which Dr. Woltjer has referred, is that if you have a tangled array of lines of force, which becomes sheared because of the differential galactic rotation, the force lines all become stretched out in the direction of the galactic rotation, i.e., in the θ direction, parallel to the spiral arms. The end result is an ellipsoidal distribution of magnetic field vectors. There will be a high probability of finding a magnetic field in the direction of positive or negative θ, and a lesser probability of finding strong magnetic fields in other directions.

An ellipsoidal distribution of magnetic field vectors (or, more simply, a prolate spheroidal distribution) would give a preferential orientation of grains perpendicular to the lines of force, oriented either by paramagnetic relaxation or by ferromagnetic relaxation. According to Henry [7], this latter mechanism has the advantage that it requires a field no greater than 10^{-6} gauss to orient the interstellar grains.

So it is possible then, with a field of this order, to get a fairly self-consistent picture in which the magnetic lines of force are tangled but are stretched out by the galactic rotation. The ellipsoidal distribution of field vectors that results is adequate to explain qualitatively and perhaps also quantitatively the interstellar polarization.

Another problem one faces, of course, with this particular field strength is how to explain the synchrotron radiation. I think it is entirely clear that if the low-field picture were correct, the synchrotron radiation would have to be explained in some other way. As Dr. Woltjer has shown, a field as low as 2×10^{-6} gauss is not adequate to explain the synchrotron radiation if we take for the density of relativistic electrons in the galactic plane the presently accepted value for the neighborhood of the earth.

So if this picture were correct, I think we should probably have to assume that the synchrotron radiation comes from many radio sources, many supernova remnants, rather than from the general galactic field of relativistic electrons moving in a galactic magnetic field. Alternatively, one might assume that for some reason the number of energetic electrons near the earth is much less than in the galaxy generally.

Another problem that I think is relevant in this connection is the problem of star formation. How does material condense together to form new stars in the presence of magnetic fields of one of these two types? There are two general methods available for bringing material together in the presence of a magnetic field. One is the diffusion of neutral atoms through the ions and across the magnetic field; this is called ambipolar diffusion. The other is gravitational contraction of the entire gas, including ions and the magnetic field.

The equation for the ambipolar diffusion rate can be derived very simply. The force F per cubic centimeter between the ions and the neutrals is just the rate of loss of momentum. The momentum lost per collision is the mass m_H of the hydrogen atom colliding with an ion, times v_D, the relative drift velocity of the ions through the neutrals; with the usual relation for the number of collisions per second, we have

$$F = n_i n_H \langle \sigma v \rangle m_H v_D \qquad (1)$$

where v is the random velocity of the hydrogen atoms and the brackets denote an average over the velocity distribution function. This, then, is the force per cubic centimeter exerted between the ions and the neutral hydrogen atoms resulting from a drift between them. We shall consider two cases of this particular formula.

The first case is that in which the force is equal to the magnetic energy density divided by a distance R; in this case we obtain the formula referred to this afternoon by Dr. Woltjer,

$$v_D = \frac{B^2}{8\pi R n_i n_H \langle \sigma v \rangle m_H} \qquad (2)$$

In the case of a contracting protostar, a cloud of gas has already contracted to rather a high density; then, as was shown several years ago [10], this drift velocity is adequate to get separation of the ions and the neutral particles. That is, when the density has increased to a value of the order of 10^4 to 1 ^{5} atoms/cm^3, the ionization level falls to such a low value that the drift velocity can be as great as a kilometer per second, and in the order of 10^5 to 10^6 years the lines of magnetic force can snap out of the protostar. Thus if the density is great enough, ambipolar diffusion can become rapid, and the protostar can get rid of a large part of the magnetic field that is present initially in the interstellar material.

I think it is quite obvious that one must get rid of the magnetic field in the material before the star can condense. If you take interstellar material with a field even of this lower value and compress it to the densities in the sun, the magnetic field will vary as the two-thirds power of the density for fairly uniform three-dimensional contraction and the energy density of the magnetic field will exceed the present average material energy density in the solar interior by several orders of magnitude. So it is clear that we have to get the lines of force out of the material before the stuff can actually contract.

Now let us see how we can produce the initial condensation in the early stages, before the fractional ionization has fallen to the low value assumed above. Let us consider the possibility that ambipolar diffusion can produce this initial contraction also, with the neutral gas contracting across the magnetic field under its own gravitational contraction. We can idealize this problem by treating an infinite cylinder. The force responsible for the ambipolar diffusion is here the gravitational force. We assume that the magnetic field is uniform and parallel to the axis of the cylinder and that no magnetic force need be considered. What will actually happen is that the gravitational field will, in the course of a very short time, produce a slight radial contraction of the cylinder, so there is a slight excess of magnetic pressure on the inside—slight in the sense that it balances the gravitational force. But this requires only a very slight contraction because the magnetic pressure is assumed to be so large. Now the ions are fixed by the magnetic field. The gravitational force acts primarily on the neutrals and there will be a drift between the ions and the neutrals; it is the drag resulting from this drift that holds up the neutrals.

The gravitational force per cubic centimeter is equal to the density $n_H m_H$ times the gravitational acceleration, which is $2GM/R$, where M is now the mass per unit length of this cylinder. It is a matter of simple algebra to substitute these quantities in Eq. (1) and to compute the time constant for contraction, i.e., the time for the drift velocity to move the material by an amount R across the lines of force, on the assumption that v_D is constant. Interestingly enough, this time t_i comes out to be a constant independent of the initial density and also of the radius R. The equation we find for t_c is

$$t_c = \frac{n_i \langle \sigma v \rangle}{2\pi \bar{n}_H G m_H} \tag{3}$$

where $\bar{n}_H m_H$ is the mean density interior to R. If we set σ equal to 10^{-16} cm², v to 10^5 cm/sec (corresponding to T about equal to 100°K), and $n_i/\bar{n}_H$ to 5×10^{-4}, we find that t_c is 2×10^8 years. Since 2×10^8 years is rather long compared to the life of the normal cloud, it would seem very difficult to separate the gas from the magnetic field by this process. So I think one would conclude that this process probably is not responsible for the initial concentration of interstellar matter into protostars.*

It would be a little more comfortable if this time were less by a hundred years or greater by a hundred years. Then we could come to a more definite conclusion. I think 200,000,000 years is really too long to use this process effectively during star formation.

We can assume that to form protostars from interstellar clouds both the gas and the magnetic field must be compressed together. About the only mechanism available to do this is gravitational self-contraction of an entire cloud. To compute the radius of a magnetized cloud which will be unstable against gravitational contraction, we can take the simple Jeans criterion, which may be justified on dimensional arguments, although it can, of course, be justified in more detail. According to this criterion, R, the radius of the unstable configuration in the absence of a magnetic field, is given by

$$R \approx \frac{V_s^2}{G\rho} \tag{4}$$

where V_s^2, the square of the sound velocity, equals kT/m_H.

In the presence of a magnetic field this criterion has to be changed. The magnetic pressure must also be considered, and we have

$$R \approx \frac{V_s^2 + V_A^2}{G\rho} \tag{5}$$

where V_A is the usual Alfvén speed, given by

$$V_A^2 = \frac{B^2}{4\pi\rho} \tag{6}$$

* *Note added in proof:* Osterbrock has since shown that the relevant cross section σ is about 10^{-14} cm². With this value adopted in Eq. (3), t_c is about 2×10^{10} years, and the process is evidently unimportant. In a dense protostar, however, the value of n_i/n_H falls to so low a value that diffusion of ions through the neutral gas can probably still provide the reduction of magnetic field intensity required for subsequent star formation.

One can look at the problem this way: The gravitational instability is determined by $dp/d\rho$, which is essentially equal to $V_s{}^2 + V_A{}^2$.

From these relations we can easily show that for a typical cloud

$$\frac{V_A}{V_s} = 7.2 \times 10^{+5}B \tag{7}$$

So for the lower magnetic field we can assume that V_A/V_s is equal to 1.4, while for the higher value this ratio is equal to 14. Thus we get two entirely different regimes if we are talking about the compression of material to form a protostar or a complex of protostars. At the higher magnetic field, the Alfvén speed is 14 times the usual sound speed and the magnetic pressure is 200 times the material pressure. As a result the critical density for gravitational instability at a particular wavelength is increased by a factor of 70 over what it is at the lower field.

Let us see what this actually corresponds to if we try to compare these results with actual clouds. With a little manipulation we can rewrite Eq. (5) as

$$\frac{M}{R^2} \approx \left(\frac{p}{G}\right)^{1/2} \tag{8}$$

where M is the cloud mass and p is the total pressure, including both gas pressure and magnetic pressure.

In the case in which one neglects the magnetic field and considers in more detail the equilibrium of a sphere surrounded by a medium at constant pressure, and asks the question under what conditions would this be unstable and start collapsing, one finds that the criterion for marginal stability in Eq. (8) must be changed a bit. Specifically, the right-hand side must be multiplied by a factor 5; p now refers to the external pressure on the cloud. This analysis was carried out by Bonnor [4], by Ebert [6], and later by McCrea [9]. In the marginally stable case the gas is quite concentrated in the center, and allowance for this effect increases the mass.

If we now forget for the moment about the magnetic field, and let p equal the pressure of the interstellar gas, which is of the order of 1.4×10^{-13} corresponding to a density of about 10 atoms/cm^3 at a temperature of $100°$ (or to an intercloud density of 0.1 and a temperature of 10^4), we find that M/R^2, the mass per unit area in the marginally stable state, is roughly 8×10^{-3} g/cm^2. This value corresponds to an extinction of 1.5 magnitudes, if we assume that the ratio of dust to gas has the same value as in interstellar matter generally.

This critical value of the mass per unit area is just about the upper limit observed for most of the large typical clouds observed in the galaxy.

There are some small clouds with larger extinctions, but they seem exceptional. If you include some turbulent pressure, which has been omitted here, then the critical value of M/R^2 would come up somewhat and would be somewhere between the values observed in typical clouds and the more extreme values.

We turn now to the case where the magnetic field has the relatively high value of 2×10^{-5} gauss. Since the total pressure is now increased by a factor of 70, Eq. (8) indicates that the critical value of M/R^2 is increased by a factor of 8.4, amounting now to 7×10^{-2} g/cm^2. The corresponding extinction is 13 magnitudes. If a mean density of 100 H atoms/cm^3 is assumed, the radius R of the marginally stable configuration is 100 pc. If such a large, dense cloud complex existed, it should be readily observable. I do not believe that any such extended cloud, with a mean extinction of more than 10 magnitudes over an area several hundred parsec across, has ever been observed. Thus it is difficult to see how we can assume that the interstellar medium is condensing into new stars, if a magnetic field as great as 2×10^{-5} gauss is present in interstellar space.

These results are quite tentative. When a uniform magnetic field is present, the details of the contraction process are certainly quite different from what they are in a spherical nonmagnetic cloud; the equilibrium of a spheroidal gas in a magnetic field has not yet been considered in detail. However, I believe that contraction along the field, which should proceed readily because the pressure available in this direction is relatively small, does not facilitate the contraction in the other direction. The main problem is how to condense the gas and the magnetic field together into a dense protostar. Contraction in the axial direction does not increase the optical thickness along the axis. And it is high optical thickness that you need to reduce the ionization. The value of n_i/n_H must be reduced sharply if ambipolar diffusion is to be of much importance.

So contraction along the magnetic field is not going to help, I think; it is probably not going to increase the force transverse to the magnetic field very much. Moreover, this is not an unstable contraction because as the cloud flattens in the direction parallel to the field the gravitational force will not go up much, while the gas pressure will increase. Hence a new stable equilibrium will be reached in which you have a flattened disk. In fact, one of the difficulties of this process, if a strong magnetic field is assumed, is that any large cloud of this sort should be much more flattened in the direction of the spiral arm than it is perpendicular to it. And I know of no observations indicating this.

I would certainly not claim any degree of conclusiveness in these arguments, especially since one can think of much more complicated magnetic topographies which would certainly have different properties. In fact, Dr. Woltjer has suggested a somewhat different magnetic topography which gets around some of these difficulties, although perhaps not all of them. But these results indicate that there are serious problems in star formation if you assume a magnetic field so great that the magnetic energy density is a hundred times the material gas density within a typical cloud. Such an assumption very much increases the difficulty of pushing cloud complexes together to form protostars.

References

[1] G. K. Batchelor, *Proc. Roy. Soc. (London)*, **A109**, 405 (1950).
[2] L. Biermann and A. Schlüter, *Z. Naturforsch.*, **9a**, 463 (1954).
[3] B. J. Bok, *Centennial Symposia*, Harvard Observatory Monograph No. 7, 1946.
[4] W. B. Bonnor, *M.N.*, **116**, 351 (1956).
[5] S. Chandrasekhar and E. Fermi, *Ap. J.*, **118**, 113 (1953).
[6] R. Ebert, *Z. Ap.*, **37**, 217 (1955).
[7] J. Henry, *Ap. J.*, **128**, 497 (1958).
[8] F. Hoyle, *Ap. J.*, **118**, 513 (1953).
[9] W. H. McCrea, *M.N.*, **117**, 562 (1957).
[10] L. Mestel and L. Spitzer, *M.N.*, **116**, 503 (1956).
[11] L. Spitzer, "Stars and Stellar Systems," Vol. 7, in press.
[12] L. Spitzer and J. Tukey, *Ap. J.*, **114**, 187 (1951).

Discussion

Dr. Biermann: Do we agree that we could get a magnetic field from a turbulent conducting medium in case the kinetic-energy density of mass motions is sufficiently large compared with the field energy we wish to have? We may consider that in the early stages of the galaxy the density of the gas was considerably higher than it is now, and the turbulence should have been more violent, owing to the presence of more massive stars, as has been discussed by Davis and myself in connection with cosmic rays. So it appears to be possible that the stronger field is a sort of relic from the early stages in the sense that it was generated in those times. After the first half billion years of existence of our galaxy the field settled down without further amplification but also without any considerable decay. Also star formation should have been easier then, because the density was so much higher. Would that be consistent with what you think?

Dr. Spitzer: At what field level?

Dr. Biermann: I would say 2×10^{-5}.

Dr. Spitzer: Then you still get into the problem with present-day star formation. And the question is, where are the dense cloud complexes whose density is high enough to bring in the lines of force? It has never been entirely clear to me how one builds up a field that is uniform over such large regions with small-scale turbulence. Maybe this could be done.

Dr. Oort: Isn't one serious objection to assuming the magnetic field to be as low as this that it would be extremely hard to understand how such expanding motions as I discussed yesterday could ever arise, unless you assume a totally new force that would be working there? I don't see how you can do it with magnetic fields that would be considerably smaller than this 2×10^{-5}. In the central regions you would need even a little more than that to get magnetic pressures that would be sufficient to cause arms of that mass to move out at velocities such as are observed. That is perhaps the most compelling argument for the very strong magnetic fields in the galaxy.

Dr. Spitzer: Could not ejection from stars provide this velocity? Although it is difficult to see how the gas ejected from stars would get organized into a spiral arm, velocities of the right order could presumably be explained by such a mechanism.

Dr. Oort: Yes, but you see the total mass contained in this 3-kpc arm is of the order of several million solar masses. And so are these other masses that are expanding at high velocities near the center. It looks very difficult to get high velocities for such enormous masses.

Dr. Underhill: With star formation on the whole we are concerned with outer regions where the field could be low, but in the inner part, where you see these rather large motions, we have no reason for believing that there is much star formation going on now. So you could have the field in one place and star formation in another.

Dr. Oort: That is not so satisfactory. You see, if you once have these strong fields in the central region, and you can make your synchrotron radiation by means of the general fields in the central region, it would seem at least very tempting to assume that the same mechanism provides the radiation in the outer regions of the galaxy. But it is not quite certain, of course.

Isn't another difficulty tied up with this to some extent in the star formation—you didn't mention it and it wasn't your subject—the problem of the angular momentum? It is of a somewhat similar nature in a way, I think. If you contract matter from interstellar space you are always faced with the fact that it would in general have 10^3 or 10^4 times too much angular momentum and you would have to get rid of that unless you assume very special conditions, which I think are hard to accept.

Dr. Spitzer: Any rotation would certainly twist the magnetic field in the neighborhood of the star. The hope would be that we could get rid of the magnetic field that we don't want and keep enough around to slow down the angular momentum. That seems to be not unpromising.

Dr. Strömgren: I believe in your paper with Mestel you were looking at possibilities for reduction of the density of free electrons through the action of the grains. I believe it has also been looked into what the effect of H^- is in that context. Is the result available, or does it still have to be worked out under the circumstances?

Dr. Spitzer: I think in the case where the contraction has started and has gone quite a way, it is fairly clear that the ionization disappears rapidly. Apart from the small ionization produced by K^{40}, cosmic-ray particles, and things of that sort, probably the electron density falls to quite a low value. I think we are probably on safe ground there. In the larger, less-dense clouds it is not obvious that you can reduce the ionization level much.

Dr. Prendergast: I suppose you could consider a cloud in which there are several reversals of the field through the cloud. Couldn't you make good use of the interface between the different subregions where the field is very small, to help star formation?

Dr. Spitzer: This gets back to Dr. Woltjer's picture, where you have a tangle of force lines. One of the problems there is that in the regions where the field is going in opposite directions one might argue that some twist of the force lines might be present, and that you would actually get a sort of force-free situation, with a continuous change of field direction between the two regions.

Dr. von Hoerner: It is not so astonishing that one gets difficulties in making stars. I would think nature has difficulties too, because otherwise no interstellar matter would be left. The fact that we have a lot of interstellar matter left shows that it is not so easy. It may be that only in exceptional cases the formation of stars is possible.

Dr. Spitzer: That is right. On the other hand, stars are being formed now at a rate which we think we know, and therefore if there is some structure that forms part of this, that is large and obvious, we ought to see it. It is not clear to me that we do.

Dr. Blaauw: On the figures you gave about the extinction ($1^m.5$ and 13^m), I understand that you favor $1^m.5$ as a representative value of what we do encounter.

Dr. Spitzer: I took this value from the familiar table by Bok [3].

Dr. Blaauw: But we do see features that have much higher absorption, of the order of say eight magnitudes, particularly in the region where star formation occurs.

Dr. Spitzer: Aren't they quite small?

Dr. Blaauw: Small but not so very small. I would say perhaps 5 pc or so. I am not thinking of the globules. For instance, in Scorpio you have these long lanes which run from Scorpio down to the galactic circle. There you have absorptions of the order of, I would say, five to eight magnitudes, and not in a very tiny thing. In the Perseus clouds there are also absorptions which are quite large. In general, if the absorptions are highest in the smallest features, you only would see them in rather dense star fields. And I suppose if you are at somewhat higher latitudes, many of them would just be lost.

Dr. Spitzer: That is an important point.

Dr. Woltjer: How much absorption do you need to significantly affect the degree of ionization of carbon?

Dr. Spitzer: Certainly if you have eight magnitudes, corresponding to four magnitudes into the center of the cloud, that will begin to have an effect.

Dr. Lüst: Is your objection against the picture of the contraction starting first along the lines of force that you don't see the flat clouds?

Dr. Spitzer: I wouldn't say that it has been established that the observations exclude the possibilities that there are such flat clouds. It is a little hard to be sure that they would look flat, especially if you are looking along the lines of force. But looking across the spiral arms you then ought to see thin clouds perpendicular to the galactic plane. I am not aware of anything that looks like that.

Dr. Oort: It might be difficult to see.

Dr. Spitzer: I agree. I don't regard this as conclusive at all. But it would suggest something to look for observationally.

Dr. Lüst: Would you also have strong objections on theoretical grounds?

Dr. Spitzer: No. A cloud in a strong magnetic field will certainly tend to contract along the lines of force first. Then if the densities are high enough it will contract across the magnetic field, pulling the lines of force with it. As the density increases and the fractional ionization falls, the lines of force will pull out of the cloud and the whole structure will then fragment, as suggested by Hoyle [8].

Dr. Oort: You have considered only the average kinetic energy of the clouds. But there are of course clouds that have velocities that are much above the average. It is conceivable that in collisions between two such clouds one might compress the matter against the magnetic fields to some extent, so that you would get higher densities and get afterward shorter times than this 10^8 years.

Dr. Spitzer: You have to be a little careful because in a normal shock the density increases by at most a factor of 4. In an isothermal shock, however, a greater increase in density is possible.

Characteristics of interstellar matter
in other galaxies

Gas in elliptical and S0 galaxies

D. E. Osterbrock

I should like to talk to you today about the observational data on interstellar matter in the elliptical galaxies. Although it is not possible to give a complete interpretation, many facts are known and several plausible inferences may be drawn. I hope you will be stimulated to think a little about the problem, particularly from the points of view of how ellipticals differ from spirals in general and from our galaxy in particular.

First, we should define what we mean by elliptical and S0 galaxies. Elliptical galaxies are objects without spiral structure, H II regions, or any kind of patchy fine structure. In the sky they are either circular or elliptical in shape, and they have a strong concentration of light to the center. Most of the elliptical galaxies that have been studied, and to which the statistics I shall quote refer, are giant ellipticals with masses of the same general order as our galaxy; that is, they contain roughly $10^{11} M_{\odot}$. In addition there exist dwarf elliptical galaxies, for instance M 32, the round companion to the Andromeda Nebula, but there are very few observations of these objects except for this one case. There are still other kinds of galaxies, the Sculptor-Fornax type, also classified by Baade as ellipticals, which are very small and loose, with very little concentration to the center. There are essentially no observations or data at all that I can talk about on interstellar matter in these Sculptor-Fornax systems.

The S0 galaxies also appear in the sky as round or elliptical objects, but there is more than one type of object in this classification group as Hubble used it. One type is round or elliptical in shape like an elliptical galaxy, but instead of having a smooth decrease of luminosity from the center outward, has instead some kind of an abrupt change in slope in the relation between surface brightness and distance. A second type is an object that would otherwise be called an elliptical, except that it has some faint dust markings in it. And finally there are objects that look something like edge-on spirals, but without any dark absorption (NGC 3115 is an example), and these sometimes appear in tables as S0, sometimes as E 7. Hubble, I believe, thought that these three types were examples of the same sort of galaxy, seen in different projections in the sky, and for that reason they are lumped together in the classification.

Now E and S0 galaxies are usually called pure population II objects, and it might be thought that there is no interstellar matter in them. However, the observations show that although fewer ellipticals than spirals contain visible interstellar matter, there is a definite fraction of the ellipticals in which gas is present. This is shown by observations of the [O II] $\lambda3727$ emission line, which is a characteristic feature of the spectra of diffuse nebulae or H II regions in our galaxy and in other spirals. It is convenient for finding interstellar gas in emission in galaxies because it occurs at a place in the spectrum where the continuous spectrum of the galaxy itself is weak. There are statistics, which are byproducts of the Lick and Mount Wilson radial-velocity surveys, of the occurrence of

Table 1

Fraction of Galaxies of Each Type in Which [O II] $\lambda3727$ is Observable in Emission

	Percentage with $\lambda3727$	
Type	Mount Wilson observational material	Lick observational material
E	18	12
S0	48	27
Sa	62	45
Sb	80	62
Sc	85	68

the $\lambda3727$ line in the spectra of galaxies of each type, and they show that among the spirals a relatively large fraction shows this emission line, while among the ellipticals there is a much smaller percentage, but it is by no means negligible—15 per cent would be a fair average.

Among the elliptical spectra that show the $\lambda3727$ emission line it occurs in all strengths, from very strong down to very weak and difficult to detect. Furthermore, it is possible to find still more cases of ellipticals showing λ3727 in emission, by taking spectra specifically for this purpose, widened and well exposed in the near ultraviolet. Of six nebulae studied in this way, one turned out to have weak λ3727 emission, so although the number is too small for statistics, there is no doubt that there is a continuous graduation in the intensity of this line from strong through weak to absent.

λ3727 is actually a double line, the two components of which are separated by 2.8 A. A measurement of the relative strengths of the two components gives the electron density in the region in which the emission arises, because the two upper levels involved have different excitation cross sections. However, in all the ellipticals the internal velocity dispersion is so large that the lines are not resolved at all, and λ3727 is just a single, very broad, blend. For instance, in NGC 4278, an elliptical with strong λ3727, the profile is a single broad line, with a width of about 12 A or about 900 km/sec. As far as I know all the ellipticals have a single broad profile like this, except for NGC 4486, also known as M 87 or Virgo A, the well-known strong radio source. It is an elliptical galaxy with the peculiarity of a so-called jet near its center. The nucleus of this galaxy shows λ3727 in emission, and as Minkowski discovered, the profile of the line may be described as almost double. The stronger component has a velocity that corresponds to the velocity of the stars in the nucleus, while the weaker component is shifted by about 10 A, or about 700 km/sec in velocity. The λ3727 emission line occurs only in the nucleus, not in the jet, which in fact emits visible synchrotron radiation, but the double profile of λ3727 may be connected in some way with the existence of the jet and the strong nonthermal radio radiation. This is not certain though, by any means.

In one of the other ellipticals, NGC 1052, we tried to get some idea of the electron density, even though the two fine-structure components were not resolved. To do this, we measured the mean wavelength of the blended profile, and then interpreted this wavelength in terms of the relative strengths of the two unresolved components. The result was that the measured wavelength was near what would be expected in the low-density limit, that is, for any electron density less than about 200 per cubic centimeter. This means that the emission spectrum comes from interstellar gas with a density similar to the density in the H II regions of our galaxy, rather than from gas with a density similar to the densities in the planetary nebulae. Although this was measured only in the single case NGC 1052, we have as a working hypothesis considered it to apply to all ellipticals with λ3727 in the emission in their spectra.

Next we shall consider the detailed observations of NGC 4278, a nearly round elliptical with quite strong λ3727. In its spectrum there also occur all the strong emission lines that are typical of diffuse nebulae,

Table 2

Observed Relative Emission-Line Strengths in NGC 4278
Compared with NGC 1976

Emission line	NGC 4278 E galaxy	NGC 1976 galactic diffuse nebula
$\lambda 3727$ [O II]	14.5	6.4
$\lambda 3869$ [Ne III]	1.0	1.0
$\lambda 4861$ H$_\beta$	5.0	5.0
$\lambda 5007$ [O III]	3.8	17
$\lambda 6548$ [N II]	1.7	1.0
$\lambda 6563$ H$_\alpha$	6.4	17
$\lambda 6583$ [N II]	5.5	2.7

as Table 2 shows, where a comparison is made with the Orion nebula. The intensities for NGC 4278 have low accuracy, because of the underlying continuous spectrum of the stars (this is particularly serious for H$_\beta$ and H$_\alpha$), and considering these inaccuracies it is fair to say that there are no exceptionally striking differences between the two emission-line spectra, except that the Orion nebula has somewhat higher ionization.

From the emission-line strengths it is possible to compute the relative abundances of those ions that give rise to the lines if the temperature is known. In Table 3 the abundances are given for two possible assumed temperatures, 10,000°, representative of the H II regions of our galaxy, and 20,000°, to show the effect of higher temperature. It can be seen that the calculated abundances of all the heavy ions are lower by about a factor

Table 3

Relative Abundances from Interstellar Emission Lines in NGC 4278

	Assumed temperature	
Ion	10,000°	20,000°
H$^+$	1.0×10^4	1.0×10^4
N$^+$	0.3	0.08
O$^+$	1.5	0.15
O^{++}	0.5	0.08
Ne^{++}	0.3	0.04

of ten with the higher assumed temperature. This result is due to the fact that cooling occurs by the forbidden-line radiation, so that if you could imagine decreasing the abundances of the heavy elements in a nebula, the effect would just be to make the temperature go up until the forbidden-line strength came to about the same level again, so that the same amount of energy would still be radiated away. Thus there must be an independent measurement of the temperature before the abundances can be determined. In an ordinary gaseous nebula, the temperature is found by measuring a line ratio such as [O III] $\lambda5007/\lambda4363$, but in even the most favorable elliptical $\lambda\,4363$ is far too faint to be measured against the integrated continuous spectrum of the stars. Thus several alternatives are open; we might assume a normal gas temperature $T = 10,000°$ and then find the total O abundance to be $O/H = 2.0 \times 10^{-4}$ (since almost all O is either O^+ or O^{++} in a typical gaseous nebula, while all H is H^+), fairly normal in comparison with the Orion nebula, for which $O/H = 3.4 \times 10^{-4}$, or we might assume a high temperature, $T = 20,000°$, and derive an abnormally low abundance ratio $O/H = 0.25 \times 10^{-4}$.

Next I should like to discuss the space distribution of the observable interstellar gas in the same elliptical galaxy, NGC 4278. Like all ellipticals, it has a very steep rise of surface brightness (in the continuous spectrum) right in to its center. To map the distribution of the gas, spectra were taken with the slit of the spectrograph held fixed across the nucleus and in various position angles, so that on the resulting spectrograms, the image of $\lambda3727$ is resolved along one space coordinate (perpendicular to the dispersion), and also in one velocity coordinate (parallel to the dispersion). The spectrograms show that the emission line is highly broadened at the center of the nucleus, with a maximum width of 900 km/sec (on the longest exposures), but that the broadening decreases outward, practically vanishing at the edge of the nucleus (4″ in diameter). Furthermore, within the nucleus the intensity of the emission line decreases sharply from the center outward. Just outside in the nucleus, the line is very weak, but probably barely visible, resolved into the two unbroadened fine-structure components, but this is not certain. The spectrograms also show that there is a gradient of the mean velocity of the gas across the nucleus amounting to about 200 km/sec/4″ diameter, in a sense corresponding to a rotation essentially about the minor axis of the galaxy.

The distance of the nebula can be estimated only from the measured red shift, and as it is only 600 km/sec, the distance is highly uncertain, but on this basis the 4″ diameter of the nucleus is equivalent to 170 pc. Thus if we were to consider the gas motions in the nucleus to be turbulent, with an average turbulent velocity of, say, $v = 300$ km/sec and a scale of $l = 170$ pc, then a very crude estimate of the decay time of the turbulence would be $l/v = 10^6$ years.

The total amount of ionized gas in the nucleus can also be estimated, from the absolute intensities of the hydrogen emission lines. Their intensities have been compared photographically with the continuous spectrum of the galaxy, and the continuous spectrum has in turn been measured both photographically and photoelectrically by Tifft at the Mount Wilson Observatory. This result is that in the continuous spectrum, the nucleus within a $4''$ diameter has $m_V = 13.1$, which corresponds to $M_V = -16.5$, which corresponds to $L = 3 \times 10^8 \, L_\odot$. And from the measured brightness of the gas in the nucleus, the total emission from the whole volume can be found, which for a known temperature is proportional to the product of the mean electron density and the total mass of gas. Thus to find the mass, assumptions must be made about the temperature and also about the mean density. Total masses calculated in this way under various assumptions are listed in Table 4, together with in each case

Table 4

Total Mass and Effective Radius of Ionized Interstellar Gas in Nucleus of NGC 4278 for Various Assumed Electron Densities and Temperatures

Assumed density N_e cm^{-3}	Assumed temperature			
	$T = 10,000°$		$T = 20,000°$	
	$M/M_\odot$	R pc	$M/M_\odot$	R pc
1	6×10^6	360	12×10^6	450
10	6×10^5	78	12×10^5	97
10^2	6×10^4	17	12×10^4	21
10^3	6×10^3	4	12×10^3	5

the radius a homogeneous gas cloud of the assumed temperature and density would have, if it emitted all the observed radiation.

It can be seen that the first line of the table is not physically possible, because it requires a radius larger than the total radius of the nucleus. Smaller computed radii would indicate the presence of density fluctuations, but a density as high as 10^3 cm^{-3}, as in the last line of the table, can be ruled out by the observational upper limit, quoted earlier, of 300 per cubic centimeter (measured, it must be remembered, in a different elliptical, but assumed to be generally valid).

The total mass of ionized gas in the nucleus, which the table thus shows is at most about $10^6 \, M_\odot$ and at least about $10^4 \, M_\odot$, is quite small in comparison with the total mass of stars in the nucleus, which have a measured $L = 3 \times 10^8 \, L_\odot$ and a mass probably of the order of $3 \times 10^9 \, M_\odot$. This estimate of the mass of the nucleus follows from assuming that the turbulent velocity of the gas balances the gravitational attraction of the stars on it, which leads to

$$M = \frac{R}{G} \langle v^2 \rangle = 3 \times 10^9 M_\odot$$

It is only an order-of-magnitude estimate, but probably the mass of stars does not differ by much more than a factor of three from it, and there is no doubt that the mass of ionized gas is much smaller. Note that the estimated mass corresponds to a ratio $M/L = 10 \, M_\odot/L_\odot$ in the nucleus.

Next it may be asked what the mechanism of excitation of the observed emission is. Two possibilities can be imagined. One is that the excitation is the same as in diffuse nebulae in our own galaxy, namely, that hot stars radiate ultraviolet light, which ionizes the gas and thus is converted into lower-energy visible photons. We ordinarily think of the elliptical galaxies as being without high-temperature stars, and they certainly do not contain any of the very high luminosity O and B stars that excite the H II regions in our own galaxy. There might be, though, lower-luminosity hot stars that cannot be seen individually. Some possible hints can be found in globular clusters, although, as is known from their spectra, globular clusters are not the same in population as elliptical galaxies, but both are at least samples of old populations.

In globular clusters there are some hot stars, both along the blue end of the horizontal branch in the H–R diagram, and also above it, off any sequence. Spectra have been taken of only a very few of these stars, and they have been described as O and B stars, while for most of them the only available information is their colors. The number of these hot stars varies quite widely from one cluster to another cluster. For an elliptical galaxy we can make the following most optimistic calculation: That is, take the globular cluster which has the largest population of hot stars—M 3; find the total amount of ionizing radiation in that cluster and scale it up to the elliptical. In both cluster and galaxy, most of the light comes from the bright giants, while the ultraviolet light comes from the hot stars. To make the calculation, the temperatures of the hot stars must be known, and with the available data they are highly uncertain. The visible light from the nucleus of the elliptical is about 10^3 times the visible light of the cluster, while the ionizing radiation that is needed in the elliptical to excite the observed emission-line spectrum is about 100 times the ionizing radiation that is available in the cluster. In other words, if the globular cluster M 3 were scaled up to have as many bright stars as there are in the nucleus of the elliptical galaxy NGC 4278, there would be 10 times as much ultraviolet light available as is needed to give all the observed emission from this elliptical. This interpretation has this attraction: One can imagine that from elliptical to elliptical there might be differences in the number of hot stars, because there are known to be differences from one globular cluster to another. We could thus understand the differences among elliptical galaxies in strength of $\lambda 3727$ purely as an ionization effect. For the amount of gas required is so small that it is hard to imagine that there is not enough in every elliptical.

Another possible explanation of the excitation mechanism, which leaves out the hot stars altogether, is to imagine that the observed velocities are truly turbulent, and that the turbulent dissipation is the energy source for the observed emission. The energy made available in this way, to use a very crude estimate, is $\epsilon = v^3/l = 100$ erg/g/sec. On the other hand, the energy that is radiated by the gas can be calculated from the tables of Spitzer and Savedoff to be $\epsilon = 5N_e$ erg/g/sec for the normal abundances and $T = 10,000°$, or $\epsilon = 1N_e$ for the lower heavy-element abundances and $T = 20,000°$. So if $N_e \leqslant 20$, there would be enough energy from this source to give all the observed radiation. However, this interpretation means that the turbulence would decay in 10^6 years, and the problem of what continues to generate it remains, for a mechanism that feeds energy into the gas is then required.

Next I should like to talk briefly about the radio observations of elliptical galaxies, first of all the 21-cm observations. Among the ellipticals an attempt to detect the 21-cm line of H in emission has been made only in M 32, as far as I know. It is a dwarf elliptical, one of the companions to M 31 and is not characteristic of the giant ellipticals to which all the other results apply. The result of Wentzel and van Woerden is that there is no detectable 21-cm radiation from M 32 and that the upper limit that can be placed on the amount of hydrogen is $M_H \leqslant 2.5 \times 10^7 M_\odot$. On the other hand, the mass in this same galaxy can be found from the observed dispersion of the stars' velocities, and the most recent result is due to Burbidge, Burbidge, and Fish, $M = 1.8 \times 10^9 M_\odot$, and the ratio of these two gives $M_H/M \leqslant 0.014$, which is just about the observed ratio in our galaxy and M 31. To date this measurement has been made only for M 32, but there are giant ellipticals of about the same apparent magnitude, and I believe that pushing this observation on those galaxies would give important results. It could be found whether or not there is a few per cent of the mass in the form of neutral H in them, and whether in fact those elliptical galaxies that do not show emission lines do have neutral gas, and also whether those that do show emission lines have neutral gas, too, as well as ionized gas.

Finally, I should like to discuss briefly nonthermal emission from the ellipticals. There are at the present time actually quite a few radio sources that have been identified with double elliptical galaxies, as shown in Table

Table 5

Double Elliptical Galaxies as Radio Sources

Object	Hubble type	Magnitude, m_{pg}	Radio index, $m_{TV} - m_{pg}$
3C 315	E + E	19	-10.7
Hyd A	E + E	16	-10.3
3C 310	E1 + E0	17	-10.0
3C 433	E + E	17	-8.7
3C 317	E + E	14	-6.7
3C 465	E + E	14	-6.2
NGC 4782/3	S0 + E0	13	-5.4
3C 75	E0 + S0	13	-4.9
NGC 545/7	S0 + E0	13	-4.8
NGC 750/1	E0 + E0	13	> -4.6

5. They are all identifications that have been called certain by Dewhirst, or Bolton, or Leslie, and that were classified as ellipticals or S0. Many of them, particularly those with large radio indices, are quite faint. I think that for these faint objects the classifications are fairly uncertain, because at faint magnitudes the images are very small, and it is hard to see what they really look like. The last pair in the table, NGC 750/1, is a double elliptical that is fairly bright and quite well known, but is not a radio source, and I have estimated an upper limit to its radio magnitude by the fact that it is not in the 3C catalogue. A fine picture of it has been published by Zwicky; it consists of two ellipticals nearly in contact, and there is material between them and also a tail behind one of them. This case illustrates that it is not true that all double ellipticals are radio sources.

There are also a number of single ellipticals that have been identified as certain radio sources, listed in Table 6. As you can see, there is quite a large number of objects, and among the brighter ones there is great diversity. One is NGC 5128, called a peculiar elliptical by Hubble, and a case of a collision or interpenetration between E and an Sc galaxy by Baade and Minkowski. Another is NGC 4486, the elliptical with the jet. Many of the others are so faint and small that a peculiarity would be difficult to recognize. On the other hand, there are a number of ellipticals that have not been observed as radio sources although attempts were made, and in these cases there are significant limits to the radio index. All spirals of the Sb and Sc classes are supposed to have radio indices of essentially $m_{TV} - m_{pg} = 0$, so that at least NGC 3115 in the last line of the table has definitely less radio emission for its light emission than it would if it were a spiral.

I am uncertain again about the interpretation. We tend to think

Table 6

Single Elliptical Galaxies as Radio Sources

Object	Hubble type	Magnitude, m_{pg}	Radio index, $m_{TV} - m_{pg}$	Peculiarity
3C 33	E0	18	-11.4	
3C 298	E0	18	-10.1	
3C 327	S0	17	$- 9.4$	
NGC 6166	E	14	$- 6.0$	Three nuclei
NGC 4486	E0	10	$- 5.9$	Jet
3C 66	E	13	$- 5.3$	Jet
NGC 4261	E3	11	$- 4.6$	
NGC 1218	E	13	$- 4.4$	
NGC 5128	Ep	6	$- 4.0$	Heavy dust
NGC 533	E3	13	$- 3.6$	lane
NGC 4374	E1	10	$- 2.0$	
NGC 584	E4	11	$- 1.9$	
NGC 4494	E1	11	$> - 0.8$	
NGC 4636	E0	11	$> - 0.3$	
NGC 3379	E0	10	> 0.2	
NGC 4649	E2	10	> 0.4	
NGC 3115	E7	10	> 1.8	

of the nonthermal emission as caused by relativistic electrons in a magnetic field. If we suppose that the emission is distributed through the whole galaxy, there must be relativistic electrons and a magnetic field through the whole galaxy. I am not clear whether the magnetic field can come from the relativistic electrons themselves, or whether it must have its origin in a more massive, lower-temperature, interstellar gas. Another possible interpretation would be that the radio emission comes from the shells of supernovae or from some other kind of radio stars. That would mean that there is a large difference in the number of supernovae shells or radio stars from one of these galaxies classified as ellipticals to another.

References

R. Minkowski and D. E. Osterbrock, *Ap. J.*, **129**, 583 (1959).

D. E. Osterbrock, *Ap. J.*, **132**, 325 (1960).

L. H. Aller and W. Liller, *Ap. J.*, **130**, 45 (1959).

J. G. Bolton, *Publ. Caltech Radio Astronomy Obs. 5*, 1960.

E. M. Burbidge, G. R. Burbidge, and R. A. Fish, *Ap. J.*, **133**, 393 (1961).

E. M. Burbidge, G. R. Burbidge, and R. A. Fish, *Ap. J.*, **133**, 1092 (1961).

D. W. Dewhirst, in R. N. Bracewell (ed.), "Paris Symposium on Radio Astronomy," 1959, p. 507.

D. O. Edge, J. R. Shakeshaft, W. M. McAdam, J. E. Baldwin, S. Archer, *Mem. Roy. Ap. Soc.*, **78**, 37 (1951).

P. R. R. Leslie, *Observatory*, **80**, 316 (1960).

B. Y. Mills, *Australian J. Phys.*, **8**, 368 (1966).

B. Y. Mills, O. B. Slee, and E. R. Hill, *Australian J. Phys.*, **11**, 360 (1960).

G. M. Wade, *Observatory*, **80**, 235 (1960).

D. G. Wentzel and H. van Woerden, *B.A.N.*, **14**, 335 (1960).

F. Zwicky, *Ergeb. Exakt. Naturw.*, **29**, 344 (1956).

Discussion

Dr. Pottasch: The derived chemical composition is very sensitive to lower temperatures. If the temperature were 5000° the abundance of all heavy elements would go way up.

Dr. Osterbrock: Right. If the temperature were lower, the abundances would go up, whereas if it were higher, they would go down.

Dr. Oort: I hope we shall soon be able to attempt 21-cm observations of elliptical galaxies. We hope to have a parametric amplifier working in the course of this year, and then the chances will be much better for reaching fainter limits.

Dr. Osterbrock: I agree with you. The expected amount of neutral hydrogen is uncomfortably close to the limit of the present observational technique, but somewhat higher sensitivity would put many ellipticals within reach.

Dr. Schwarzschild: To investigate the possibility of very blue stars, has one ever attempted a sort of a UBV photometry—of course the U band has to avoid the [O II] line—to see whether there is already in the accessible ultraviolet substantial excess over K giants ?

Dr. Osterbrock: Yes, in a very primitive way. That is, Tifft measured photoelectrically a number of ellipticals and also spirals. He had one filter in the ultraviolet short of $\lambda3727$. There was an ultraviolet excess in NGC 4278 with respect to the everage of other ellipticals, but it was not very large. As well as I can remember there was one other elliptical with a still larger ultraviolet excess but it doesn't show $\lambda3727$ emission. But there was in his data by no means a complete coverage of all ellipticals.

Dr. Lüst: Since these ellipticals are also radio sources, is it not possible that there are low-energy cosmic-ray particles responsible for the ionization of the gas?

Dr. Osterbrock: I don't know quantitatively but I would well imagine that it is possible. There is not a correlation of $\lambda3727$ with radio emission in ellipticals. So you would have to imagine that the $\lambda3727$ without radio emission arises where there are a lot of low-energy particles but no relativistic particles.

Dr. Oort: As far as I know the radio spectrum is not very different for these ellipticals.

Dr. Woltjer: Concerning the possibility that the magnetic field in these nonthermal galaxies would be produced by the relativistic particles themselves, I think the answer is quite simple. If this were the case you would have a system of positive energy which would explode very violently.

Dr Spitzer: Because there is not enough mass to be held gravitationally ?

Dr. Woltjer: Yes.

Dr. Oort: Wouldn't it be likely that the amount of gas near the nucleus would depend to some extent on the flattening of the nebula considered? If you have a spherical nebula one would expect that the gas might collect near the nucleus, whereas if you had a rapidly rotating nebula it would be spread out more over the disk and you would not see anything very conspicuous near the nucleus. So some differences of that kind also might well occur.

Dr. Osterbrock: Yes. According to Dr. Spitzer's analysis of some years ago, random motion would quickly damp out and the gas would be left as a thin layer if there is any rotation at all. That might be what is seen in the spectrum of NGC 4278 outside the nucleus. As you know the ellipticals are a mixture of objects, and the E0 class is partly made up of round objects and partly of spheroids seen face on. It is therefore hard to answer your question from the observations. There is no systematic correlation of the observed degree of ellipticity with the occurrence of $\lambda 3727$, although the statistics are rather small.

Dr. Oort: Isn't that rather remarkable, that there shouldn't be such a correlation?

Dr. Osterbrock: To me there is much that is very remarkable. At the center of NGC 4278 there certainly appear to be random motions, for you can see that the gradient of rotation across the central part is about 200 km/sec, while the broadening of the line is quite a bit larger than that.

Dr. Oort: Is it certain that that broadening is really due to internal motions and not to an extremely rapid variation in rotational velocity quite close to the nucleus where you couldn't recognize it as rotation?

Dr. Osterbrock: No. Then of course it would have to have a rotational velocity curve that goes up very sharply then falls and then rises again, all within 4″ or 170 pc.

Dr. Spitzer: Might this perhaps be a mild form of what one sees in a more exaggerated form in the Seyfert type with stellar nuclei? These systems show enormous velocities of 1000 km/sec.

Dr. Woltjer: Is there any correlation between the occurrence of the emission lines in the ellipticals and their location in or outside clusters?

Dr. Osterbrock: In the dense nearby clusters the occurrence of $\lambda 3727$ in ellipticals is zero. There are four dense clusters relatively close to us for which there are good spectra and for which the types are known from the Hubble catalogue. Among 25 ellipticals in these clusters not a single one has $\lambda 3727$. In the very distant clusters there are galaxies classified as ellipticals that have $\lambda 3727$ in emission, but they are so faint and small that the identity of those galaxies with the well-known close ellipticals is not certain.

The distribution of gas in spiral and irregular galaxies

E. Margaret Burbidge

Introduction

Three methods are available at present for investigation of the inter-stellar medium in external galaxies:

1. Direct photography using appropriate filter combinations to isolate specific emission lines which give information on the distribution of the ionized gas. This method also gives all the information so far available on the distribution of obscuring material.

2. Radio astronomical investigations with 21-cm line techniques, which give information about the distribution and the amount of neutral atomic hydrogen.

3. Spectroscopic investigations with nebular spectrographs.

None of these techniques has yet been exploited adequately. The methods of filter photography were applied by Shajn and Hase [24], [25], [26] to a number of nearby galaxies. Beyond this there has as yet been no systematic investigation along these lines. Much more information on the distribution of dust in external galaxies is available in the large collection of plates of galaxies taken over the last 60 years with large reflectors. For example, an extensive pioneering survey of the dust in flattened edge-on spirals was made by Curtis [7].

21-cm investigations of a number of comparatively nearby systems have been published in recent years, e.g., M 31 [10], M 33 [32], and M 82 [17]. The most extensive spectroscopic investigations have been made by Mayall and Humason. Radial velocity investigations have led to estimates of the frequency of occurrence of [O II] $\lambda3727$ in elliptical galaxies [11], and the only extensive investigation of the frequency of this emission feature in spiral and irregular galaxies has been made by Mayall [13]. In addition, a number of investigations of the small class of galaxies which show strong emission lines, i.e., the galaxies studied by Seyfert [23] and some radio sources such as Cygnus A [2] and NGC 1275 [14], have been made. Finally, investigations of the state of the gas in two other elliptical galaxies have been made by Minkowski and Osterbrock [16], [18].

Since 1958 we have been investigating the rotations and internal motions in a number of spiral, barred spiral, and irregular galaxies. The emission features that are used in these studies are predominantly H_α and [N II]λ6583, also [S II]$\lambda\lambda$6716, 6731, and occasionally H_β, [O III]$\lambda\lambda$4959, 5007, and [O II]λ3727.

In this paper we shall give an account of the information that we have on the distribution and relative intensities of these emission features in 33 irregular and spiral galaxies. We shall then compare the relative intensities with those observed in planetary nebulae and in H II and diffuse emission regions in our galaxy. Finally, we shall consider the theoretical intensity ratios under various physical conditions.

Observations

In his fundamental paper on the occurrence and distribution of emission from the [O II] doublet at $\lambda\lambda$3726, 3729, Mayall [13] showed that in barred and normal spiral galaxies of types b and c, and in irregulars, ionized gas was nearly always present in considerable amounts. Page [20] in his study of velocities in double galaxies with the B-spectrograph at the prime focus of the 82-inch telescope, used the H_α and nearby [N II] lines because he noted that all galaxies in which the [O II] doublet appeared had H_α emission which was stronger than [O II]. Mainly for this reason (although also for the reason that with low dispersion the [O II] doublet is blended and the mean wavelength of the blend depends on the relative strengths of the two lines and hence on the density of the gas), we decided to use the emission lines of H_α and, where possible, [N II]λ6583 in our program of measurement of rotations and internal motions of galaxies. Some 200 spectra are now available for a number of barred spiral, normal spiral, and irregular galaxies, and these can be used, as well as for the primary purpose of measurement of velocities for which they were obtained, to give information on the distribution of the ionized interstellar gas in these galaxies and the physical conditions in the gas.

In this section we give a description of the distribution of the ionized gas in 33 galaxies arranged according to structural classification. The information that we can give consists of what emission lines are visible (indicating the degree of excitation), how the various lines are distributed in the galaxies (indicating the variation in stellar content and/or the gas-to-stars ratio), and a rough estimate of the relative intensity of the neighboring lines H_α and [N II]λ6583. Our spectra are not calibrated, having been obtained primarily for velocity measurements, so true intensities cannot be obtained. However, it is found by eye estimates that the ratio H_α/[N II]λ6583 can vary from a value near 5, through a value near 3 which appears to be characteristic of spiral-arm emission regions of both low and moderately high excitation, through values near unity which are found in some nuclei and nuclear bulges, to values so much less than unity that H_α disappears in the nuclei of some galaxies. This ratio must contain information on the conditions of excitation of the gas—whether it is radiative or collisional, and perhaps on what the radiation and electron temperatures are, since the Balmer series is usually produced by recombination after radiative ionization while the forbidden line spectrum is usually produced by collisional excitation by electrons in an ionized gas. The ratio might be affected also by variations in the relative abundance of the elements in the gas with location in the galaxy, but we shall as a working hypothesis assume that relative abundances are the same as the relative abundances in our own galaxy. The galaxies described below are arranged, within each structural classification division, roughly in order of decreasing excitation, although some attention is paid to the structural similarities of galaxies within these subdivisions.

Irregular
NGC 5253: Very strong emission lines, concentrated to the center of the galaxy. Made up of knots (giant high-excitation H II regions). H_α and other Balmer lines, [O III], [O II], [S II], [N II], [Ne III]λ3869, appear, with H_α and [O III] strongest. $H_\alpha \gg$ [N II].

NGC 4449: Made up of knots (moderately high excitation giant H II regions). Strong emission lines are concentrated to the center, but appear throughout the galaxy, showing extensive ionized gas. H_α, H_β, [O III], [O II], [S II], [N II] appear, with H_α and [O III] strongest. $H_\alpha \gg$ [N II].

M 82 (NGC 3034): Extensive dust, as shown by Morgan and Mayall. Region *A*, surrounding what is apparently the nucleus, is riddled with dust lanes (see Fig. 1) and shows very strong emission lines of H_α, H_β, H_γ, [N II], [S II], and weak [O III]. The excitation is evidently fairly low, because [O III] $\ll H_\beta$. The emission lines extend quite strongly across the prominent dust lane (*B*), although no continuous spectrum is visible here. They cease abruptly just after going into region *C*, which shows a strong continuous spectrum with absorption lines indicating spectral type *A*. A moderately long exposure shows still no emission in the dust

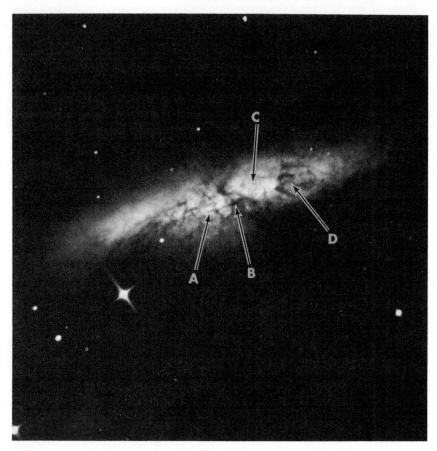

Fig. 1

lanes in region D. This will be discussed further below, and in a separate publication.

Barred Spirals: SBc

NGC 5383: H_α, [N II], and weak [S II] appear in the nuclear region, which has a structure consisting of a central small amorphous nucleus and a bright fast-rotating region around it with dust lanes emerging that form part of the bar. The H_α/[N II]$\lambda6583$ intensity ratio is approximately 3. H_α and [N II]$\lambda6583$ are also visible in the bar and outer arms, much weaker than in the nucleus but with the same intensity ratio.

NGC 7640: On fairly short exposure spectra, only H_α emission is seen, widespread throughout the galaxy which is seen nearly edge-on, of fairly uniform intensity throughout, but strongest in an H II region outside the nucleus.

Barred Spirals: SBb

NGC 3504: This has a prominent bright nucleus which is fast-rotating and shows very strong emission lines with moderately high excitation. H_α, [N II], [S II], [O II], and [O III] are seen in order of decreasing intensity; H_β and H_γ are also in emission. The intensity ratio H_α/[N II]λ6583 $\sim$ 3. Outside the nucleus only H_α and [N II] are seen, weaker than in the nucleus, and with the same intensity ratio. Evidently this galaxy has a nuclear population containing young stars of high temperature and luminosity.

NGC 1097, 1365, 6951: These are all similar in having fast-rotating bright nuclei with considerable structure in them. NGC 1097 and 6951 have in the very center small amorphous nuclei like NGC 5383, and bright spiral rings around them consisting of emission knots. NGC 1365 has dust arms emerging on opposite sides and leading into the bar. In the nuclear regions H_α and [N II] are the strongest features and the intensity ratio H_α/[N II]λ6583 $\sim$ 3, except in NGC 6951, where the lines are of nearly equal intensity; [S II] is weakly visible, indicating fairly low excitation (no [O III] is seen).

NGC 1530: Only H_α and [N II] are seen in the nucleus, and the intensity ratio H_α/[N II]λ6583 $\sim$ 3. The same emission lines are also present in the outer parts, with the same intensity ratio.

NGC 613: Emission lines are strong in the nucleus, showing H_α, H_β, [N II], and weak [S II]. No [O III] is seen; the excitation is moderately low. The intensity ratio H_α/[N II]λ6583 just exceeds unity in the nucleus; only these two lines, much weaker and with intensity ratio approximately 3, are seen in the arms.

NGC 7479: Emission lines of H_α and [N II] occur in the nucleus and strongly throughout the length of the bar, showing concentrations of ionized gas in large H II agglomerates along the bar. It is noteworthy that Mayall found [O II] emission only in the nucleus, not along the bar. In the nucleus the intensity ratio H_α/[N II]λ6583 < 1, while it has the usual value of about 3 along the bar.

NGC 1300: Emission lines of H_α, [N II], and [O II] are seen in the nucleus; [S II] and [O III] are not seen, indicating low excitation. H_α and [N II] are seen in the outer regions also, less intensely. In the nucleus H_α/[N II]λ6583 < 1, while this ratio is approximately 3 outside the nucleus.

NGC 5921: Emission lines of H_α and [N II] are seen but are quite weak. In the nucleus $H_\alpha/[N II]\lambda6583 \ll 1$; in H II regions outside the nucleus this ratio is approximately 3.

NGC 1398: No emission lines at all are seen.

Barred Spirals: SBa

NGC 4314: This is classified as peculiar in the Hubble Atlas [21]. It has an inner spiral structure in the nuclear region, like NGC 1097 and 6951, and this region shows H_α and $[N II]\lambda6583$ in the normal 3:1 ratio. [S II] and [O III] are not seen; the excitation is hence low. No emission lines have been detected in the bar and outer regions, which are smooth and apparently devoid of H II regions.

Normal Spirals: Sc

NGC 4631 and 3556: These are viewed rather edge-on and little spiral structure is visible, but the former has been classified Sc in the Hubble Atlas and the latter shows a fairly regular dust arm. They probably verge on the irregular in structure. Both have widespread emission of fairly uniform intensity throughout, with little central concentration. NGC 4631 is of higher excitation than NGC 3556; the former shows H_α, [O III], [S II], [O II], and [N II] in that order of intensity (H_β is also in emission, and $H_\alpha \gg [N II]$). NGC 3556 shows only H_α and [N II]; emission lines do not appear in the extensive regions of dust, and $H_\alpha/[N II]\lambda6583$ is about 3.

NGC 253: This has widespread emission throughout but a concentration in the nucleus. H_α, [N II], and [S II] are seen; the excitation is thus moderately low except in isolated emission patches, where [O III], H_β, and H_γ can be seen. The intensity ratio $H_\alpha/[N II]\lambda6583$ changes on going from the nucleus, where it is near unity, to the outer regions, where it is, as usual, about 3.

NGC 1385: Emission is widespread; the ratio $H_\alpha/[N II]\lambda6583$ changes from about 1.5 in the nucleus to about 3 outside. [S II] is weakly visible outside the nucleus.

NGC 6503: This has widespread emission throughout, of fairly even intensity, with no nuclear concentration. H_α, [N II], and [S II] are seen, showing that the excitation is moderately low (no [O III] is seen). In the nuclear region the intensity ratio $H_\alpha/[N II]\lambda6583$ is near unity; in the nucleus itself the emission is weaker and the ratio is less than 1; in the main body the ratio is approximately 3, while it may exceed 3 in the strongest emission patches in the arms.

NGC 157: Emission is widespread, showing H_α, [N II], and [S II]. In the outer parts the ratio $H_\alpha/[N II]\lambda6583$ probably exceeds 3, while in the nucleus the ratio is about unity.

NGC 3198: Emission is stronger in the arms than in the nucleus.

H_α/[N II]λ6583 changes from near unity in the nucleus to about 3 in the arms; the excitation is low.

NGC 6643: Only H_α and [N II] are seen, indicating low excitation, and they are widespread throughout the galaxy with little nuclear concentration, but there is increased emission intensity in prominent H II regions in the arms. H_α/[N II]λ6583 changes from about 1.5 in the nucleus to about 3 in the arms.

Normal Spirals: Sbc

NGC 2903: H_α and [N II] are distributed throughout the galaxy but are concentrated in the prominent spiral arms. [S II] and weak [O II] are visible in the nuclear region. The intensity ratio H_α/[N II]λ6583 hardly changes on going from the nucleus to the spiral arms; it is about 3 throughout.

NGC 5055: H_α and [N II] are distributed throughout the galaxy, right out to the outer parts, with concentrations in the more obvious H II aggregates in the spiral arms and gaps in the dusty regions. H_α/[N II]λ6583 is approximately 3 in the arms; in the nucleus itself no emission lines occur and only absorption lines are seen.

Normal Spirals: Sb

NGC 4258: This is a somewhat atypical Sb; it was included in Seyfert's list of galaxies with nuclei having enormously strong, broad emission lines of high excitation, although it clearly does not belong to this class—it does not have the characteristic broad strong H_α in the nucleus. In the nucleus it has [O III], [O II], [S II], [N II], and H_α in about this order of intensity; the ratio H_α/[N II]λ6583 is about 0.3. Emission lines in the nucleus are rather broad, and could be interpreted as indicating random velocities of about 350 km/sec. In the nuclear bulge only H_α, [N II], [S II], and [O II] are seen; the lines are narrower here and H_α/[N II]λ6583 is about unity. Outside this, emission lines appear only in isolated patches, where they are very strong, and H_α, [O II], [O III], [S II], [N II], and even H_β, H_γ, and H_δ can be seen in some areas. H_α/[N II]λ6583 varies in these outer parts from about 3 to values somewhat larger than this. H_β is more intense than [O III]. The excitation is evidently moderately high both in the nucleus and in the outer emission patches.

NGC 3646: Emission lines of H_α and [N II] occur strongly both in the inner elliptical region and in the peculiar outer structure. The ratio H_α/[N II]λ6583 is about 3.

NGC 4736: In H II regions in the inner bright arms, emission lines of H_α, H_β, [N II], [S II], [O II], and weak [O III] occur; the excitation is thus moderately high. H_α/[N II]λ6583 is about 3 here. In emission patches in the outer arms, low-excitation emission showing only H_α, [N II], and [O II] occurs, with approximately the same H_α/[N II] ratio as in the inner arms. Right in the nucleus, emission is weaker and only [N II] and [O II] are seen; H_α does not appear. This is an extreme case of the lowering of the H_α/[N II] ratio in the nuclei of some galaxies.

NGC 4826: H_α, [N II], and [S II] are seen in the knotty region in the inner spiral arms. In the nucleus itself H_α and [N II] are seen, with H_α/[N II]λ6583 about 0.3. The ratio increases on going away from the center; in the nuclear bulge it is just greater than unity, and in the inner-arm region it is about 3, as usual. The outer arms are very smooth and show no emission. Exposure conditions are right for showing [O III] if it were present in the nucleus, but it is definitely absent.

NGC 1832: This has emission spread right through the galaxy, as in the Sc and Sbc galaxies described above; the emission is located in the numerous H II aggregates in the arms. H_α and [N II] are the only features seen, so the excitation is low. There is only a very slight concentration of emission in the nuclear region; here the ratio H_α/[N II]λ6583 slightly exceeds unity, and it increases to the usual value of about 3 in the arm regions outside. [S II] and [O III] are definitely absent in the nucleus; our spectra are too weak at λ3727 to show whether [O II] is present or not.

NGC 5005: This has weak emission of only H_α and [N II] in the arms; the excitation is thus low. In the nuclear region weak emission is also present; in the nucleus itself only [N II] and [O II] are seen, so this is an extreme case of a low H_α/[N II]λ6583 intensity ratio, as in the nucleus of NGC 4736. In the nuclear bulge only [N II] is seen, so the low ratio persists further out than in NGC 4736. A little further out H_α appears and the ratio grows to about 2. In the arms the ratio is about 3.

NGC 7331: Emission lines are very weak. As in NGC 4736 and 5005, no H_α is seen in the nucleus itself; [N II] and probably [O II] are present. In the spiral arms weak H_α and [N II] are present, with H_α/[N II]λ6583 about 3. In the nucleus itself several of our exposures are of the right intensity to show [O III] if it were present, but it is definitely absent.

Normal Spirals: Sa

NGC 3623: This is the only Sa in which we have so far been able to detect emission lines. Weak H_α and [N II] are seen in the arms with H_α/[N II]λ6583 about 3. In the nucleus itself and in the nuclear bulge only weak [N II] and [O II] are present; H_α is absent. This galaxy resembles NGC 5005 and 7331 in class Sb with regard to the degree of excitation and the distribution of ionized gas.

Relative Intensities of Emission Features in Our Galaxy

In the general emission regions that we observe outside the nuclei in spiral galaxies, the excitation is usually fairly low and the emission often extends over many kiloparsecs. Consequently we might expect the nearest analogue in our own galaxy to be the diffuse extended regions studied by Struve and Elvey [30], [29]. In their pioneer work they showed the existence of large areas of low surface brightness where H_α was in emission. They were not able to say anything about the $H_\alpha/[N \; II]$ intensity ratio since on their dispersion H_α and $[N \; II] \lambda\lambda 6548$ and 6583 were blended. However, H. M. Johnson [12] made a study of these features in diffuse emission regions and in galactic nebulae with the same spectrograph that we use in our observational work on external galaxies (the B spectrograph). Johnson found that, after H_α, the most frequently observed line was $\lambda 6583$, while [S II], [O III], [O II], H_β, and occasionally He I $\lambda 6678$ were also observed. For all the regions that he studied, he tabulated intensities relative to H_α; the mean ratio $H_\alpha/[N \; II]\lambda 6583$ was 3.2, and the range of values found lay between 1.1 and 7.7. Nowhere did he find this ratio to be less than unity.

Johnson's mean ratio $H_\alpha/[N \; II]\lambda 6583$ is thus the same as the "normal" ratio of 3 which we observed in the general emission in spiral arms of external galaxies and also in those nuclear regions of barred spiral and irregular galaxies that contain much gas and presumably population I stars, such as NGC 3504. The lines seen most commonly by Johnson, i.e., H_α, [N II], and [S II], are also the lines that we have found most generally. Thus we have confidence that in the spiral-arm regions in external galaxies, where $H_\alpha/[N \; II]\lambda 6583$ is about 3, and in some nuclear regions, the normal physical conditions in extended H II regions in our own galaxy should apply. It should be noted that [O II]$\lambda 3727$ is probably as widespread as and of comparable intensity to [N II]$\lambda 6583$, but the B spectrograph with the grating blazed at H_α, as used by both Johnson and ourselves, is inefficient at the wavelength of the [O II] doublet.

Work on emission regions in our own galaxy has also been done by Page [19] and recently by Courtès [6], who used a Fabry–Perot interference etalon. Courtès recognized that the most usual value of the ratio $H_\alpha/[N \; II]\lambda 6583$ was 3, and he divided the regions that he studied into five classes, with $[N \; II]/H_\alpha > 0.3$; $= 0.3$; < 0.3; [N II] weak; and [N II] absent. He found only two regions in which [N II] was almost as strong as H_α, namely, in M 20 and in some filaments at $20^h 15^m$, $+ 43°$. Thus nowhere did he find a ratio like that which we find in the nuclei of some spiral galaxies, e.g., NGC 5005, with $H_\alpha/[N \; II]$ considerably less than unity.

We may next look at the intensities found in typical planetary nebulae.

As an example, Aller [1] gives the following values for NGC 7027, on a scale where $H_\beta = 100$:— [N II]λ6583 = 240, H_α = 650, [O III]λ5007 = 1170, [O III]λ4959 = 420, H_β = 100, [Ne III]λ3869 = 51, [O II]λ3729 = 4.6, [O II]λ3726 = 9.4. Thus the excitation is very much higher than in the extended emission regions which we have been discussing, as evidenced by the high [O III]/[O II] ratio. Even in this case, where [O III] is more intense than H_α, we have H_α/[N II]λ6583 $\simeq$ 3. White [33] measured the relative intensities of H_α and [N II]λ6583 in a number of planetaries; he found a variation from zero intensity of [N II] (the most common value) to H_α/[N II]λ6583 = 0.3 in NGC 2440. Only in 3 out of 22 cases did the value drop below unity. The mean ratio was 2.3. For comparison, his average value in the Orion nebula was 4.

We conclude that there is a general similarity between the degree of excitation found in spiral-arm emission regions in external galaxies and in the diffuse Struve–Elvey H II regions in our own galaxy. The intensity ratio H_α/[N II]λ6583 is about the same in both cases. We do not find in our own galaxy evidence for the general occurrence of a ratio of H_α/[N II]λ6583 $\ll$ 1, as found in the nuclei of some external spiral galaxies. There is one noteworthy place where the H_α emission intensity is very low, namely, in filaments in the Cassiopeia radio source (Cas A) (Minkowski and Aller [15]). It is therefore of interest to see how the ratio was explained here.

Minkowski and Aller pointed out first that there is no source of radiation in Cas A and the emission lines result from cascade following excitation by collisions with electrons. Weak H_α could be explained by collisional excitation at low electron temperature ($T_e < 15,000°$), if the electron density $N_e < 10^5$ cm^{-3}. But in Cas A they had to explain additional peculiarities, namely, [O I] and [O III] were strong while [O II] was weak. The weakness of [O II] could be explained if $N_e \sim 10^4$ cm^{-3}, for collisions of the second kind are much more important for the destruction of metastable states in O II than they are in O I or O III. But if $T_e < 15,000°$, as the absence of H lines would imply, O II or even O I could not be collisionally ionized, and the O III must have been left over from a previous state of the gaseous mass, presumably connected with the supernova explosion thought to have originated it.

Thus a small intensity ratio of H_α to the forbidden lines in this case had to be explained by a nonstationary process connected with the availability not long ago of a large amount of energy no longer present. Such a mechanism would be highly unlikely to operate over large-scale regions in a number of normal spiral galaxies. Further, we do not find [O III] in these regions; what we have to explain is simply a low ratio H_α/[N II] where the ionization potentials of H and N I are rather close together.

Finally, it might be suggested that the emission lines in the nuclei of spiral galaxies might be the integrated result of a large number of planetary nebulae, which belong to the stellar population found in the nuclear region of our own galaxy. But in typical planetary nebulae in our galaxy the strongest feature seems to be the [O III]λ5007 line, and White's mean ratio in 22 nebulae for H_α/[N II]λ6583 was 2.3. In our cases in the nuclei of spirals, [O II] and [N II] are the strongest and [O III] is not seen. Consequently we do not believe that the effects that we have observed can be due to the integrated effect of numbers of planetaries.

In the next section we shall discuss the theoretical intensity ratios to be expected in extended H II regions of the Struve–Elvey type and we shall consider a way of producing the low H_α/[N II] ratio found in the nuclei of galaxies.

Theoretical Intensities in Extended Regions of Emitting Gas

We shall first consider the theoretical line intensities in gas having a low electron density and subject to dilute radiation, where radiative ionization of hydrogen, nitrogen, oxygen, and sulfur, radiative excitation of hydrogen, and collisional excitation of metastable states in nitrogen, oxygen, and sulfur occur. A summary of the calculations of relative line intensities has been given by Aller [1]. The theoretical expressions that we have used are taken from Seaton [22].

In our observations of external galaxies, we have only eye estimates instead of accurate relative intensities. Also, we do not observe all the emission features necessary for a complete solution of the problem in terms of the electron temperature T_e and the electron density N_e. Further, we are dealing with large emitting volumes over which N_e and T_e may vary, so that only an average value is applicable. Consequently, we shall as a first attempt *assume* that T_e, N_e in the extended spiral-arm regions in external galaxies have the values characteristic of extended H II regions in our own galaxy. We therefore take $T_e = 10{,}000°$K. As long as N_e $\lesssim 10^3$ cm^{-3}, or perhaps $\lesssim 10^2$ cm^{-3} in the case of [O II], collisional de-excitation of the metastable states in nitrogen, oxygen, and sulfur is unimportant. With the quantities tabulated by Seaton [22], his equations for the line intensities, for $T_e = 10{,}000°$, are

$$I(H_\alpha) = 2.838 \times 10^{-24} b_3 N_p N_e \qquad (1)$$

$$I([N\ II]) = 7.654 \times 10^{-21} N_{N^+} N_e \qquad (2)$$

$$I([O\ II]) = 3.466 \times 10^{-21} N_{O^+} N_e \qquad (3)$$

$$I([S\ II]) = 1.502 \times 10^{-20} N_{S^+} N_e \qquad (4)$$

where for the forbidden lines the intensities are the sums of the two lines in the transition in each case.

We have now to consider the value of b_3, the factor by which the population of state 3 in hydrogen differs from that at thermodynamic equilibrium at $T = 10,000°$. With radiative ionization and excitation there are three possibilities, considered by Baker and Menzel [3] and Baker, Menzel, and Aller [4] and applied by them to planetary nebulae. In case A[2] a given level in hydrogen is populated by electron capture and downward cascading in an optically thin nebula excited by a star with Lyman continuum radiation but no radiation in the Lyman lines. This corresponds to case (a) + (b) considered by Strömgren [27] in his study of the physical conditions in the interstellar gas. In case B, which is usually thought to be better applicable to planetary nebulae than case A[2], the nebula is optically thick to Lyman radiation; this is the case considered earlier by Zanstra and Cillié and corresponds to Strömgren's case (a) + (b) + (c). In case C, which is also discussed by Chamberlain [5], we have an optically thin nebula excited by radiation approximating that from a black body even in the frequencies of the Lyman lines, so that direct radiative excitation of H from the ground level to the various excited levels can occur. Values of b_3 in these three cases are given in the first three lines of Table 1.

Table 1
Values of b_3 for Cases A[2], B, C, and the Collisional Case

	10,000°	20,000°	40,000°
A[2]	0.0393	0.146	0.296
B	0.089	0.330	0.670
C	1.60	1.60	1.53
Coll. (optically thin)	0.60	1.35	1.55
Coll. (optically thick)	1.50	3.47	4.00

Cases A[2] and B on the one hand, and case C on the other, can be distinguished by the values they predict for the Balmer decrement, in particular, the ratio H_α/H_β. In A[2], H_α/H_β is about 1.9 and in B it is 2.5; this ratio is insensitive to temperature. In case C, however, $H_\alpha/H_\beta = 5.32$ for $T = 10,000°$, and 3.63 for $T = 20,000°$ (Chamberlain [5]). Now Struve and Elvey [30] found a value of 5 for this ratio in extended diffuse H II regions, suggesting that case C with $T = 10,000°$ is applicable here.

On our spectra we rarely observe H_β; it is only seen when H_α is unusually strong and consequently the Balmer decrement is apparently quite steep. Relative intensities cannot be estimated over such a large wavelength range without accurate calibration, but we can at least be certain that in general $H_\alpha/H_\beta > 2$ in the spiral-arm regions that we have observed in external galaxies. Thus case C seems to be applicable here also. When the exciting radiation comes from general stellar radiation from numbers of stars of a range of spectral types and with a velocity dispersion, case C seems to be the best from a physical standpoint also.

We have now to consider the degree of ionization in dilute radiation with $T_e = 10,000°$. The modified Saha equation given by Strömgren [28] can be used; in this, since we are interested only in ratios of the degree of ionization for the various elements, all factors cancel out but the partition functions and the exponentials in T_i, the temperature of the ionizing radiation. Ratios of the degrees of ionization in N, O, and S to that in H are given in Table 2.

Table 2

Values of Ratios of Degree of Ionization

T_i	$\dfrac{N_p}{N_H} \Big/ \dfrac{N_{N^+}}{N_N}$	$\dfrac{N_p}{N_H} \Big/ \dfrac{N_{O^+}}{N_O}$	$\dfrac{N_p}{N_H} \Big/ \dfrac{N_{S^+}}{N_S}$	$\dfrac{N_p}{N_H} \Big/ \dfrac{N_{O^{++}}}{N_{O^+}}$	$\dfrac{N_p}{N_H} \Big/ \dfrac{N_{S^{++}}}{N_{S^+}}$
10,000°	0.717	1.150	0.0231	Large	Large
20,000°	0.413	1.137	0.150	Large	64.6
40,000°	0.314	1.130	0.384	113	3.80

For the relative abundances of the elements we take the values of Goldberg, Müller, and Aller [8], recognizing that abundances in the sun may well not be representative of abundances in the interstellar medium in external galaxies, and also that the abundances may very well differ between galaxy and galaxy and that the abundance of sulfur is particularly uncertain.

Relative intensities can now be calculated. We take Eqs. (1) to (4) (for $T_e = 10,000°$), and the value of $b_3 = 1.60$ (case C) from Table 1. For the ratios of the degree of ionization (Table 2) we choose $T_i = 20,000°$ as representative of the average temperature of the stars producing the dilute radiation field. With the abundance ratios given by Goldberg, Müller, and Aller, we find

$$\frac{I(H_\alpha)}{I([N\ II])} = 2.57$$

$$\frac{I(H_\alpha)}{I([O\ II])} = 1.63$$

$$\frac{I(H_\alpha)}{I([S\ II])} = 2.27$$

where $I([N\ II])$ is the sum of the intensities of $\lambda\lambda6548, 6583$; $I([O\ II])$ is the sum of the intensities of $\lambda\lambda3726, 3729$; and $I([S\ II])$ is the sum of the intensities of $\lambda\lambda6717, 6731$.

These results represent the observations in spiral-arm regions in galaxies quite well. We have estimated $I(H_\alpha)/I([N\ II]\lambda6583) = 3$ as the most common value; $\lambda6548$ is always weaker than $\lambda6583$ and is usually not seen unless the emission is rather strong, so it contributes a fairly small part to the sum of the intensities. Thus the $H_\alpha/[N\ II]$ ratio is in very good agreement with the observations. The $H_\alpha/[S\ II]$ ratio on our spectra is more variable, and the variation in the ratio of the degree of ionization of sulfur to hydrogen is seen from Table 2 to be considerable over the range of T_i taken. The second I.P. of sulfur is low enough that double ionization will begin to deplete the S^+ in the probable range of temperatures.

In regions where [S II] is stronger than [N II], which occur in a few of the galaxies described earlier, e.g., NGC 4449, where the effect is quite striking, [O III] appears, which suggests a higher T_i (from Table 2); but this is the direction in which H_α/S [II] decreases relative to $H_\alpha/[N\ II]$. Possibly in these galaxies we are looking at great aggregates of denser H II regions, like the Orion nebula, rather than at diffuse low-density nebulosity.

We conclude that the mechanism outlined in this section for the production of emission lines in the widespread spiral-arm regions in external galaxies, with $T_e = 10,000°$, $N_e < 10^3$ cm^{-3}, and a general radiation field that includes radiation in the Lyman line frequencies, well represents the observations. This mechanism will apply also in the diffuse extended H II regions in our own galaxy, and in the nuclei and nuclear regions of those galaxies where $H_\alpha/[N\ II]$ has the usual value of about 3, [N II] > [S II], and [O III] did not appear (e.g., NGC 5383, 1365, 2903).

However, these conditions will clearly not explain the ratio $H_\alpha/[N\ II]$ < 3 and sometimes $\ll 1$, which is found in some nuclei and nuclear regions. From Table 1 we see that the population of the excited level 3 in hydrogen can be much reduced if cases A^2 or B, which are usually applied to planetary nebulae, can be applied here. With $T_e = 10,000°$, we find $H_\alpha/[N\ II] = 0.063$ in case A^2 and 0.143 in case B. This would be in agreement with the observations, and here we have no estimate for H_α/H_β which can be used to rule out these possibilities. However, they do not seem to be physically realistic.

We saw that case C applied in spiral-arm regions where early-type stars of population I should be present. Yet case C required radiation that resembles that from a black body in not having strong Lyman absorption lines. We assumed that the variety of stellar types and the velocity dispersion ensure that radiation is available at Lyman line frequencies. In the nuclei of the spiral galaxies that we are now considering, most of the radiation field should be provided by K giants, according to our spectra, or at least by a mixture of K giants, main-sequence stars of types G–K, and some horizontal-branch-type stars of higher temperature, and the velocity dispersion should be higher. We conclude that if cases A^2 and B do not apply in the outer parts of galaxies, where population I stars are present, they are even less likely to apply in the nuclei. As mentioned earlier, lack of [O III] while [N II] and [O II] are the strongest features does not suggest the type of excitation characteristic of planetary nebulae.

At first sight it seems hard to account for lack of H_α when [O II] and [N II] are seen, for the ionization potentials of H, N, and O are so similar. Of course, it can always be suggested that the abundance of hydrogen in the nuclei is actually low. If the gas that is giving rise to the emission lines in these inner regions does not partake of any general circulation in the galaxy, is not "left-over," uncondensed gas, but is gas that has been ejected from the highly evolved stars in which hydrogen has been largely consumed, our observed low $H_\alpha/[N\ II]$ or $H_\alpha/[O\ II]$ ratios could be accounted for easily. This should be borne in mind as a possible explanation. However, there is another possibility which does not involve anomalous abundance effects, and which we wish now to suggest.

With the stellar population likely to be present in the nuclei under discussion, radiation may be less important than collisions in producing not only excitation of the metastable states in nitrogen, oxygen, and sulfur but also ionization of hydrogen and these elements and excitation of hydrogen. Chamberlain [5] considered the case where collisions alone, or collisions with radiation, occur at various electron temperatures. He was interested in explaining the excitation in the Network Nebula, where an exciting star has never definitely been identified. Values of b_3 for the pure collisional case in an optically thin and an optically thick nebula are given in the last two lines of Table 1, taken from the paper by Chamberlain.

Intensity ratios may be calculated for the collisional case by means of the same equations as used previously from Seaton [22], but the values of b_3 for the case of collisional excitation of hydrogen, computed by Chamberlain, have to be used. It is probably appropriate to use his case of the optically thin nebula. For $T_e = 10,000°$, b_3 is reduced by a factor of 3 over the radiative case C, and Eqs. (1) to (4) will be the same, so a reduction by a factor of 3 in the ratios of H_α to the various forbidden lines will be achieved and the ratios of the forbidden lines to each other will stay the same. This is not sufficient; we need to explain a drop in H_α/[N II] to at least 1/5 and sometimes to 0.1 or even lower. Let us consider the case for $T_e = 20,000°$. Although a certain proportion of doubly ionized oxygen occurs through radiation at temperatures in the range 20,000° to 40,000°, electrons whose energy distributions correspond to these temperatures have mean energies of only a few electron volts, and the proportion of electrons of sufficient energy to doubly ionize oxygen (I.P. = 35 ev) will be extremely small. Ionization of hydrogen, and single ionization of nitrogen, oxygen, and sulfur will be reduced, but the proportion of electrons with energies in the range 10 to 14 ev is not so small. We need to calculate values of the ratios of the degrees of ionization by collision, like the values of radiative ionization given in Table 2. But we have not been able to find any data on collisional ionization cross sections. In the absence of these data, we shall simply use the values for $T_i = 20,000°$ in Table 2, which include merely the Boltzmann factors and normal partition functions, but we recognize that these values might be quite largely in error.

With $b_3 = 1.35$ from Table 1, and the same abundance ratios used before [8], we find

$$\frac{I(H_\alpha)}{I([N\ II])} = 0.18$$

$$\frac{I(H_\alpha)}{I([O\ II])} = 0.04$$

$$\frac{I(H_\alpha)}{I([S\ II])} = 0.14$$

These conditions will give the lowered H_α intensity that we need. This calculation also gives a strengthening of [O II] relative to [N II], which was observed in the nuclei where the H_α/[N II] ratio was very low. It still gives too high an intensity for [S II], as in the radiative case, but in view of the lack of knowledge of cross sections for collisional ionization and uncertainty in the abundance, this is not significant. If we go to a higher T_e, the reduction in the relative H_α intensity becomes even more striking. For

$T_e = 40,000°$, Chamberlain's value of $b_3 = 1.55$, and the radiative ionization ratios for $T_i = 40,000°$ from Table 2, we find

$$\frac{I(H_\alpha)}{I([N\ II])} = 0.026$$

$$\frac{I(H_\alpha)}{I([O\ II])} = 0.0052$$

$$\frac{I(H_\alpha)}{I([S\ II])} = 0.077$$

Again, [O II] is about five times as strong as [N II], and in this case [S II] is only a third the intensity of [N II].

We conclude that physical conditions consisting of an electron temperature in the range 20,000° to 40,000° and a radiation field that is relatively unimportant will reproduce the lowered $H_\alpha/[N\ II]$ and $H_\alpha/[O\ II]$ ratios seen in the nuclei and nuclear bulges of some galaxies. The importance of there being no significant radiation field is seen if we are to explain the absence of [O III] at such electron temperatures. That the radiation field may be unimportant in regions where the stellar population may resemble that of the old galactic cluster M 67 (except for an increased number of low-mass main-sequence stars) seems to be perfectly acceptable. That a high electron temperature can be maintained against cooling by line radiation is more questionable. Until absolute measures of the energy emitted in the forbidden lines have been made, so that the energy balance can be calculated, we cannot say whether this is feasible or not.

Conclusions

This investigation can be summarized as follows:

a. Our spectroscopic study of this sample of galaxies has further substantiated the well-known result that irregular galaxies have the highest proportion of ionized gas and that this gas fraction decreases steadily through barred spirals of types SBc and SBb, and normal spirals of types Sc, Sbc, Sb, and Sa. The ionized gas is distributed most widely in irregular galaxies, and in general the excitation is higher there than it is in other types. This indicates that such systems contain a large number of massive, luminous stars. There is much ionized gas in the central regions and in the nuclei of those irregulars which have nuclei, and hence there must be a population containing high-luminosity stars right in the nuclear regions.

b. Among the irregular galaxies that we have studied M 82 is especially interesting. The spectra suggest that in regions which look similar on direct photographs there are striking differences either in the ratio of gas to stars, or in the mass functions of the stars, i.e., in the relative numbers of the most massive, high-luminosity stars to the fainter ones. Thus both regions A and C in Fig. 2 have a network of dust lanes, but A shows strong emission lines and C does not. The presence of dust in both regions suggests that there is plenty of gas in both; this leads to the tentative conclusion that they contain very different proportions of high-mass, hot stars. Strömgren [28] showed that O-type stars are much more efficient than A-type stars in ionizing the gas around them. Perhaps because of the different factors that influence the rate of star formation (e.g., the local value of the magnetic field and the velocity field) more massive stars have formed in the last million years in region A than in region C. The presence of emission lines in the prominent dust lane B also suggests that high-luminosity stars are embedded in the dust. A detailed account of the spectroscopic features and motions in M 82 is in preparation.

c. Barred spiral galaxies of types SBc and SBb tend to contain much ionized gas in their nuclear regions, indicating the presence of massive luminous stars. The features which are seen and their relative intensities are consistent with the mechanisms of radiative ionization and radiative plus collisional excitation which are used to account for the spectra of extended H II regions in the spiral arms of our own galaxy.

d. Spiral-arm regions in barred and normal spirals of all subdivisions may contain H II regions where the conditions of excitation are similar to those in the extended H II regions in our own galaxy. The degree of excitation may vary somewhat in galaxies within any one subdivision, and in regions in the same galaxy, but in general the values $T_e = 10,000°$ and $N_e < 10^3$ cm^{-3} seem to be appropriate.

e. Emission lines sometimes occur in the prominent dust regions of galaxies (e.g., M 82) and sometimes do not (e.g., NGC 2903, 5055). This may either be due to a much deeper obscuring layer in some galaxies than in others or to a lack of exciting stars in the dust regions of some galaxies. Another example of a galaxy with emission lines in the dust lane is NGC 5128. This galaxy was not discussed above because it is a strong radio source and consequently the emission lines which are seen (H$_\alpha$ and [N II]λ6583) may be connected with the nonthermal energy source that gives rise to the radio emission.

f. Of the normal spirals in classes Sc and Sbc, some may have nuclei like the SBc and SBb galaxies mentioned in (c), in that they contain much ionized gas and highly luminous stars, the mechanisms of emission being the normal processes in H II regions.

g. The nuclei of other Sc and Scb galaxies and the nuclei in the majority of Sb galaxies contain less ionized gas than the galaxies mentioned in (c) and (f). Our most striking observational result is that between the outer parts and the nuclear regions the ratio of the strengths of H_α and [N II]λ6583 decreases from about 3, the usual value in a normal H II region, to values in the range $\sim$1 to 0.1. This reversal in intensity is evidently widespread and is more common in Sb and Sa galaxies with large, prominent nuclei and well-developed nuclear bulges, but it appears even in some Sc galaxies with small nuclei. To explain this rather general result we can either appeal to differences in relative abundances or to quite different conditions of excitation. If we explain the effect in terms of relative abundances then we must conclude that in the inner regions of all these galaxies there is a deficiency of hydrogen with respect to nitrogen and oxygen as compared with the abundances of these elements in the solar neighborhood in our own galaxy and also in the outer parts of the same galaxies. Before accepting such a fundamental result, it is necessary to determine whether such an effect could be produced by the conditions of excitation. We have found that such an explanation is possible for the extreme cases (e.g., NGC 4736, 5005, 3623). Here we may suppose that radiative processes are comparatively unimportant and that collisional ionization and excitation take place in the gas with an electron temperature of 20,000° to 40,000°, or with energies of a few electron volts, since such excitation may be nonthermal. Whether such an argument is acceptable depends on the energy requirements, i.e., estimates of the energy supply required to maintain such a high electron temperature against cooling, mainly by line emission. This cannot be done adequately until absolute measurements of the emission line intensities have been made.

However, some tentative ideas can be mentioned. The energy supply may be nonthermal and may consist of corpuscular emission from the outer layers of the stars. Most of the light in such regions comes from K giants, but low-mass K- and M-type dwarfs may be present in large numbers. The effect may be related to the expansion of material from the central regions of our own galaxy [34]. The origin and mechanism providing energy for this radial motion remains unknown. However, if similar flows exist generally, they may be maintained by some kind of circulation with material flowing inward from above and below the equatorial plane in the nuclear region. The dissipation of kinetic energy in the inner regions might give rise to high electron temperatures.

This work has been supported in part by a grant from the National Science Foundation.

References

[1] L. H. Aller, "Gaseous Nebulae," Chapman and Hall, London, 1956.
[2] W. Baade and R. Minkowski, *Ap. J.*, **119**, 206 (1954).
[3] J. G. Baker and D. H. Menzel, *Ap. J.*, **88**, 52 (1938).

[4] J. G. Baker, D. H. Menzel, and L. H. Aller, *Ap. J.*, **88,** 422 (1938).
[5] J. W. Chamberlain, *Ap. J.*, **117,** 387 (1953).
[6] G. Courtès, *Ann. Ap.*, **23,** 115 (1960).
[7] H. D. Curtis, *Lick Obs. Publ.*, **13,** 43 (1918).
[8] L. Goldberg, E. A. Müller, and L. H. Aller, *Ap. J.* (*Suppl.*), **5,** 1 (1960).
[9] G. Haro, *Ap. J.*, **55,** 66 (1950).
[10] H. C. Hulst, E. Raimond, and H. van Woerden, *B.A.N.*, **14,** 1 (1957).
[11] M. L. Humason, N. U. Mayall, and A. R. Sandage, *Ap. J.*, **61,** 97 (1956).
[12] H. M. Johnson, *Ap. J.*, **118,** 370 (1953).
[13] N. U. Mayall, I. A. U. Symposium No. 5, Cambridge University Press, New York, p. 23.
[14] R. Minkowski, in R. N. Bracewell (ed.), "Paris Symposium on Radio Astonomy," Stanford University Press, Stanford, Calif., 1959, p. 315.
[15] R. Minkowski and L. H. Aller, *Ap. J.*, **119,** 232 (1954).
[16] R. Minkowski and D. E. Osterbrock, *Ap. J.*, **129,** 583 (1959).
[17] J. H. Oort, Princeton Conference on Interstellar Matter in Galaxies, 1961.
[18] D. E. Osterbrock, *Ap. J.*, **132,** 325 (1960).
[19] T. L. Page, *Ap. J.*, **108,** 157 (1948).
[20] T. L. Page, *Ap. J.*, **116,** 63 (1952).
[21] A. Sandage, "The Hubble Atlas of Galaxies," *Carnegie Institution of Washington Publ. 618*, 1961.
[22] M. J. Seaton, *M.N.*, **114,** 154 (1954).
[23] C. K. Seyfert, *Ap. J.*, **97,** 28 (1943).
[24] G. A. Shajn and V. T. Hase, *Publ. Crimean Ap. Obs.*, **7,** 87 (1951).
[25] G. A. Shajn and V. T. Hase, *Publ. Crimean Ap. Obs.*, **8** (1952).
[26] G. A. Shajn and V. T. Hase, *Trans. I.A.U.*, **8,** 693 (1954).
[27] B. Strömgren, *Ap. J.*, **89,** 526 (1939).
[28] B. Strömgren, *Ap. J.*, **108,** 242 (1948).
[29] O. Struve, *J. Wash. Acad. Sci.*, **31,** 217 (1941).
[30] O. Struve and C. T. Elvey, *Ap. J.*, **89,** 119, 517 (1939); **90,** 301 (1939).
[31] H. Suess and H. C. Urey, *Rev. Mod. Phys.*, **28,** 53 (1956).
[32] L. Volders, *B.A.N.*, **14,** 323 (1959).
[33] M. L. White, *Ap. J.*, **115,** 71 (1952).
[34] H. van Woerden, W. Rougoor, and J. H. Oort, *Compt. rend.*, **244,** 1691 (1957).

Discussion

Dr. Strömgren: If you have the normal abundance of oxygen, ionic cooling would be very effective. Can the mechanisms that you suggest for heating at 40,000° overcome this?

Dr. E. M. Burbidge: I don't know. It turned out that the nitrogen would be as effective a cooling agent as oxygen, judging by the intensity ratio that one predicted.

Dr. Osterbrock: In our galaxy, in the planetary nebulae, the stronger [N II] line λ6484 can vary with respect to Hα, all the way from being, say, three times stronger than Hα down to much weaker than Hα. I always thought that the interpretation could be, that in those nebulae where [N II] is strongest, N is N^+, while the planetaries with the weak [N II] could be interpreted by supposing that N^+ is ionized to N^{++}. For a "normal" abundance ratio $N/H = 1 \times 10^{-4}$ by number the computed relative strengths are λ6584/Hα = 1.6 at $T = 10^4$ and 6.8 at 2×10^4 if all the N is in the form of N^+.

Dr. E. M. Burbidge: If there were appreciable double ionization of N, it seemed to us that [O III] would appear in these regions also. Isn't it true that in planetary nebulae [O III] is always very much stronger than H_β, and usually stronger than H_α and [N II] also? In the cases I discussed we do not observe [O III] at all.

Dr. Osterbrock: Would you be able to see the [O III] if it were there? Do you see H_β?

Dr. E. M. Burbidge: I am not certain we would see [O III] unless it were very strong. I had assumed that the degree of ionization was low because I didn't see it. Of course we should go into this with calibrated spectra to work it out properly. We did not see H_β in the nuclear regions where [N II] is stronger than H_α.

Gas in clusters of galaxies

F. D. Kahn

What I shall talk about is more uncertain than anything yet discussed here. This report is on gas in clusters of galaxies, which, as far as I know, has never been observed.

I should like to discuss the reasons why one infers that such things may exist. The reasons go back to the virial theorem, according to which, in a cluster of gravitating matter,

$$\tfrac{1}{2}\ddot{I} = 2\Omega + T$$

where $I = Mr^2$, $\Omega = \tfrac{1}{2}\Sigma\Sigma \, GMM'/|\mathbf{r} - \mathbf{r}'|$, and $T = \tfrac{1}{2}\Sigma \, M\dot{r}^2$. If $2T + \Omega \neq 0$ the cluster cannot be in a steady state but must be either expanding or contracting. It will oscillate if $T + \Omega < 0$. If $T + \Omega > 0$ the energy is positive, and the cluster expands to infinity.

The position was summarized by Professor Oort [1] at the Solvay Conference three years ago. Comparisons of T and Ω were made for the Virgo cluster. The masses of the individual galaxies were estimated from their luminosity, and the gravitational self-energy Ω was found. To estimate T you look at the velocity dispersion. Of course you can only look at the dispersion of the radial component because you rely on the Doppler shifts. It was found that T was in fact about 25 times larger than Ω. It was assumed that if you see a velocity dispersion relative to the center of mass in the radial direction, you can assume dispersions of the same order in the two transverse directions, where they cannot be observed directly.

A factor of 25 is rather hard to argue away. But it is instructive to consider how these estimates are affected by our estimate of the size of the universe. It would make a considerable difference if we had the Hubble constant wrong.

Suppose we estimate that for a particular galaxy the luminosity is L_0, the mass M_0, the typical distance in the cluster involved is R_0, and that V_0 is a typical radial velocity. If we increase the scale of the universe by a factor λ, the luminosity becomes $\lambda^2 L_0$, and the estimated mass of the galaxy $\lambda^2 M_0$. The radius goes up to λR_0, and V does not change. The kinetic-energy content goes like λ^2. The gravitational energy goes like M^2 divided by R, and so like λ^3. If you make the universe larger the discrepancy between T and Ω gets less bad. But you might not be willing to make the universe large enough to explain away a factor of 25.

Another approach to the problem is that of van den Bergh [2]. To check the masses concerned, he treated galaxies close together in a particular cluster as binaries, and then estimated their masses. He compared the $M{:}L$ ratio thus obtained with that found by means of the virial theorem for the cluster. For the Virgo cluster he found from the binary galaxies a mass–luminosity ratio much less than 280, while the virial theorem would require for the cluster as a whole a mass-to-luminosity ratio of about 700. This determination is clearly independent of the factor λ because T and Ω now scale the same way.

There are other discussions of these problems, and in almost every one it has been found that the gravitational self-energy is not large enough if you estimate the mass in the ordinary way.

You could save the situation by introducing into the cluster some material which you do not see very well. You can either introduce populations of rather dark stars which do not show up, or you can introduce a large mass of gas. Of course the gravitational attraction on the galaxies toward the center of the cluster will now be larger, and you can work out various kinds of expression to indicate how the presence of gas affects their velocity dispersion. A discussion of this problem has been given by Limber [3]. He finds that a few coefficients have still to be left lying about. These depend on the particular structure of the cluster and the distribution of gas. The general effect is shown by the formula below. Here G refers to galaxies and g refers to gas. The relation is

$$\langle V_G^2 \rangle = C_{GG} \frac{GM_G}{R}\left(1 + \frac{C_{Gg} + D_{Gg}}{C_{GG}}\frac{M_g}{M_G}\right)$$

Limber gives various values of the coefficients for different models. In general, of course, introducing the gas makes $\langle V_G^2 \rangle$ larger.

It should be added at this point that there are several small clusters, of which one called Stephan's quintet is the one most written about.

In Stephan's quintet there is a similar situation but only, as the name implies, five galaxies [4].

In the particular case of Stephan's quintet some people are willing to assume that the line-of-sight velocity dispersion among those five galaxies is not typical of their dispersions in the other directions. Then you might just about make Stephan's quintet gravitationally stable, and might not have to introduce intergalactic matter to keep it so. But I understand that there are several objects like this, all with the same property, and one would not want to make the same assumption of asymmetry for all the clusters.

At this point it is interesting to report an observation by Zwicky [5], which is to my mind even more disturbing than the observation of absorbing matter in the halo of our galaxy, described earlier by Professor Oort. What Zwicky finds is that if he has a large cluster of galaxies in a particular part of the sky, and he counts fainter galaxies which would be expected to lie behind it, then he gets a considerable deficiency of those galaxies. It is as though the presence of the cluster somehow reduces the transparency of that part of the universe and we do not see as many galaxies behind as we should.

This reduction in the density of galaxies in the sky is by a factor of between 5 and 12, and corresponds to about one magnitude absorption through a cluster. If intergalactic matter is similar in composition to interstellar matter, there is something like 7×10^{-3} g/cm^2 of matter in the line of sight. In that case a cluster which has a diameter of 10 Mpc contains 2.3×10^{-28} g/cm^3, and the total mass of gas in it equals about 10^{15} solar masses. This is a considerable contribution. But it goes very much against the grain to assume that any kind of dust gets into intergalactic space.

It has at various times been suggested that you might be able to do other things with the intergalactic gas if it exists. For example, suggestions have been put forward by Burbidge, by Shklovsky, and by de Vaucouleurs, who have all mentioned the possibility that it might be possible to have gas in intergalactic space in the same state as one imagines it to be in a galaxy, and that this diffused material is permeated by a magnetic field, for the strength of which the typical estimate given is of the order of 10^{-7} gauss. With the magnetic field and possibly irregular gas motions being present you would expect that there would also be high-energy electrons about. The density suggested for them is 10^{-13} cm^{-3}, and their typical energy would be of the order of 1 Bev. This would lead to synchrotron emission from clusters of galaxies.

Nothing like this has ever been verified observationally, although I might mention at this point that some of the radio galaxies one observes are rather embarrassingly large. In Cygnus A we have a small visible object in the middle and a large radio object extending for hundreds of thousands of parsec straddling it. This is an object whose origin is often attributed to the effect of the collisions of two galaxies, but it seems to be a structure almost on an intergalactic scale.

Finally there has also been a suggestion that our own galaxy is involved in some intergalactic matter [6]. It arose from a consideration of the dynamics of the local group, whose apparent instability raises a difficult problem. Most of its mass is in the Andromeda nebula, and one can easily get a fair idea of the value of Ω. Now Andromeda and our own galaxy approach each other at a speed of 125 km/sec, but the system apparently has positive energy. Dr. Woltjer and I tried to see what we could do by putting intergalactic matter into the group. The first problem was to see what must be the properties of this intergalactic matter if it has

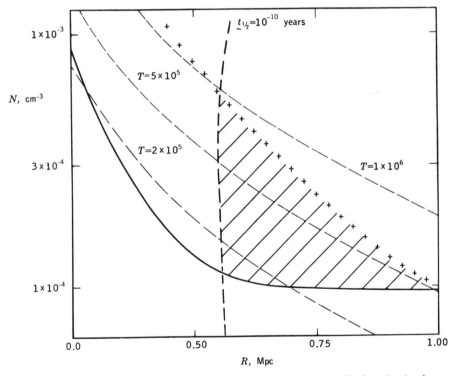

Fig. 1. Possible physical conditions in the intergalactic gas. Each point in the diagram corresponds to a given value of the mean density of the gas (N cm^{-3}) and of the outer radius of the configuration R. Points below the solid line do not satisfy the dynamical requirements for the local group. Configurations to the right of the dashed line and to the left of the crosses have cooling times longer than 10^{10} years and masses less than 10^{13} ⊙.

continued to exist for the time that we expect the local group to have existed. One finds that one is squeezed into a rather small part of a diagram by various physical considerations (Fig. 1). The shaded area is the possible region where the values of n_e can lie. The possible densities derived are of the order of 10^{-4} up to about 10^{-3} particle/cm^3.

Of course you could argue the other way and say that you have restricted the possibilities for the particles so much that a small further shift of one of the curves will make their existence impossible. Alternatively you could see this as a possible way of investigating what the intergalactic gas can be like.

But it was clear that the gas temperature is forced to be rather high, about 2×10^5 °K, and the gas would thus be fully ionized. This is probably the typical condition in which one finds intergalactic matter anywhere. There seems to be one way in which one could verify its existence. Consider how our galaxy plows its way through this intergalactic matter. A mechanical effect is produced on the halo of the galaxy and the galactic plane will be tilted a little at its extremities, in the way that it has been observed to do.

I would only mention now that one of the consequences of such a model seems to be that it may allow a certain amount of intergalactic matter to flow into the galaxy. One imagines that inside the halo there is a magnetic field, and outside there is plasma. Closer study shows that this sort of boundary is often unstable, for as Professor Biermann said yesterday, you often find plasma flowing across a magnetic field much faster than you think it could. It seems likely that the intergalactic matter will diffuse into the galactic halo and somehow come into the galactic plane. This is one way in which the intergalactic gas can be lost. It is hard to make any predictions about the rate at which such loss would occur.

References

[1] J. H. Oort in R. Stoops (ed.), "La Structure et l'evolution de l'universe, " 1958, p. 163.
[2] S. van den Bergh, *M.N.*, **121**, 387 (1960).
[3] D. N. Limber, *Ap. J.*, **130**, 414 (1959).
[4] D. N. Limber and W. G. Matthews, *Ap. J.*, **132**, 286 (1960).
[5] F. Zwicky, "Handbuch der Physik," vol. 53, 399 (1959).
[6] F. D. Kahn and L. Woltjer, *Ap. J.*, **130**, 705 (1959).

Discussion

Dr. G. R. Burbidge: I would like to say that there are two sides to this argument about the virial theorem. It has been proposed by Ambarzumian and by other people that in fact the virial theorem does not apply and that the clusters of galaxies are not stable. One has to admit this possibility. The second point is that an argument for the presence of intergalactic matter which appeals to me comes from the mean density of the universe for various assumed models, where one normally finds densities near 10^{-29} g/cm³, whereas the mean density one gets from the visible matter, just from the density of galaxies in space, appears to be about 10 or 100 times smaller. To my mind this is probably a nice argument, although rather uncertain, since we do not know which cosmological model to use. As far as the small groups are concerned, I think the difficulties there are quite severe if you do wish to satisfy the virial by putting a lot of intergalactic matter into a small group. You find the density is very high because the systems are so small. One wonders, in fact, why one sees separate systems, or why one can see fairly regular galaxies.

Dr. Woltjer: In the first place, I wonder if one can really say at the moment that cosmologically one can exclude even a completely empty universe. Essentially it depends on the curvature of the redshift-distance relation. I think at the moment one can only be definite about an upper limit if one accepts conventional models. As to the small clusters, there I think the situation is extremely serious. One can argue—and I suppose we will continue to argue for the coming years—about what happens in the case of the Virgo cluster and the other large clusters. But if one puts intergalactic matter in the small groups one needs a density that is not much less than the density of the galaxies themselves. On the other hand, if one supposes that they are expanding, it means that the time scale is of the order of 50 or 100×10^6 years, which seems equally disturbing. This trouble arises not only in Stephan's quintet but in the other very concentrated groups as well.

Dr. G. R. Burbidge: I don't think this is necessarily the case, because you are presupposing that the galaxy forms at the same time as the group. Since I don't know quite how the system is formed, I hesitate to say this. I quite agree that the time scale for expansion is of the order you quote, and this is one order of magnitude or more less than the age of the galaxies or of the universe.

Dr. Oort: In many of these groups there are elliptical galaxies that couldn't be quite that young.

Dr. G. R. Burbidge: This is perfectly true. The question is: Do you want to say that the galaxies form in the group at the same time that the group formed? It is implicit in your argument.

Dr. Oort: The question is: How could you get such a small compact group? The difficulty really extends to the double nebulae that Page has discussed, although the discrepancy may not be quite so large as for Stephan's quintet. That stresses the difficulty that Dr. Woltjer mentions, I think, that you get similar things in double nebulae also. At the same time I would not think that, if you consider the cosmological problems, it is probable that the clusters would actually be in an equilibrium of some kind. But that is another problem.

I would like to make two remarks, though. The first with regard to the absorption in clusters of nebulae, which Dr. Kahn mentioned. My recollection is that I wasn't at all convinced when I saw the data that Zwicky had that there was really much evidence for such an absorption. The second point concerns the sizes of the radio sources you mentioned. Wouldn't it be possible to think, as Shklovsky has recently suggested, that they are just expanding at the rate of a few thousand kilometers per second, and that in that case the present dimensions of the order of a megaparsec are quite reasonable? Shklovsky thinks, and that is not a bad idea perhaps, that everything might have come about by a very large number of supernova explosions in the beginning, and that this matter just expands into space.

Dr. Woltjer: Wouldn't one in that case suppose that the nonthermal sources would be connected with young galaxies instead of with the ellipticals? In the second place isn't there some trouble that if these halos expanded so fast that, as a consequence, the relativistic electron gas in the halo will cool down?

Dr. G. R. Burbidge: This depends on what you start with. You can do this with not such a large factor.

Dr. Woltjer: It increases your energy difficulty.

Dr. G. R. Burbidge: Originally, yes.

Dr. Strömgren: Some years ago there was an estimate that in our galaxy the number of high-velocity stars would be sufficient to make some contribution to the mass, but I suppose that that argument is now changed somewhat.

Dr. Oort: I wouldn't exclude it altogether from present evidence. There might be enough stars, faint subdwarfs, say, to make up for the missing mass. But there are some difficulties.

Dr. Woltjer: Isn't it very difficult to see how the original mass fragmented for 95 per cent in subdwarfs and for the rest in galaxies?

Dr. Spitzer: If we knew more about the process of fragmentation we could answer this question.

Dr. Oort: After all, stars were formed in the halo in the early days.

Dr. G. R. Burbidge: Could I ask one more question about the situation of the local group? Whether or not you need extra mass to satisfy the virial is perhaps again a little open to question. I have just received a paper which uses exactly the same data you use, and the author concludes that the system is stable. The question I have is: Suppose you have a density one order of magnitude less, which, as I said, I am perfectly willing to accept as pervading the whole of the universe, can you then do much the same dynamical things with that material as you did with the material that you had to put into the local group?

Dr. Kahn: The magnitude of the effect would depend on pressure differences on the different parts of the galactic halo, which, in turn, would be proportional to the density of the intergalactic gas far away. If this were ten times smaller it would be hard to get the observed effects.

Small-scale dynamics
of interstellar matter

Energy balance of the interstellar medium

L. Biermann

We are mostly interested in the balance of the kinetic energy, but this cannot be separated very well from the total energy balance of the interstellar medium. Therefore, we shall first write down some processes which affect the heating rate of the H I regions. We can assume that H I is present in clouds, as was discussed already, of say 10 H atoms/cm³ in 1/10 or 1/20 of the available space. For the mass density in these regions we shall take $10^{-22.7}$ g/cm³, which allows for a certain admixture of helium.

We have then first the ionization by starlight, which is mainly the ionization of the carbon component and therefore evidently depends on the abundance of C. The figure I write down is taken from the recent discussion by Spitzer for the "Compendium of Astrophysics," which I think is based on a relative abundance of C of $10^{-3.5}$. That gives then $10^{-27.2}$ erg/cm³/sec and $10^{-4.5}$ erg/g/sec in these clouds. If the carbon should be less abundant, as assumed by some people, this rate would go down somewhat.

Next we have to consider the collisions between clouds. These were discussed by Dr. Kahn in recent years, and again I write down the figure given in Dr. Spitzer's article, which is $10^{-26.8 \pm 0.4}$ erg/cm³/sec. The rate of conversion into heat depends greatly, according to theory, on the assumed strength of the magnetic field; if the field is weak we have stronger dissipation, and vice versa. This is accounted for by the factor $10^{0.4}$, respectively $10^{-0.4}$. These figures are equivalent to $10^{-4.1 \pm 0.4}$ erg/g/sec.

Next we have heat contributed by ambipolar diffusion. For this I take

153

as the basis the discussion of Schlüter and myself given at the symposium in Cambridge, Mass., in 1958. But I assume the value for the magnetic field strength to be 2×10^{-5} gauss, which is the value that was arrived at by Leverett Davis and myself in a recent paper, the content of which will come up later. Essentially it is identical with the value proposed by Dr. Woltjer. With this high value of the magnetic field strength, and using the same abundance of the ions as the one I quoted, one arrives at $10^{-3.1}$ erg/g/sec. The figure is fairly uncertain.

Next we have the cosmic rays. The general picture is that the cosmic-ray particles are confined by the interstellar magnetic fields, each particle for a certain time, after which most of them escape from our galaxy; during this time (of the order of some 10^6 years) they collide with interstellar material.

For the higher energy particles, a large part of the energy goes into nuclear reactions, radiations of some sort, and a fraction into ionization. Here I write down again a figure which goes back ultimately, I think, to work of Olbert, Morrison, and Rossi; its value (cf. Spitzer, loc. cit.) can be converted into $10^{-4.2}$ erg/g/sec.

One point worth mentioning is the following: If it should turn out that low-energy cosmic rays are much more abundant than we were led to believe until now, this figure would have to be raised, not only in proportion to the total energy density, but one would have to allow for the relatively increased loss of energy by ionization. So it is conceivable that on this basis the figure might go up by as much as one power of ten. Before too long we shall probably know more about this point by new observations.

One might inquire about the amount added by the dissipation of turbulent energy. The expression given by the theory of isotropic incompressible turbulence is equal, apart from a factor of order unity, to v^3/l, with v as the characteristic velocity and l as the connected characteristic length; using, say, 7 km/sec for v and for l something like 12 pc or so, we would get 10^{-2} erg/g/sec. This of course should be compared with the rate given previously for collisions. The turbulence is certainly not incompressible, and the magnetic field will tend to make it anisotropic and reduce the dissipation rate. Hence the figure derived from the collision rate is quite certainly more trustworthy.

Now I turn to those processes by which the state of motion of the interstellar material, which looks like a turbulent state of motion, can be maintained. The figures I shall use are those which have been discussed at previous symposia at Cambridge, England, and Cambridge, Mass., and again by Dr. Spitzer.

One of the main mechanisms here appears to be the expansion of the H II regions around the early-type stars. This was first suggested by

Professor Oort in 1953 and by members of our group at the same time.

The figures can be found in the proceedings of the first Cambridge symposium and are, respectively, equivalent to 10^{-4} erg/g/sec for the big complexes of clouds, which were considered by Oort, and 10^{-2} to 10^{-1} erg/g/sec given in the communication by Schlüter and myself. The second figure was supposed to refer to all stars that have H II regions around them. The energy transmitted to the H II regions has been evaluated again more recently with greater care, by Dr. Spitzer. The figure he gives (which does not refer to the available mechanical energy; see below) is equivalent to 0.7×10^{-2} erg/g/sec.

To use Spitzer's discussion a little bit more, he takes as a basis the region around the sun with a radius of 1 kpc; assuming a thickness of 300 pc, the total volume is 10^9 pc^3 or 3×10^{64} cm^3, which is of the order of 1 per cent by volume of the galactic disk. Of course this refers to conditions in the vicinity of the sun and it is certainly a difficult question to derive a figure that could be used for the total galactic system. If one uses the statistics of Dr. Spitzer for the stars from O5 to B1 inclusive and then tries to convert them into bolometric magnitudes—using recent data given by Professor Blaauw in the Nijenrode lectures of 1960—one gets for the total luminosity of stars O to B1, included in this volume, a value of approximately 2×10^7 in solar units, or 8×10^{40} ergs/sec. Here no allowance is made for the contribution of the giant-type stars and of super giants. If I try to make an estimate on the basis of some figures given by Blaauw, to which extent such stars might contribute additional luminosity, my impression is that they might lead to an extra factor of 2. If this would be used as a basis for an extrapolation to the whole galactic system, the figure would be 2×10^9 (resp. 4×10^9) in units of the sun's luminosity and that would mean that, with $1 \times 10^{11} M_\odot$ for the mass of the galaxy, these stars of very early type alone would contribute a luminosity per unit mass of 0.02 in solar units. To put it another way, if we assume that a reasonable estimate for the total mass-to-luminosity ratio would be something like 10, then we would have a contribution of 20 per cent (or 40 per cent) from these stars. Here we consider the luminosity that is found when one adds up the (bolometric) luminosities of all the stars.

I should like to come back once more to the earlier figure of 8×10^{40} ergs/sec. In order to derive the amount that goes into heat energy, only the fraction of the total radiation that belongs to the Lyman continuum has to be counted. Of this fraction per quantum ionizing an H I atom something like kT goes into heat, which can then be partly converted into mechanical energy. It is not surprising that this fraction turns out to be only 4×10^{38} ergs/sec, which is only 0.5 per cent of the total and leads to the figure of $10^{-2.1}$ erg/g/sec in our list. In this connection it is perhaps interesting to remark that if by any chance these stars also emit energy in the form of corpuscular radiation, then evidently the standard to which we should refer this additional nonthermal energy would be the integral luminosity; if these stars would lose mass at a substantial rate, a subject we shall discuss later, then at a rate corresponding to something like 1/10 of 1 per cent of the luminosity, they would contribute additional mechanical energy. This corpuscular radiation would make collisions in the vicinity of the star and would contribute to maintaining the motion of the interstellar material.

Next I should like to remind you of an effect that has also been discussed by Professor Blaauw—that of all the stars of type B0 or earlier, about one-fourth are fast moving, that is, moving through the galaxy with a velocity of the order of 50 or 100 km/sec, in some cases even more than that. If we consider the cloudy or spotty distribution of interstellar material, it is clear that, if we have such a large fraction of hot stars moving through it, that these stars will give rise to unequal heating and very irregular accelerations, possibly by the mechanism proposed by Dr. Oort and Dr. Spitzer. I think these fast-moving stars are, again, a group that contributes quite effectively to maintaining a state of motion that at least in appearance could be described as turbulent.

With regard to the observational evidence, I should like to make the following remarks. First of all it has been pointed out, for instance by Bok at the first Cambridge meeting, that there are quite a number of early-type stars without any interstellar matter around them. I think that came up here earlier. For the fast-moving stars this is easily understood, because their velocity is so high that they separate fairly rapidly from the clouds from which they originate. For other stars we may have differential motions between stars and matter, but I shall leave this point perhaps to the later discussion on the dynamical effects of interstellar magnetic fields.

So, on the whole, the observational evidence appears to be reasonably in favor of the picture that a substantial part of the kinetic energy which maintains the irregular turbulent motion of the interstellar matter may be provided by this mechanism. But I am aware of some criticism of this concept, which I hope will come up in the discussion.

Next we have another source of energy which is, as far as integral amount is concerned, of the same order of magnitude but which has become apparent only quite recently. These are the supernovae of type II, the ones that belong to the population I. I shall write down some figures based on information which I got in Pasadena and used in my own work: In supernovae of type II, assuming we have a shell of 1 solar mass emitted with something like 7000 km/sec, the kinetic energy is of the order 10^{51} ergs. The maximum may be larger. It is quite possible that we have 10 solar masses or even more which are driven away with much smaller velocity. Dr. Blaauw has recently proposed a picture in which the type II supernovae are connected with the origin of the fast-moving early-type stars, in such a way that these are stars of 50 to 100 solar masses which explode by an instability connected with their very large mass. In this picture the total emitted mass is of the order of 50 or 100 solar masses, but the velocity should be only 50 to 100 km/sec. That would then give an amount of energy somewhat less than the amount given before.

With regard to the frequency of these supernovae, the most probable figure I know of is, say, something like one per 200 years, which is $10^{9.8}$ sec. I should like to add to this. In the literature there are estimates which are as high as one supernova per, say, 50 years, or even 30 years. As I understand the position, the high figures occasionally quoted are largely based on combinations of data which effectively use different nonconsistent distance scales for the reduction of the observations. The distance scale comes in in several ways. If one consistently uses a figure corresponding to a redshift of say 75 km/sec/Mpc one gets the frequency that I quoted.

So much, then, for the supernovae of type II. Those of type I have an energy that is smaller by two powers of 10, so I think for the present purpose we can disregard them. The first figure then gives 10^{41} ergs/sec, or 3×10^{-2} erg/sec/g of interstellar material. This is of the same order as that contributed by stars in the form of UV heat energy.

Notice that we have here, in fact, a very powerful source of energy. Of course the question of which part of this amount could be directly used for maintaining the state of motion of interstellar material would require more discussion.

Finally, what regards the balance of kinetic energy, some of the figures recorded here are already related to this—for example, the ambipolar diffusion, which is an efficient sink of kinetic energy. I should like to add, as another mechanism in this category, the secondary acceleration of cosmic rays. According to a picture that has been current for a number of years, although not always agreed to—the power law for the energy spectrum of the cosmic radiation has to be explained by a mechanism of the kind first proposed by Fermi, which might also operate under somewhat less restricted conditions, which have been extensively discussed by L. Davis and others.

On theoretical grounds it is difficult to be sure that the physical conditions are really favorable for a mechanism of this sort to be operative in our galaxy. I shall not try to summarize the pros and cons regarding this assumption. I think it is fair to say that as far as the theory is concerned it could operate, although one would not assume it if one would not have independent reasons to do so.

With regard to this independent evidence, the strongest argument in favor of the assumption that some mechanism of this sort is indeed operative is provided by the fact that the power law extends over so many powers of 10, and that every recent addition to our knowledge of the energy spectrum has so far given no ground for suspicion that the power law might not be a general law. Some of these points were discussed by Dr. Lüst, so I need not perhaps go into them, but I may just remind you that the power law is established between 1.4×10^{10} ev, up to at least 10^{17} ev, and that everything that is known about the frequency of particles with energies up to 10^{19} ev is indeed consistent with an exponent that is almost constant. That is to say, it varies from roughly 1.5 or 1.6 to something like 1.9 or 2.0.

I should point out, however, that Cocconi in a recent discussion has put forward another picture, which he calls an eclectic theory of the origin of cosmic radiation. In this picture he ascribes the energy distribution of cosmic rays essentially to primary acceleration. That is to say, low-energy cosmic rays are provided by active stars; at higher energies they are possibly provided by very active stars or by novae and supernovae. Cosmic-ray particles of very high energies, 10^{18} ev and beyond, might come from intergalactic space, owing to conditions which are different from those that prevail in our own galaxy. In this picture the fact that the exponent is so nearly constant and varies so smoothly is a sort of accident. One certainly would expect that with progressing knowledge one would find irregularities of some sort in the power law.

At the present time it is quite impossible to be confident regarding which of the two possibilities is really the right one. Personally, I still feel that the arguments I tried to indicate for the secondary (Fermi-type) acceleration to be operative are really rather strong and that the other picture requires a somewhat improbable combination of circumstances. But I should not like to be dogmatic about it.

I think it is quite possible, although not definitely established, that secondary acceleration of cosmic rays does occur in our galaxy in the galactic halo. For this purpose I need not discriminate among the various galactic theories of cosmic radiation which can be found in the literature.

As to the amount in question, secondary acceleration of cosmic rays would require an amount of the order of 10^{-2} erg/sec/g of interstellar gas, corresponding to something like 4×10^{40} ergs/sec. This last figure again pertains to the whole galaxy and just means that an amount of the order of 1/10 of 1 per cent of the current energy output has to be converted into cosmic-ray energy. Perhaps I should remind you that in this picture the energy required for the primary acceleration of cosmic-ray particles and that energy required for secondary acceleration are approximately of the same order of magnitude. This results from the fact that its exponent is so near unity. So, irrespective of what kind of theory one makes, 10^{40} to 10^{41} ergs/sec is the order of magnitude of the energy required to maintain the present level of intensity of cosmic radiation. That this figure is comparable with the contribution by the supernovae of type II is one of the reasons why these have recently been made mainly responsible for producing cosmic rays.

You see that the figure is also comparable to the UV energy contributed by the luminous stars of early types. So one should not, for the purpose of the theory of cosmic rays, give preference to one single group of active stars on the basis of an energy argument.

To sum up, if the picture of a secondary acceleration of cosmic rays in interstellar space is correct, we have another loss of the order of 10^{-2} erg/g/sec, which has to be provided in order to keep the state of motion of interstellar material at its present level.

Discussion

Dr. Spitzer: How firm is your result on the secondary acceleration of cosmic rays? Must the energy of cosmic rays really come from the energy of the motion of the clouds? This poses a very serious problem in maintaining the kinetic energy of the gas. The efficiency of converting stellar ultraviolet radiation into kinetic energy is surely going to be substantially less than 100 per cent. For example, ultraviolet energy of O and B stars will go mostly into radiation by the interstellar medium. In the case of the supernovae, this energy is going in at an exceedingly high temperature. I would think that the efficiency of conversion of that into kinetic energy of a much larger mass would be very low. It seems very difficult to account for energy losses much greater than 10^{-4} in your units, unless you find some entirely new energy source. Also, I had the impression previously that you were assuming that the cosmic rays were mostly accelerated a long time ago and stored in the halo. Is that picture now out?

Dr. Biermann: I think it is something which can still be kept in mind. Davis and I proposed this picture on the basis of the first results on the size of the galactic halo, which gave a volume that was bigger by 1 power of 10 than is now usually believed to be true. Also three years ago the time scale was considered to be of the order of 5 or 6×10^9 years, while now we feel that 10 to 12×10^9 years might be more acceptable. But the main point is really the change in the volume of the halo. That is, of course, not the whole story. Yesterday we heard of the possibility that we have material in the local group, and that opens up the possibility for a sort of complex theory with part of the cosmic-ray particles being stored in the larger local group with larger scale magnetic fields. But the subject is so complex that I intentionally left it out of this discussion.

Dr. Spitzer: Isn't the prospect of getting 10^{-2} erg/g/sec out of the kinetic energy of the gas exceedingly remote?

Dr. Biermann: I don't quite think so. The velocity of expansion of the H II regions is of the order of 10 km/sec. That is of the same order as the ordinary motion of the clouds. And so I would be inclined to think that quite a substantial fraction could be converted into kinetic energy. I don't quite see why only something of the order of 1 per cent should go into kinetic energy.

Dr. Spitzer: When neutral gas streams from an H I region into an H II region the conversion efficiency from radiant energy to kinetic energy will be reasonably high if the gas comes out fast enough so that the atoms get ionized only once. If on the way out through this insulating layer the atoms are ionized and recombined many times, then the energy goes into visible light and Lyman α rather than into kinetic energy. A conservative estimate of the number of times a particular atom is ionized and recaptured before the process is over would be some 5 to 10 times.

Dr. Biermann: The way we estimated this figure before the first Cambridge meeting, was as follows: We considered that the pressure of the H II region, something like 10^{-11} cgs, effectively drives the interstellar material out, and produces acceleration just corresponding to the surface and to the pressure.

Dr. Kahn: I think that a lot of the energy output from early-type stars just goes into maintaining the H II regions at about 10,000°. If you work out a dynamical model, only a few per cent goes into kinetic energy of motion. And the rest is just used to excite O^+.

Dr. Biermann: I did allow for this. The number I gave is $\frac{1}{2}$ per cent of the total radiation; 10 per cent is in the Lyman continuum, for this whole group of stars, and of this 10 per cent you get again only something of the order of 10 per cent into heat, because most of it is used for ionization.

Dr. Spitzer: This is the energy that goes into the kinetic energy of ejected photoelectrons.

Dr. Biermann: Yes. But part of the energy that goes into ionization is recovered, because it decays into Lyman α, and Lyman α is reabsorbed and you get a pressure in Lyman α.

Dr. Kahn: That Lyman α pressure isn't very well coupled to the gas.

Dr. Pottasch: I recently made a determination of the temperatures of O stars from the surface brightness in the Balmer lines, assuming the Zanstra mechanism to be operative. The O5 and O6 stars had a UV temperature about twice that used by Dr. Spitzer. This would push your figure for the energy up by about a factor of 10.

Dr. Biermann: I should have remarked that Dr. Spitzer applied a correction for the fact that the Lyman continuum is below what you would expect on the basis of the temperature. What you say is that in effect the reduction was less than the one which has been applied.

Dr. Pottasch: Yes.

Dr. von Hoerner: I wonder why did you not mention the differential galactic rotation and turbulent friction as one of the supplies of energy?

Dr. Biermann: I recall that the differential galactic rotation was considered an efficient source before 1953. One reason why we dropped it then was that it was difficult to convince ourselves that the state of motion really gave rise to a rotational instability.

Dr. von Hoerner: I don't mean the rotational instability. I just mean the usual turbulent friction when you have any kind of shear.

Dr. Biermann: But if you take the kinetic energy that might be gained by redistribution of angular momentum, and if you divide that by the time scale, the figure is on the low side.

Dr. Strömgren: I would say it is the same as you have here, V^3/l. This is exactly the same formula that you take in the next bigger elements. And so the result will be the same, again 10^{-2}.

Dr. Biermann: The rotation corresponds roughly to 10^{14} ergs/g. Dividing this by, say, 10^{10} years gives $10^{-3.5}$ erg/g/sec, which is an upper limit.

Dr. Oort: It might of course be that you would have to increase this number because the interstellar medium is being replenished by dying stars, and so new rotational energy is put in continuously. But I don't think, personally, that it is very likely that the differential galactic rotation would be a source of turbulent energy because the whole phenomenon of clouds and cloud motion looks very different from what one would expect from such frictional processes.

Dr. Biermann: Yes. But perhaps I may say that the gas from stars is in a sense included in the figure I gave for the corpuscular emission. The interstellar mass is by its origin, at least to some fraction, connected with the corpuscular emission. Since the rotational velocity in our galaxy is comparable with the velocity of the corpuscular radiation, it is indeed likely that when you compute the energy this way you get higher values.

Dr. Field: Wouldn't you expect that around each star that is emitting corpuscular radiation there would be a rather small region analogous to the H II regions where most of the particles are stopped? So therefore there would be a small efficiency, perhaps, for conversion into large-scale kinetic energy of the gas; that is, most of this energy presumably would go into radiation.

Dr. Biermann: Only if the velocity is high enough. That comes back to a question we had before. If the material is mostly emitted with some 100 km/sec, say, like the steady component of the solar corpuscular radiation, then I think you have a reasonably effective conversion. Since these stars are distributed irregularly and since a part of them is moving quite fast, I think there is a good case for assuming that the fraction which is to become kinetic energy is not very small.

Dr. Kahn: There would be a region where that motion has to be reconciled with the motion of the surrounding interstellar gas. And that is where you lose energy into radiation if you aren't careful.

Dr. Biermann: Yes, that is right. It is certainly something that could be looked into in more detail.

Dr. G. R. Burbidge: Should one include also the energy contained in the material which is expanding from the center regions of the galaxy—I know one has problems here of understanding where the energy comes from, and what causes it to move in this way—but one also has to consider the dissipation if further out there is no outward expansion. Could this not be quite a sizeable contribution?

Dr. Oort: It wouldn't be any higher than this 10^{14} ergs/g. Taken over the whole galaxy it would be much lower.

Dr. Kahn: How does the ambipolar diffusion depend on the field strength?

Dr. Woltjer: It depends through the term $\nabla \times \mathbf{B} \times \mathbf{B}$. If you increased the field, then to keep equilibrium you may have to make the field more and more force-free and thereby you would not increase the diffusion term very much.

Dr. Spitzer: For the supernovae I think the argument on the conversion efficiency is very much more difficult.

Dr. Biermann: That is right. Going along with the Blaauw picture we have much more material, moving at a much smaller velocity, of only a few hundred kilometers per second, and this should not lose too much energy going into light. For the particles of some thousands of a kilometer per second things may be quite different. Wouldn't you agree that with particles which arrive at 300 km/sec you have a good chance of getting most of it into kinetic energy?

Dr. Spitzer: No, not at 300 km/sec. To use this kinetic energy at 30 km/sec with the greatest efficiency, you must distribute the energy through a mass that is greater by a factor of 100 than the mass in which it was originally concentrated. You don't want to do that by snow-plowing because that conserves the momentum and not the energy. You must convert this energy into heat and use the heat as a pressure source to accelerate the new material. And the inefficiencies in such a process due to radiative losses are very large.

Dr. Woltjer: If you want to accelerate cosmic rays in the halo—I wouldn't agree that one really has to—what fraction of the energy of the supernovae of type II could one convert directly into hydromagnetic waves if the supernova shell expands into the interstellar magnetic field?

Dr. Biermann: Possibly conditions might be more favorable then, if the speed is quite high. It may be that quite a substantial fraction of the hydromagnetic wave energy could go into cosmic rays. That might be a way to get an efficient secondary acceleration of cosmic rays.

Dr. Strömgren: Regarding the supernovae calculation, you mentioned that 1 per 200 years is a fairly conservative estimate. In the discussion in Pasadena that you referred to, was it agreed that this was fairly reliable? My impression is that the recent discoveries in fairly large numbers by Humason and Zwicky have strengthened the estimate for the supernovae of type I but not particularly for type II; in external galaxies many of them may be in strong absorption regions and therefore below the limit of detection.

Dr. Biermann: If I remember correctly, the figure of 200 years might mean something between 100 and say 300. We had the impression that going down to 50 was not indicated by the data.

Dr. Field: In principle couldn't one get an estimate of the number of supernovae of type II in our galaxy by looking at the number of supernovae remnants, which are now detected by radio means, and their distribution in distance, and in age?

Dr. Biermann: They had some discussion of this point also in Pasadena, especially with Bolton. Bolton appeared to advocate somewhat higher frequencies, partly on the basis of the distribution in space of known remnants. But Davis and I felt that there was no very strong reason to push the frequency higher. It is difficult to be more definite because of the statistical uncertainties.

Dr. G. R. Burbidge: Not too long ago Shklovsky tried to estimate the frequency by using the radio-source data, and he came up with a very high figure, something like 1 every 30 years.

Dr. Field: Shouldn't it be borne in mind that we are not interested in a typical galaxy but our galaxy and therefore we shouldn't take too seriously the estimates from extragalactic systems? It could be higher by a factor of 10 in our own galaxy.

Dr. Biermann: Yes, but I had the feeling that when one looks at what appear to be remnants and combines it with probable ages, there was no strong reason to assume a higher figure than was in the estimate of about 100 to 300 years.

Dr. Struve: Since Shklovsky's high frequency of supernovae has been mentioned let me say that these estimates are based on a diagram he made of the locations of the supernovae with respect to the sun; they occupy a space about one-quarter or one-fifth of the galaxy. This is the reason the 200-year interval is reduced to something like 40 years.

Dr. Biermann: Could one not say that it is somewhat difficult to rely on statistics with so small numbers?

Dr. Struve: Oh, yes. But at the same time it is a striking thing that Cas A has an absorption of 6 magnitudes or so.

Dr. Field: By the same token, certainly, the type I supernovae have an astonishing concentration in the area around the sun, considering that there were three in a thousand years. Again one suspects that the frequency in our galaxy may be much larger than that of the average galaxy.

Dr. Biermann: Yes, but these are negligible in the energy balance as compared to the type II. Their energy is 2 powers of 10 less.

Dr. Woltjer: I think the point Dr. Field raised depends very much on what you assume for the distance of the historic supernovae. If you put in more realistic distances the difficulty largely disappears. I would place two of the supernovae at about 2 kpc distance and one at about 10 kpc—which is still somewhat disturbing but not so bad as with the older distances.

Dr. Biermann: May I try to summarize? I got the following impression from the discussion. If we estimate the balance of kinetic energy from probable losses by collisions between clouds and by ambipolar diffusion, then we are in the range of between 10^{-3} to 10^{-4} erg/g/sec. If that is what has to be replaced, we could do it with a reasonable fraction of the heat energy in the ultraviolet (kT per Lyman continuum quantum of 10^{-2} erg/g/sec), or of the energy contributed by supernovae (of similar amount), and by corpuscular radiation of active stars. That would seem to be a possible way of getting these figures straight, but only if we are justified to disregard the secondary acceleration of cosmic rays as requiring 10^{-2} erg/g/sec.

Dynamics of the interstellar gas

F. D. Kahn

I should like to restrict my discussion and in fact spend most of the time talking about what goes on in the H II regions. There is a good reason for that. The mechanism by which the energy in the interstellar gas is dissipated by the so-called turbulence in space is extremely obscure. It is made more so by the fact that one doesn't know how important the magnetic field is in this process, and anything one might say on the subject would be extremely tentative.

On the other hand, the question of the input of energy in the H II regions around hot stars has recently been discussed in a fair amount of detail in a number of papers. I would, therefore, like to describe how these calculations are done and roughly what one would expect to see. The mechanism by which the energy is put in is fairly familiar. We have heard about it earlier in this conference.

We have a hot star. It is surrounded by hydrogen, some of which will be ionized out to some distance, and then unless the system is in a steady state—and usually it will not be in a steady state—there will be gas flowing across the ionization front, or the boundary, of the H II region. You will remember from Professor Strömgren's paper [1] 22 years ago that this boundary is sharp relative to the size of the region. Often the distance from the star to the ionization front is several parsec, perhaps, whereas the region of transition between the neutral gas and ionized gas will be much narrower, say, 0.01 pc wide, at the usual density.

On crossing the boundary, gas atoms are ionized and the electrons so produced acquire extra thermal energy, namely, the excess of the energy of the ionizing photon above that required for separating an electron from a proton. Therefore, from the mechanical point of view there is an input of heat into the gas, and this tends to make the gas move. It should be added that there is also quite a considerable input of heat in the main body of the H II region, whenever one of the atoms there is reionized. A lot of this heat will be lost to O^+ ions, which can radiate away this energy (cf. Spitzer [2]).

Let me first concentrate on what goes on at the boundary of the ionization front. One can classify ionization fronts into two kinds, and these can be subclassified into two further kinds (cf. Kahn [3]).

We may have conditions in which the radiation from the star does not contain very many photons in the Lyman continuum. The ionization front will therefore move slowly into the gas ahead. Alternatively one can look at it this way: There is a star with a given output of radiation. If a dense cloud of gas is put in front of it, and the ionization front moves into that, its progress will be slow. This is the dense case, and the name given to it is D-type.

There are in general two possibilities for the motion of the gas behind the ionization front. It can either move supersonically, or it can move subsonically.

The closer study, made by Axford [4], about which I shall speak, shows that the possibility of a transition from subsonic ahead to supersonic behind in such a case is rare and requires rather special conditions. Because there is a considerable change in the motion of the gas, this is called a strong D-type front.

Gas moves subsonically on both sides of a weak D-type front. This can occur but is often found to be unstable. If we have such a D-type front, the gas ahead will tend to readjust its motion if it can, by expanding toward the star. Conditions at the ionization front will then be just such that ahead they are subsonic and behind they are exactly sonic. That is the critical condition. We expect such transitions to occur, for example, at the boundaries of bright rims with elephants' trunks, where there is a transition from a dark cloud to a bright rim.

Between the densities at which D-type fronts can occur and those where the other class of ionization fronts becomes possible, there is a range for which no ionization front can be made to lie between the neutral and the ionized gas. This is a forbidden range. But at sufficiently low density one can have a front moving supersonically into the neutral gas ahead.

We can call a front such as this R-type, to remind us of "rarefied." Again, conditions behind may be subsonic or supersonic. In general, both kinds of transition are allowed. In a study of the structure of an ionization front one sees that a strong R-type transition, from supersonic ahead to subsonic behind, requires one to insert a shock wave somewhere, but that can be done if the ionized gas is being pushed from the rear. On

F. D. Kahn

the other hand, the weak transition, from supersonic ahead to supersonic behind, is usually found when there is nothing pushing on the ionized gas behind. This will, for example, occur where you have an interstellar gas cloud in empty space and you suddenly let a star shine onto it and ionize it. If the intensity of radiation is high enough, the ionization front so produced will advance faster than a shock can into the neutral gas, and the ionized gas behind will expand away toward the star.

Now suppose that you set up an experiment like this: You have a star, you expose some gas to the radiation of the star, and you arrange the density of the gas such that neither kind of ionization front can occur. It seems that what happens then is that the ionization front will be preceded by a shock front, whose passage causes the density of the gas to adjust so that a D-critical front can occur behind it. In this particular case we get the well-known rocket mechanism of Oort and Spitzer [5], because here we have a means of accelerating a whole slab of neutral gas.

One can now treat these transitions not so much as discontinuities, but rather as objects with a structure. This is rather instructive, because it shows just why some of them are possible and others are not. My description is based essentially on the recent paper by Axford. Axford was able to include many different effects such as ionization and recombination, cooling of the gas by O^+ ions, and of course the dynamical effects. He used essentially the following equations:

Rate of change of intensity J of ionizing radiation:

$$\frac{dJ}{dr} = \frac{\alpha}{M} J\rho(1 - x) \tag{1}$$

Note that, like Strömgren in his classical paper, he neglects the contribution to the photon flux due to recombinations to the ground state.

Ionization balance:

$$u\frac{dx}{dr} = \alpha J(1 - x) - \frac{\beta_0 \rho x^2}{M T^{3/4}} \tag{2}$$

Equation of state:

$$p = \frac{k}{M}(1 + x)\rho T \tag{3}$$

Equation of motion:

$$u\frac{du}{dr} = -\frac{1}{\rho}\frac{dp}{dr} \tag{4}$$

Equation of continuity:

$$\rho u = F = \text{const} \tag{5}$$

Equation of energy balance:

$$u\frac{d}{dr}\left(\frac{3p}{2\rho}\right) - \frac{pu}{\rho^2}\frac{d\rho}{dr} = \frac{\alpha kT_*}{M}J(1-x) - \frac{3}{2}\beta_0 kT^{1/4}\frac{\rho x^2}{M^2} - \frac{\rho^2}{M^2}L_{ei}(T) \tag{6}$$

The frame of reference is chosen such that the ionization front is at rest, hence no time derivatives occur. The meaning of the symbols is as follows:

J = flux of Lyman continuum photons

r = distance, defined so that it increases toward the star

α = cross section of H atom for Lyman continuum photons

ρ = density of gas

x = fractional ionization of the gas

M = mass of H atom

u = velocity of gas

$\beta_0/T^{3/4}$ = radiative recombination coefficient, summed for all final states of the H atom

T = gas temperature

p = gas pressure

k = Boltzmann's constant

T_* = temperature of star from which ionizing radiation comes

$L_{ei}(T)$ = rate of cooling of gas by O^+ ions, per unit mass of gas (for the purpose of this calculation $L_{ei} = 0$, when $T < 4000°K$, and $L_{ei} = 0.97 \times 10^{-31}(T - 4000)^2$ erg/g/sec otherwise)

The formula is based on values given by Spitzer, and assumes an abundance of O^+ ions typical of population I objects.

Note that the second terms on the right-hand sides of Eqs. (2) and (6) represent contributions made by proton–electron recombinations to the balance of ionization and temperature, respectively. It is instructive to consider an ionization front in which recombination and cooling can be neglected, and we shall do so in a moment.

We just note that the full equations reduce to the following dimensionless form:

$$\frac{d}{dj}(j - x) = E\frac{x^2}{j(1-x)\theta^{3/4}}\frac{\bar{\rho}}{A} \tag{7}$$

$$\frac{dG}{dj} = D\frac{dx}{dj} + DH(\theta)\frac{d}{dj}(j - x) \tag{8}$$

The relation between j, x, and the normalized distance ϕ is given by

$$\frac{d\phi}{dj} = \frac{1}{j(1-x)\bar{\rho}/A} \tag{9}$$

Axford's notation has been changed a little. In the equations,

$j = MJ/F$, a normalized photon flux

$$G = [4/(BU_i)^2]\left(\frac{5p}{2\rho} + \frac{u^2}{2}\right), \text{ a normalized enthalpy}$$

$\bar{\rho}$ is a normalized gas density
θ is T/T_*
D and E are constants typical of the ionization front
$H(\theta)$ is a term representing the heat losses due to recombination, and
radiation by O^+ ions

Further,

ρ_0 = gas density ahead of the ionization front
U_i = gas velocity there
p_0 = pressure there

$$BU_i = \frac{p + \rho u^2}{F} = \frac{p_0 + \rho_0 U_i^2}{F}, \text{ a constant of the motion}$$

We also need to know

$$Y = \frac{4p/\rho}{(BU_i)^2} \quad \text{and} \quad \bar{w} = 2u/BU_i$$

It can then be readily shown that

$$G = 1 + 2Y \pm \sqrt{(1 - Y)} \quad \text{and} \quad \bar{w} = 1 \pm \sqrt{(1 - Y)}$$

There is thus a relation between G and Y, another between $\bar{w}$ and Y.

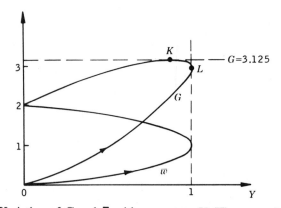

Fig. 1. Variation of G and $\bar{w}$ with respect to Y. The arrow heads show the direction in which the Mach number M increases. Relative to the ordinary speed of sound $M_{ad} = 1$ at K. Relative to the isothermal speed of sound $M_{iso} = 1$ at L. Two values of $\bar{w}$ are possible for a given G. The choice depends on whether conditions are subsonic or supersonic.

This gives rise to a diagram (Fig. 1) that can be used to decide what kind of ionization fronts you can get.

Now at an ionization front there is an increase in the value of G because energy is fed into the gas from the radiation that is absorbed. Therefore we prescribe the value of G at the head of the ionization front. If cooling is neglected we require G to be increased by a certain amount ΔG before we let the gas stream out into the ionized region. We can now decide whether under given conditions such an ionization front is possible or not.

To give typical examples, suppose we have an ionization front that is moving subsonically relative to the medium ahead, and where $G = 1$, say, in the gas ahead. We require further that the value of G be increased by $\Delta G = 1.5$, say. Then obviously behind the ionization front G must equal 2.5.

At the same time $\bar{w}$ must change from the value it takes below $G = 1$, to the one it takes below $G = 2.5$. Therefore, if we are interested in finding out how G and $\bar{w}$ vary, we can do the following: We use the equations given before to find the relation, say, between G and x, the fractional ionization of the gas. When recombination and cooling within the ionization front are ignored, we find that x increases from zero ahead to unity at the back. The amount of energy now given to the gas just goes up linearly with the degree of ionization, so that G is linear in x.

If we are now interested in the value of the velocity as a function of x, we find the relation by picking out corresponding points on the $\bar{w}$ curve, as illustrated in Fig. 2.

This is a weak D-type front. There is absolutely no difficulty in setting up such a front, when recombination and cooling are neglected, provided the final value of G is less than or equal to 25/8. When there is equality the velocity of motion behind the front is sonic. This is the D-critical case. The impossibility of having a strong D-type front without cooling arises because we would have to enter the G curve in the subsonic region and then cannot from there make a shock transition to the supersonic region.

The only way to get such a front is by allowing other forms of variations of G with x. If the gas can lose some heat at a later stage, there may exist a curve such as in Fig. 3, where x and G go up together initially because the gas is being heated on being ionized. But now so many O^+ ions are produced that cooling sets in and G levels off and then decreases. If one can arrange things so that the maximum value reached by G is just 25/8, then it is possible to go up over the maximum in the G, Y curve. This leads to a motion that is subsonic ahead and supersonic behind.

Now suppose that we try to add more energy than that to the gas and force G to exceed 25/8. Then, of course, we are in trouble, because

F. D. Kahn

there is nowhere to go on the G curve. This is the case in which conditions are such that the simple fronts that I described before do not allow an ionized region to touch the neutral gas.

Estimates are given on p. 199 of reference [3]. For example, at a distance of 9 pc from an O9 star, surrounded by H II region containing 10 H$^+$ ions/cm^3 one requires a density of 500 atoms/cm^3 in the neutral gas in order to get the D-critical condition. If one had more than that, it would be D-type.

It seems in general that when one tries to put in too much energy to allow a D-type front to occur, then one must abandon the picture of motion in steady state. The problem then has no steady-state solution, and one has to work out the initial-value problem. If the radiation falls on the boundary of a neutral gas cloud, and if the intensity of the radiation lies in the forbidden range, then a shock is sent ahead into the neutral gas, pushed by the pressure in the rear, and the distance between the shock and the ionization front keeps increasing.

When we go into the equations, we find that the effect of sending the shock ahead is to reduce the values of G and ΔG by the time the ionization front comes along. Therefore all we need to do is reduce them at

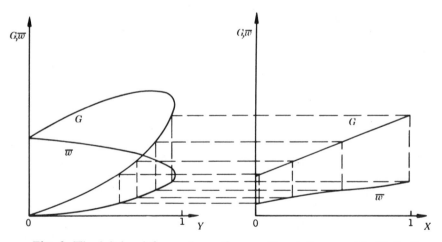

Fig. 2. The left-hand figure shows the way G and $\bar{w}$ vary with Y. In the right-hand figure one enters, first, the variation of G with x, the fractional ionization. This can be found from Eqs. (7) and (8). Since recombination is being neglected, G is linear in x. To find $\bar{w}$ on the right-hand figure, find G for a given x, and read off the corresponding $\bar{w}$ from the left-hand figure.

If a plot is desired of G, $\bar{w}$, and x in terms of the distance ϕ, then one must solve for ϕ in terms of x in Eq. (9), and construct another diagram in the same way.

least so much that the maximum value taken by G is just 25/8. This determines how strong the shock will be.

Finally, for an R-type transition, we enter the G, Y curve on the supersonic side. Here we can start to fit in R-type fronts, provided again that we do not force G to exceed 25/8.

Suppose we want to add a given ΔG. We can do it in two ways. We can let our G travel up on the supersonic side; in this case we would have a motion that is supersonic ahead and supersonic behind; that is to say, the ionization front just races through the gas and leaves it hot while producing little acceleration. Alternatively we can have an ionization front which moves supersonically up to a certain point, makes a shock transition to the subsonic side, and goes to its final value there (Fig. 4). This will be a strong R-type front, one separating a state of supersonic motion ahead and subsonic motion behind.

In general things are not changed much by including cooling terms except for the curiosity we have already discussed of being able to get a strong D-type front.

One might ask if it is legitimate to insert a shock into the ionization front the way it is done here. Would such a shock be thin enough, or should we really treat it as a structure of finite thickness?

Now the thickness of the ionization front is approximately a mean free path for a Lyman continuum photon in hydrogen gas, while the

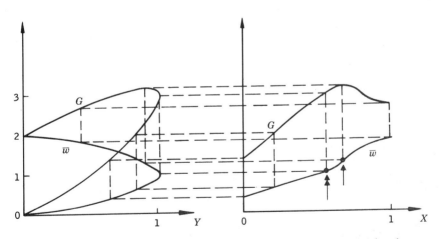

Fig. 3. If G climbs to a maximum of 25/8 and then decreases again, the gas can make the transition from subsonic flow ahead to supersonic flow behind the ionization front. The flow is exactly sonic relative to the ordinary speed of sound at the point shown by the single arrow, and relative to the isothermal speed of sound at the point shown by the double arrow.

thickness of the shock front is approximately the mean free path for a hydrogen atom. The ratio of those two quantities is found to be $(3\sqrt{3}/8g)137$, so that the shock may be treated as a discontinuity, since g, the Gaunt factor, is of order unity. In a fully ionized gas the mean free path will be different by a factor $(kT_*/\chi)^2$ approximately, and the shock will still be thin. Here $T_* =$ temperature of star, $\chi =$ ionization energy. For further details I refer you to Axford's paper, because we really must get on to a study of the H II region as a whole.

What happens if we shut off an H II region by means of an ionization front? That has been considered by Goldsworthy [6] in a companion paper. The problem he sets himself is this: Suppose we immerse a star in a region of neutral hydrogen gas. At time $t = 0$ we switch on the star. Under what conditions can we find reasonable solutions for the flow that follows?

If you leave the problem quite general, if you do not restrict the possible initial density distribution around the star, and if you allow temporal variations in the radiative output of the star, then you have set yourself a problem that is rather too lengthy to tackle even with a computer. Goldsworthy therefore looks for a system which gives him insight into the essence of the problem, but which can be mathematically handled; to do so he considers a situation which allows a similarity solution.

The types of physical effect taken into account include almost everything that is important. He found he could get better solutions if he

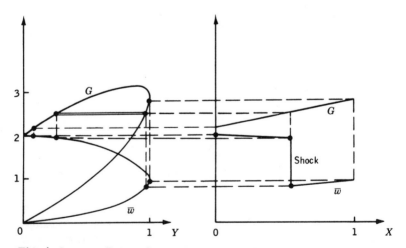

Fig. 4. A strong R-type front. Note that, at the shock, there is a jump from one side of the G, Y curve to the other. The value of G does not change at the jump, because the enthalpy does not change at a shock, when the motion is steady.

assumed that he had a cylindrical star instead of a spherical one. Later approximate calculations showed that there wasn't too much difference between cylindrical and spherical stars. He assumes initially, in the cylindrical problem, that the neutral gas density before ionization varies inversely as r, the distance from the star. He assumes that the output of radiation from the star remains constant. He includes the effects of ionization, recombination, and cooling; even gravitation can be allowed for, but he has found this to be unimportant. His preliminary results enabled him to get a reasonably simple approach to the problem.

He finds, first of all, that the cooling mechanisms which operate in the H II regions are so powerful that even on a dynamical picture it is an extremely good approximation to say that they are such as to make the temperature T satisfy

$$\frac{T_*}{T} - \frac{3}{2} - 2.4 \times 10^{25} T^{-1/4} L_{ei}(T) = 0 \tag{10}$$

Therefore H II regions are characterized by a temperature T_c, which is determined by the nature of the exciting star and the abundance of O^+ ions.

The second point is that, as in the classical case discussed by Professor Strömgren, the value of x remains very close to unity within the H II region, except at the ionization front. Again there is not much difference between the dynamic case and the static case.

Finally, again as in that case, the bulk of the Lyman continuum radiation which is poured out by a star is consumed in keeping x close to unity. Only a fraction of it, 1 per cent or so, actually reaches the ionization front. The implication is that most of the photons go to balance recombinations, and most of their energy to balance radiation by O^+ ions. Finally, he can show that the ionization front is thin on the scale in which he is interested, and he regards it as a discontinuity. He then gets the following equations.

Within the H II region,

$$D_1 \eta \frac{d\mathfrak{U}}{d\eta} = \mathfrak{U}(1 - \mathfrak{U})^2 + (1 - 2\mathfrak{U})\eta^2 \tag{11}$$

and

$$\mathfrak{A} = \sqrt{\left(\frac{5}{3}\right)} \eta \tag{12}$$

there is also an equation for $\omega = \rho r$, where ρ is the gas density. In Eqs. (11) and (12)

$$D_1 = (1 - \mathfrak{U})^2 - \eta^2, \quad \eta = (t/r)(2kT_c/M)^{1/2}$$

$$\mathfrak{U}r/t = u = \text{gas velocity}$$

Note that $\mathfrak{A}r/t = (10\,kT_c/3M)^{1/2}$ = ordinary sonic speed in fully ionized hydrogen at temperature T_c, while $\eta r/t = (2kT_c/M)^{1/2}$ = isothermal sonic speed there.

We see that $\eta \to \infty$ as $r \to 0$, that is, as the star is approached. The motion, if any, in the H I region obeys

$$D\eta\frac{d\mathfrak{U}}{d\eta} = \mathfrak{U}(1 - \mathfrak{U})^2 + \mathfrak{A}^2\left(\frac{3}{5} - 2\mathfrak{U}\right) \tag{13}$$

and

$$\frac{D\eta}{\mathfrak{A}}\frac{d\mathfrak{A}}{d\eta} = \frac{1}{3(1 - \mathfrak{U})}\left[(3 - 4\mathfrak{U})(1 - \mathfrak{U})^2 + \mathfrak{A}^2\left(\frac{3}{5} - 2\mathfrak{U}\right)\right] \tag{14}$$

where $D = (1 - \mathfrak{U})^2 - \mathfrak{A}^2$. Once again there is also an equation for ω, and $\mathfrak{A}r/t$ = local sonic speed.

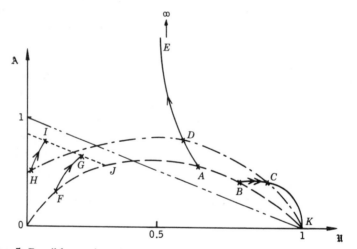

Fig. 5. Possible motions in and around H II regions. Arrowheads show the direction toward the star.

$\to\!\!-$ = typical solution curves for motion in the H II region. In particular near the star $\mathfrak{A} \to \infty$ and $\mathfrak{U} \to 1/2$ along the curve AE.

$\to\!\!\succ\!\!-$ = the solution curve for motion in the H I region, initiated at B by a strong shock.

$-\;-\;-\;-$ = locus of points in the $\mathfrak{U}$, $\mathfrak{A}$ plane which can be reached by an R-type transition from $\mathfrak{U} = 0$, $\mathfrak{A} = 0$, i.e., from the undisturbed gas.

$-\;\cdot\;-$ = locus of points which can be reached by a D-type transition from C, a typical point in the gas behind the strong shock.

$-\;-\;-\;-$ = locus of points in the H II region from which an isothermal shock transition can be made onto the curve AE.

$-\;\cdot\;\cdot\;-$ = line separating region of subsonic flow above from that of supersonic flow below. An ionization transition which crosses this line is strong; otherwise it is weak.

The possible regimes are as follows. If the intensity of radiation from the star is high or the gas density low, a weak R-type ionization front moves off ahead. To follow the motion within the H II region we go along an integral curve from F to G. Note that the motion here is supersonic. To reconcile conditions in this outer part of the H II region with those in the part nearer the star, an isothermal shock must be inserted at G. This takes us onto a point on the curve AE. The motion further inside the H II region is now described by points on this curve. Figure 6 illustrates the nature of the flow in this case. For a lower intensity of radiation the point F, which describes conditions just inside the H II region, has to be moved upward. When it reaches J, the ionization front is coincident with the isothermal shock, which takes us to A. The two together form a strong R-type front.

For a still lower intensity of radiation, a shock precedes the ionization

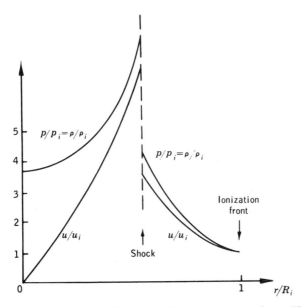

Fig. 6. The nature of the flow behind an R-type ionization front. Here a weak front precedes the H II region; behind it the pressure, density, and gas velocity tend to increase as the inner part of the H II region is approached. This section of the flow is terminated by an isothermal shock. Behind the shock the gas velocity, as well as the pressure and density, fall off on approaching the star. This produces a partial evacuation of the inner H II region.

Note that as the intensity of the stellar radiation decreases so does the ratio of the width of the outer part of the H II region to that of the inner part. Ultimately the shock and ionization fronts coalesce.

front. Since the undisturbed interstellar gas is very cool, this shock is strong; the Rankine–Hugoniot equations then show that conditions just behind it are described by the point $B(\frac{3}{4}, \frac{1}{4}\sqrt{5})$. The motion in the shocked neutral gas is described by the section BC of the curve BCM; at C a D-type ionization front occurs. If this is a weak front, the motion in the H II region is then given by section DE of curve ADE. As the intensity of incident radiation drops, the point C moves away from B. Thus the gap between the shock and ionization front widens, and there is an increase in the ratio of the amount of shocked neutral gas to that of gas in the H II region. Note also that in the limiting case, where B and C coincide, the shock and ionization front again travel together; the D-type transition would now take us back from B to A, and the combined front is again equivalent to a strong R-type transition.

Alternatively, if a strong D-type front can be inserted at C, then the integration of the motion within the H II region begins at H. From here we follow the flow to I, whence an isothermal shock takes us onto AE, and thus into the heart of the H II region. As pointed out earlier, this configuration needs special conditions to be able to occur. Figure 7 shows two typical cases of weak D-type fronts following a strong shock.

This just about completes the description of the different kinds of solutions. It is interesting that you can get shocks both ahead and behind the I front. These are both required to some extent by observation.

I should now like to say a few words about work recently done by Vandervoort. He has considered whether the ionization fronts we are talking about are stable or not. As I understand it, the problem he has solved is this: He considers a plane ionization front and treats it as a discontinuity. He neglects its structure, and this is quite fair if you are dealing with regions whose sizes are large compared with the thickness of the front, and provided that the corrugations put on it don't have wavelengths small compared with its thickness.

With neutral gas ahead, and ionized gas behind, and a given type of transition—Vandervoort actually only considers weak D-type transitions at the ionization front—you can impose a perturbation on the gas, so as to produce a corrugated ionization front. The perturbation should vanish far away both in the ionized gas and in the neutral gas, and yet grow with time. The kinds of results he finds are as follows.

Suppose you consider an ionization front in a D-critical condition, so that the ionized gas is moving away at just sonic speed. One finds that if the incident flux of radiation has symmetry about the normal to the ionization front, then there is no instability. But a rather nice kind of instability is found if there is an ionization front which is formed when radiation is falling obliquely on it.

Suppose we disturb such an ionization front by corrugating it slightly.

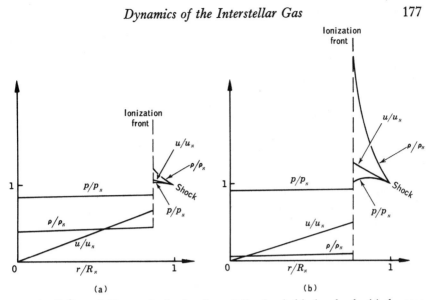

Fig. 7. A weak D-type ionization front following behind a shock: (a) the case illustrated here is typical of the regime. Goldsworthy gives the following values for the velocities of the shock and ionization fronts:

	O5	O9	B2	
u_s	18.5	16.4	15.4	km/sec
u_s	16.2	14.4	13.5	km/sec

(b) In the case illustrated here the relative thickness of the shocked region is about as large as it can be. Goldsworthy gives these values:

	O5	O9	B2	
u_s	7.1	6.3	5.9	km/sec
u_i	5.8	5.1	4.8	km/sec

Some sections of the front now receive a greater flux of radiation and others a smaller flux. The former are then pushed on faster and the latter more slowly. The result is to drive waves along the front, away from the source of radiation, and to amplify them. Vandervoort has at the back of his mind the idea that you might form elephants' trunks in the neutral gas by this means. I do not know whether this can be done. There will come a time when the effect no longer works because the faster-moving part of the corrugation will start turning away again from the source of radiation. The process only works as long as by turning that part of the front you can increase the amount of radiation incident on it per unit area.

Vandervoort finds another kind of instability when conditions at the ionization front are not exactly critical but are D-type. This may be because then the ionizing radiation does not produce enough pressure on the neutral gas to hold it back. He gives various plots of how the instability rates vary. Figures 8 and 9 show typical curves.

I should now like to say a few words about radiation pressure. We want to be sure that in considering the H II regions we have not left out a major source of energy. The only energy we have used so far is that which you get by subtracting the ionization energy of hydrogen from the energy of a Lyman continuum photon.

Now, it has been shown many times that, after ionization, recombination occurs. When recombination occurs either you get re-emission of the Ly-continuum photon, or recombination occurs to an excited state. The atom then cascades to the ground state and in the process you get some Lyman series photon. This may be an Lα photon. If not, it degrades into one after some further absorptions and re-emissions. The Lα photon now is more or less trapped in the H II region. It goes up and down between the 1*s* and 2*p* state and can never get out. The only alternative is that the recombination and subsequent cascade leave the atom in the 2*s*

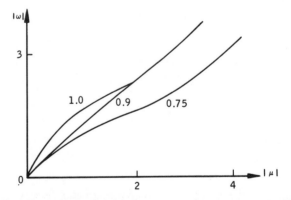

Fig. 8. Variation of the circular frequency of waves in an ionization front. $|\omega|$ is expressed in units of ka_1, where k is the wave number and a_1 the speed of sound on the neutral side. $|\mu|$ is an obliquity index; it equals zero when the radiation is incident normally on the front, and infinity when the radiation shines along it. The numbers by the curves give the Mach number on the ionized side.

state and then the atom makes a transition to the ground state by a two-quantum jump. There, of course, you lose Lα intensity, but this happens in only about a third of the cases. About half the energy of the incident Lyman continuum photons thus is trapped in the H II region in the form of Lα radiation.

The only way in which this radiation can transfer its energy to that of thermal motion of the hydrogen gas is as follows. A hydrogen atom absorbs the Lα quantum and then remains in the excited state, for rather less than 10^{-8} sec^{-1}, so that under conditions found in an H II region you would hardly expect a collision to take place and remove the excitation energy. Therefore, all that can happen to the hydrogen atom is that, on absorbing the photon and re-emitting it, it experiences a recoil in some direction. On the average the energy thus given to the atoms leads to a systematic red shift of the photon given by

$$\frac{\delta v}{v} = \frac{hv}{Mc^2}$$

There is also a Doppler shift because the atoms will in general be moving. This shift will as often be to the red as to the blue, so there is here no net loss of energy from the radiation.

Finally the radiation has to leak out somehow, somewhere. If the radiation has given up a lot of energy to the gas, it will come out considerably reddened. If a particular photon loses before its escape an amount of energy $h\Delta v_*$, that is the amount of energy given up to the gas. We can ask ourselves what fraction of the Lα energy could possibly be transferred in this way.

Obviously, Δv_*, the red shift that the average photon can suffer, is limited by the fact that far enough from the Lα line center even the H II

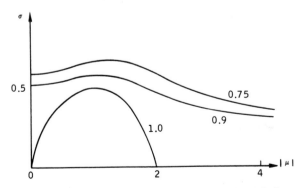

Fig. 9. The instability rate depends on μ and on the Mach number in the ionized gas. σ is also expressed in units of ka_1.

region becomes transparent to it. Now you know roughly how many hydrogen atoms there are in the line of sight in the H II region, because a condition is already set by the fact that all but about 0.1 per cent of the Lyman continuum radiation will be absorbed there.

Arguing in this way we find that in an H II region one could at most absorb 0.01 per cent of the energy of an Lα photon before it is red enough to escape. This corresponds to an amount of energy small compared with that being poured into the H II region by the ionization process we have already discussed. This will as a rule liberate some 10 per cent of the energy of the continuum radiation. The recoil effect produces a very small addition to that energy, which is of no consequence.

Now this Lα radiation is sent off into a H I region. Could it have some effect there? Under present conditions in space it would be killed pretty quickly by the presence of dust. So there you have no reason to expect anything striking.

However, here is a rather speculative point. If there were no dust grains present in the very early days of the galaxy, could this effect then have been of consequence? One would expect so. Of course, this means that in those early days very much more energy could have been poured into the neutral gas than is poured in now, and therefore perhaps more violent motions might have been set up.

One ought also to remember that the estimates one gets for the rate of expansion of an H II region depend on the fact that there are many O^+ ions within the H II region, and that these radiate away a lot of thermal energy. Again, if in the early days there was less oxygen about than there is now, it would have been possible to pour much more heat into the H II regions. So once again there might be a difference between the kind of motion that is set up now and that which used to be set then.

I realize that there are a very large number of topics that I ought to have covered but have not. The sort of problem that Professor Biermann mentioned this morning—to find out how the supernovae affect the interstellar gas—certainly deserves careful study. No complete study comparable with the ones reported here has been done for that problem. It certainly ought to be done, and certainly ought to be discussed at future meetings.

References

[1] B. Strömgren, *Ap. J.*, **89,** 526 (1939).
[2] L. Spitzer, *Ap. J.*, **120,** 5 (1954).
[3] F. D. Kahn, *B.A.N.*, **12,** 187 (1954).
[4] W. I. Axford, *Phil. Trans. Roy. Soc. London*, **A253,** 301 (1961).
[5] J. H. Oort and L. Spitzer, *Ap. J.*, **121,** 6 (1955).
[6] F. A. Goldsworthy, *Phil. Trans. Roy. Soc. London*, **A253,** 277 (1961).

Discussion

Dr. Biermann: Is it possible that by the mathematical formalisms you use you tend to pay more attention to cases in which the rate of conversion into kinetic energy is low because you tend to consider cases that in a certain sense are stationary? Might it not be that, when you fix attention, say, to rapidly moving stars—which are continuously escaping their own H II regions—where things are quite different, or when you consider the whole spectrum of combinations of stellar temperatures and densities in interstellar space, that there might appear a certain number of combinations where one could see immediately that the rate of conversion into kinetic energy might be better?

Dr. Kahn: The conclusion about the rate at which energy is lost actually can be reached without going through all the mathematics. It depends on what you assume for the intensity of radiation, the density of gas, and the density of O^+ ions—or whatever ion is responsible for the cooling. Unless you change the kinetic energy of motion in a time which is short, compared with the time t_c in which the gas would, if left by itself, cool by a factor e, you will lose a lot of the input of heat in just keeping up the temperature of the gas. You can thus argue all the time in terms of the characteristic time, in which the nature of the motion changes, and the cooling time t_c. This time t_c is embarrassingly short—of the order of 2000 years. There are not many things you could do with H II regions on that time scale.

Dr. Spitzer: What has happened to the old argument that the only stable fronts of D-type were the D-critical ones?

Dr. Kahn: In Goldsworthy's case there is gas trapped in a cylindrical or a spherical region behind the ionization front. There can be no outward flow at the center of the H II region. Therefore the conditions that obtain behind the ionization front must be reconciled with the motion of the gas throughout the H II region. In that case, there may exist stable ionization fronts which are sub-sonic inside. In contrast, when a plane ionization front produces ionized gas which runs off into a vacuum, the only condition allowed behind the front is that the motion should be sonic there. If it were subsonic the implication would be that there would be a finite density of gas at infinity downstream. In order to fit on the expansion wave, which takes you to zero density there, you have to have sonic conditions behind the front.

Dr. Spitzer: So an ionization front far away from the D-critical condition would be of interest in interstellar cases?

Dr. Kahn: I think it could be, yes.

Dr. Spitzer: But the strong D-case is not relevant?

Dr. Kahn: The strong D-type fronts are rare birds. No.

Dr. Spitzer: I was surprised by the very low velocities he obtained for the R-type front. Isn't that right, that at least under appropriate conditions one can get an enormously greater velocity for an R-front? If you take an ordinary case and turn on an O star in a uniform medium, then about 5 or 10 pc from the O star the velocity is about 2000 km/sec.

Dr. Kahn: I think the answer is this: The front which gives a relatively low velocity is the one in which you just get a strong R-type ionization front moving by itself without a shock behind. If you imagine the star being turned up in intensity so that a faster ionization front has to move out, then you can only recon-cile the motion in the gas behind this front with a state of rest in the gas near the star by inserting an isothermal shock in the ionized region (see Fig. 6).

Dr. von Hoerner: Has it been checked whether the similarity hypothesis that was introduced is a good description or not, either by a comparison with exact numerical integration or by a stability analysis?

Dr. Kahn: No.

Dr. Christy: In connection with bomb explosions, which pose a very similar problem, some of these solutions have been checked against observations. In the book called "Effects of Atomic Weapons" the results of the solutions are discussed in a general way.

Dr. Strömgren: In your discussion of the Lα effects you referred to the case of the early phase of the galaxy when there might be no grains. If in the same case we assume a very low or vanishing oxygen content, how would this affect conditions?

Dr. Kahn: The general picture one would have is that in the early phase of the galaxy there would be very little means by which the gas could cool to reasonable temperatures. This has two effects. One, the gas gets warmer and warmer as the kinetic energy of the motion dissipates, and so the typical Mach numbers would be small. On the other hand, the transformation of radiant energy into kinetic energy would be more efficient, particularly in H I regions. So you would expect that there used to be faster motions and not as much dissipation as you would get at those velocities if you applied present-day conditions.

Dr. Biermann: I should like to remark that according to considerations which L. Davis and I made two or three years ago when we discussed the possibility of an early origin of cosmic rays, all the conditions for the secondary acceleration being operative were much more favorable. This seems directly connected with what you say. Therefore, if one has reason to believe that the storage volume of the cosmic radiation is really large enough, then I think there is really quite a good case for this possibility.

Thermal instabilities in the interstellar medium

George B. Field

I have in mind a mechanism that would generate interstellar clouds. In line with general thinking at the present time, I assume that clouds form out of an intercloud medium of lower density than that inside the clouds. As suggested by Spitzer, I assume that the intercloud medium is in pressure equilibrium with the clouds. Since the clouds are found to have internal pressures of about 10^3 (expressed as particle density times temperature), and the intercloud medium appears to have a density of about 10^{-1}, the temperature of the intercloud medium must be about 10^4.

Pressure balance is postulated to prevent the clouds from expanding. As we have heard from Dr. Woltjer, a strong magnetic field might do the same thing. Hence the following discussion is probably applicable only if the field strength is negligible, i.e., less than a few $\times 10^{-6}$ gauss.

The physical mechanism I want to discuss may be called thermal instability. Usually the intercloud medium will be in a thermal steady state, the heat gains balancing the heat losses. In this way a particular temperature is established in the intercloud medium. If, however, a limited region should find itself with a slightly higher density than the average, its cooling rate might rise and its equilibrium temperature fall below the average. If the temperature should fall far enough it might overcompensate for the density increase in the region, so that the pressure in the region would fall below the average value. In this event the pressure in the surrounding matter would compress the region of high density, leading to even higher density. In this way the intercloud medium could be unstable toward the formation of condensations. Presumably such condensations would continue to rise in density until at the low temperature appropriate

183

to clouds the pressure again would equal 10^3. The final result is a cloud—
a region of high density and low temperature—in pressure equilibrium
with a medium of low density and high temperature.

I shall look first at the general instability problem and then at a
specific model for the intercloud medium in the steady state. Finally, I
shall apply the theory to the intercloud medium.

The theory of thermal instability has been treated by several authors,
notably Parker [1] and Weymann [2]. Parker considered the formation of
cool regions in an incompressible gas; obviously the effects of compres-
sibility are paramount for us, so we cannot use his results directly. Weymann
first treated the compressible case. We shall use his results with certain
changes in notation.

We take the unperturbed state to be an infinite, homogeneous, static
gas of specified density ρ_0. Various radiative effects (heating by cosmic
rays, photoionizations, cooling by free–free emission, collisional excitation)
tend to change the energy content of the gas. We include all such processes
in a *heat-loss function*, $\mathscr{L}(\rho, T)$, the losses being counted positive and the
gains negative. $\mathscr{L}$ represents the ergs lost per gram per second, for a given
ρ and T. In the steady state we may ignore conduction and convection, so
the condition of conservation of energy is stated simply as

$$\mathscr{L}(\rho_0, T_0) = 0 \tag{1}$$

Equation (1) establishes the equilibrium temperature T_0 for any assumed
density ρ_0.

To treat perturbations around such a steady state we use the linear-
ized equations expressing conservation of mass, momentum, and energy.
The perturbation is taken of the form, $\exp(2\pi i x/\lambda)$, and the time depen-
dence of the perturbation is found to be $\exp(nt)$, where $\mathscr{I}(n)$ is the oscillation frequency and $\mathscr{R}(n)$ is the growth rate (if positive) or damping rate
(if negative). The equation for n may be written (after Weymann)

$$y^3 + (\lambda/\lambda_1)[1 + (\lambda_2/\lambda)^2]y^2 + y + (\lambda/\lambda_1)[y^{-1}(\lambda_2/\lambda)^2 - \beta] = 0 \tag{2}$$

where

$y = \lambda n/2\pi V_s$

$\lambda_1 = 2\pi R V_s/\mu(\gamma - 1)\mathscr{L}_T \simeq$ distance traveled by sound in one
cooling time

$\lambda_2{}^2 = (2\pi)^2 K/\rho_0 \mathscr{L}_T \simeq$ square of distance for which conduction is
important in one cooling time

$\gamma =$ ratio of specific heats

$\beta =$ instability parameter $= \gamma^{-1}[(\rho_0 \mathscr{L}_\rho/T_0 \mathscr{L}_T) - 1]$

In the above expressions $\mathscr{L}_T$ and $\mathscr{L}_\rho$ are the T- and ρ-derivatives of
$\mathscr{L}$ evaluated at equilibrium. V_s is the sound speed, R the gas constant,
μ the molecular weight, and K the thermal conductivity.

For the special case of the intercloud medium ($n_H = 10^{-1}$, $T = 10^4$) one finds that $\lambda_1 = 4 \times 10^4$ pc and $\lambda_2 = 30$ pc. Therefore, if we restrict attention to $\lambda \simeq 100$ pc (suitable for forming clouds of 10 pc diameter and $n_H = 10$), then $(\lambda/\lambda_1) \ll 1$, $(\lambda_2/\lambda)^2 \ll 1$. This amounts physically to ignoring conduction and to assuming pressure equilibrium in the unstable mode. The three roots of Eq. (2) are then approximately,

$$y_1 = \beta(\lambda/\lambda_1)[1 + 0(\lambda/\lambda_1)^2] \qquad n_1 = \frac{\gamma - 1}{\gamma} \frac{\mu}{RT_0}(\rho_0 \mathscr{L}_\rho - T_0 \mathscr{L}_T)$$

$$y_{2,3} = \pm i[1 + 0(\lambda/\lambda_1)^2] - \tfrac{1}{2}(1 + \beta)(\lambda/\lambda_1)[1 + 0(\lambda/\lambda_1)^2] \qquad (3)$$

$$n_{2,3} = \pm i \frac{2\pi V_s}{\lambda} - \frac{(\gamma - 1)^2}{2\gamma} \frac{\mu}{RT_0}[(\gamma - 1)^{-1}\rho_0 \mathscr{L}_\rho + T_0 \mathscr{L}_T]$$

Roots 2 and 3 are sound waves which are usually damped by radiative cooling. Root 1 is exponentially growing provided

$$\rho_0 \mathscr{L}_\rho - T_0 \mathscr{L}_T > 0 \qquad (4)$$

We may rewrite Eq. (4) as

$$T_0 \mathscr{L}_T \frac{d \log p}{d \log \rho}\bigg|_{\rho = \rho_0} < 0 \qquad (5)$$

so that if $\mathscr{L}_T > 0$, the condensations grow when the calculated equilibrium pressure drops with increasing density. This criterion accords with our previous description.

Often $\mathscr{L}$ is of the form

$$\mathscr{L}(\rho, T) = \rho \mathscr{L}'(T) - \mathscr{L}'' \qquad (6)$$

with $\mathscr{L}''$ independent of ρ and T. Then

$$\rho_0 \mathscr{L}_\rho - T_0 \mathscr{L}_T = \mathscr{L}''\left(1 - \frac{d \log \mathscr{L}'}{d \log T}\right) \qquad (7)$$

where the derivative is evaluated at the equilibrium point. Thus, if the gains are independent of ρ and T ($\mathscr{L}''$), while the losses increase with density ($\mathscr{L}'$), there will be instability provided that

$$\frac{d \log \mathscr{L}'}{d \log T} < 1 \qquad (8)$$

Thus $\mathscr{L}'$ must climb faster than T to stabilize the situation. Only then will the loss of cooling power in a dense cool region tend to raise the temperature again. We note that very often condition (8) will be fulfilled so that such instability must be expected rather generally in astrophysical situations.

Now I shall turn to a model of the intercloud medium. If in fact T is high there, we must look for means to explain it. One way is to postulate some heating process acting everywhere in the interstellar medium independent of density and temperature. Such a process might not be important in the clouds where the density is high and the cooling rate correspondingly large. But under such conditions of low density as obtained in the intercloud medium, where the cooling rate is very low, the process could maintain a high temperature. One such process is ionization caused by cosmic rays. This process was considered by Spitzer [3], with the result that each H atom was supposed to gain 4.1×10^{-30} erg/sec from ionizing collisions with cosmic rays. His data was based on cosmic-ray fluxes determined near solar maximum; recent measurements near solar minimum give larger fluxes. Mr. Charles Kennel of our observatory has looked into the question again and has revised the figure upward about a factor of 10 to 3.9×10^{-29} erg/sec. It appears that even this may be an underestimate since (1) it does not take account of the larger fraction of heavy nuclei in the recent measurements reported earlier here by Lüst— and heavies are more efficient ionizing particles, (2) it does not account for the particles below several hundred Mev which may be excluded from the solar system even at solar minimum, and (3) the energy lost in nuclear collisions is neglected altogether. Conceivably all these could raise the cosmic-ray heating by another factor of 10 or more. Thus, if one uses recent estimates by Morrison, Olbert, and Rossi [4] and by Ginzburg [5], one finds 2.8×10^{-28} erg/sec, about seven times Kennel's estimate. In any case, we shall see that for densities $n_H \simeq 10^{-1}$, heating by cosmic rays is quite important. As it is rather insensitive to density and temperature we may identify cosmic-ray heating with $\mathscr{L}''$ in Eq. (6).

To calculate the $\mathscr{L}'$ term due to radiative losses we must consider whether the intercloud medium is H I or H II. Actually we are committed already to H I, since if it were H II cosmic rays would be utterly insufficient to keep it ionized. As the observations are not conclusive on this point (Strömgren [6]) we are at liberty to assume H I. In that case we may use the cooling mechanisms discussed by Spitzer [7] and revised by Seaton [8]. The results for L, the power lost per free electron for unit n_H, are shown in Fig. 1. Seaton's results have been revised by Mr. Kennel in two ways. First, he included the heat gained by photoionization of various atoms, which becomes significant relative to loss by collisional excitation at low temperatures. In fact the revised L so defined goes to zero at about $15°$, giving what may be called the "Spitzer equilibrium" for quiet clouds. At high temperatures several levels of Fe^+ have been included in an approximate manner, raising the curve above Seaton's for $T \geqslant 10^3$. The final

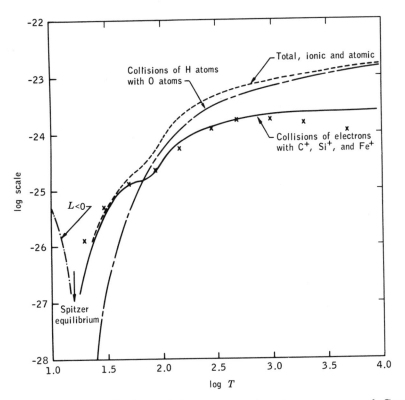

Fig. 1. *L*, power lost by each electron per unit n_H in ergs per second. Crosses indicate data from Seaton, 1955.

curve includes most processes operative in a quiescent H I region with little dust or molecular hydrogen: gains by photoionization of atoms and H⁻, and losses by H⁻ free–free transitions and electron–ion collisional excitation.

The dashed line shows the effects of losses by collisional excitation of O atoms by H atoms. It is thought that electron exchange will be effective in exciting the triplet *P* states of oxygen. Since the probability of this process has not yet been exactly evaluated we have used the kinetic cross section estimated by Burgess, Field, and Michie [9] multiplied by an estimated effectiveness for electron exchange of 10 per cent. Apparently H–O collisions may be an important cooling agent above about 100°K. Further calculations are made both with and without this atomic cooling.

Identifying the cooling curves of Fig. 1 with the $\mathscr{L}'$ of Eq. (6) we have simply

$$\rho_0(T_0) = \frac{\mathscr{L}''}{\mathscr{L}'(T_0)} \qquad (9)$$

as the equation of thermal equilibrium. Evidently,

$$\mathscr{L}' = \left(\frac{n_e}{n_{\mathrm{H}} m_{\mathrm{H}}{}^2}\right) L$$

$$\mathscr{L}'' = \frac{3.9 \times 10^{-29}}{m_{\mathrm{H}}} \qquad (10)$$

Therefore, the $\rho_0 - T_0$ relation of Eq. (9), graphed in Fig. 2, is invariant to increases in n_e/n_{H} or L and $\mathscr{L}''$ by the same factor. In the calculations we assumed $n_e/n_{\mathrm{H}} = 2 \times 10^{-4}$ (following Seaton [8]). A better value

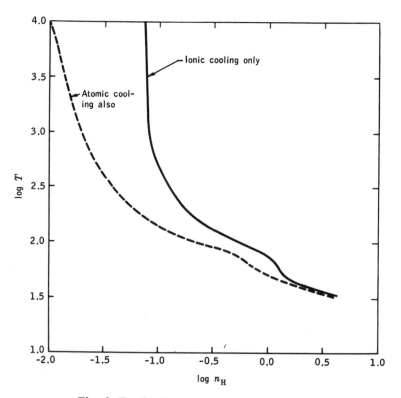

Fig. 2. Equilibrium temperature versus density.

now appears to be 5×10^{-4} (Suess and Urey [10]), so to counter that $\mathscr{L}''$ would have to increase 2.5 times. Also we ignored the electrons contributed by cosmic-ray ionization; this component will probably approach $5 \times 10^{-4} n_H$.

Returning to Fig. 2, it appears that indeed cosmic rays will maintain T near 10^4 for n_H near 10^{-1}, at least if atomic cooling is small. I do not stress the very uncertain values of Fig. 2, but only the general shape of the curves, which confirms our notion that such a rare gas will be hot. So hot, indeed that the pressure actually climbs as the density decreases, as shown in Fig. 3. Hence, at least in the case of ionic cooling only, $n_H T$ approaches 10^3 at low densities.

According to Eq. (5), any equilibria to the left of the pressure minimum will be unstable and will form condensations that are over on the right of the graph; their details are not studied here. It is interesting that the very mechanism needed to keep the intercloud medium hot also guarantees that it is unstable. The growth rates for the instabilities are calculated using Eq. (3) and the data of Fig. 1 and are shown in Fig. 4. Even the minimum e-folding time of 2.5×10^8 years appears rather long compared, say, to cloud collision times $\simeq 10^7$ years. One could decrease this time by a factor of 10 by increasing both the cosmic-ray heating and the cooling (perhaps by O–H collisions). This would shift the dashed curve of Fig. 2 to the right by $\Delta \log n_H = 1$, also eliminating the unsatisfactory vertical portion of the ionic cooling curve.

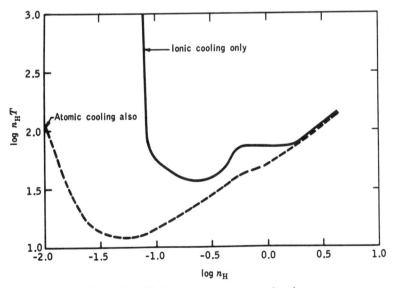

Fig. 3. Equilibrium pressure versus density.

We can follow the development of a condensation under pressure equilibrium by the equation

$$\left(1 - \frac{d\log\mathscr{L}'}{d\log T}\Big|_{T=T_0}\right)n_0(t - t_*) = \int\limits_{T}^{T_*} \frac{d(T/T_0)}{(T_0\mathscr{L}'/T\mathscr{L}'_0) - 1} \tag{11}$$

This expression diverges logarithmically as $t_* \to 0$ and $T_* \to T_0$, in accordance with the exponential growth of the early stages. Hence it is necessary to start at a finite value of $\Delta T = T_* - T_0$. Starting from $\Delta T = -0.05T_0$ and $\Delta\rho = +0.05\rho_0$ we obtain the curve of Fig. 5, with $T_0 = 10^4$ and $n_{HO} = 0.076$ (ionic cooling only). As expected, the early phases take a period equal to (growth rate)$^{-1}$—some three billion years in the present example. The growth of the condensation accelerates greatly in the later phases, owing to enhanced cooling at higher density. Hence a larger initial condensation ($\Delta\rho \sim 3\rho_0$) could reduce the time scale by more than a factor of 10. One notes in passing that probably Seaton's curves for cooling of a cloud after a collision should be revised for cooling under constant pressure.

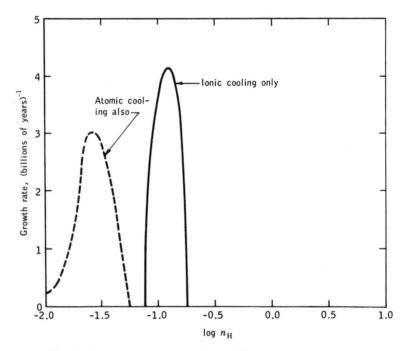

Fig. 4. Growth rate of thermal instabilities versus density.

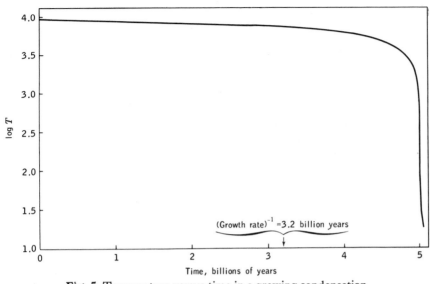

Fig. 5. Temperature versus time in a growing condensation.

Finally, these ideas may be applied to the galactic halo. Spitzer [11] has suggested a halo of density 10^{-3} and temperature 10^6 in pressure equilibrium with the clouds. He considered that corpuscular radiation could maintain the high temperature because of the low density, in analogy to our considerations of the intercloud medium. The gas of such a halo is quite unstable, and should form clouds with a time scale of 0.6 billion years. Perhaps such clouds play a role in the large-scale circulation suggested by Woltjer in connection with the observed mass loss from the galactic nucleus.

References
[1] E. N. Parker, *Ap. J.*, **117,** 431 (1953).
[2] R. Weymann, *Ap. J.*, **132,** 452 (1960).
[3] L. Spitzer, Jr., *Ap. J.*, **107,** 6 (1948).
[4] P. Morrison, S. Olbert, and B. Rossi, *Phys. Rev.*, **94,** 440 (1954).
[5] V. L. Ginzburg, "Progress in Elementary Particle and Cosmic Ray Physics," Vol. 4, Interscience, New York, p. 339.
[6] B. Strömgren, *Ap. J.*, **108,** 242 (1948).
[7] L. Spitzer, Jr., *Ap. J.*, **109,** 337 (1949).
[8] M. J. Seaton, *Ann. Astrophys.*, **18,** 1 (1955).
[9] A. Burgess, G. B. Field, and R. W. Michie, *Ap. J.*, **131,** 529 (1960).
[10] H. E. Suess and H. C. Urey, "Handbuch der Physik," Springer, Berlin,1958, Vol. 51, p. 296.
[11] L. Spitzer, Jr., *Ap. J.*, **124,** 20 (1956).

Discussion

Dr. Strömgren: Would you have any comment on possible differences in the functioning of the mechanism and the time scales when you are in and out of spiral arms? The cosmic-ray intensity would presumably be the same, but the cloud density and the other densities and maybe the radiation field would be different.

Dr. Field: If the cooling and heating mechanisms are similar, one will find instability both in and out of the arms. But the time scale should be considerably shorter in the spiral arms if the density is higher there.

Dr. Underhill: This is all for no magnetic fields?

Dr. Field: Yes, if the field were strong it certainly would not work in this simple manner. One possibility is that one might have some hope of forming the filaments that are observed in the interstellar medium, by using the fact that the thermal conductivity will be very different across and along the lines of force. So perhaps one could set up growing perturbations of the sort across the lines of force but not along them, and thereby get filamentary structure.

Dr. Woltjer: You have three phases now: Gas at $100°$, gas at $10,000°$, and the halo medium at 10^6 degrees, all three at the same pressure. What produces the phase difference between the two hot gases—the $10,000°$ component and the 10^6 degrees component?

Dr. Spitzer: I can't answer that question offhand, but there are a number of facets that can be examined. If the hot material surrounds cold clouds, you are going to get a conduction loss.

Dr. Woltjer: That would make only a very thin shell.

Dr. Spitzer: I don't know what that will do. Maybe you could get a million degree medium directly enveloping the cloud. I have the impression that you then get in trouble with the interstellar calcium-line observations. There is some reason to suspect that you may get some interstellar calcium lines formed even when the color excess is very small, when you are looking through the intercloud medium. This result is not definite enough for one to claim it as a fact. Looking at the difference between Na and Ca, for example, the number of Na atoms seems to have a correlation with color excess, which does not seem to be present in the case of the interstellar Ca to such an extent.

Dr. Woltjer: So you mean essentially that that is just an observational argument not based on a theoretical reasoning.

Dr. Spitzer: I hesitate to admit that I believe in something just because of observations! This, incidentally, is one of the areas in which very much better information could be obtained with satellite spectroscopy in the ultraviolet, because then the lines formed in the intercloud medium could readily be observed, unless the gas is too hot.

Strong shock fronts

Sebastian von Hoerner

Supersonic Turbulence and Shock Fronts

The different states of motion. The internal motion of a gas can be in one of two states: laminar flow or turbulence. In case of low velocities we have laminar flow with a high degree of correlation between the velocities of neighboring gas masses. If we increase the velocities, there will be a sudden change into the turbulent case with smaller correlation. The governing quantity is the Reynolds number,

$$R_e = \frac{lw}{\lambda v} \quad \begin{cases} < 3000 \text{ for laminar flow} \\ > 3000 \text{ for turbulence} \end{cases} \tag{1}$$

Here l is the characteristic length scale within the flow, w is the velocity difference over distance l, λ is the mean free path of the molecules, and v is the velocity of sound. The turbulent state can be divided into two cases: the subsonic one and the supersonic one, determined by the Mach number

$$M = \frac{w}{v} \quad \begin{cases} < 1 \text{ subsonic} \\ > 1 \text{ supersonic} \end{cases} \tag{2}$$

The degree of internal correlation of the gas velocities can be measured by comparing the velocities v_1 and v_2 at two points in the gas, which are separated by the distance l. We define $w = [\langle (v_1 - v_2)^2 \rangle]^{1/2}$ and write

$$w = cl^{s_0} \tag{3}$$

In the case of homogeneity and isotropy c and s_0 are constants, except

193

Table 1

State of motion	R_e	M	s_0
Laminar	<3000	} <1	1
Turbulent, subsonic			1/3
			(for $M \ll 1$)
Turbulent, supersonic	>3000	} >1	?
Uncorrelated shock fronts			0

that s_0 in general might depend on l. The constant c is a scale factor for the velocity differences, and the exponent s_0 is a measure of the degree of correlation. For laminar flow $s_0 = 1$, and in case of incompressible turbulence ($M \ll 1$) $s_0 = 1/3$. Later on we shall discuss the assumption that $M > 1$ might lead to a field of uncorrelated shock fronts, and in this case the vanishing correlation would demand $s_0 = 0$.

Astronomical examples. The values of R_e and M were roughly estimated for some interesting objects and are shown in Table 2. The Reynolds numbers always indicate the turbulent case. The Mach numbers lie within the range $0.1 \cdots 10$, and in five out of seven examples we have $M \geqslant 1$.

Table 2

	R_e	M
Sun		
Photosphere	10^9	0.3
Chromosphere	10^7	1
Galaxy, large scale	10^7	10
Interstellar matter		
H II	10^9	1
H I	10^5	10
Orion nebula		
$l = 2$ pc	10^9	1
$l = 0.005$ pc	10^5	0.1

We want to emphasize that the astrophysically most interesting state of motion is the case of *supersonic turbulence*, and that there is an urgent need for a usable treatment of this state.

Theory. Up to now only the case of the *incompressible* turbulence could be treated sufficiently. We may visualize the turbulent case as a hierarchy: The largest elements of length l_1 are divided into a small number of smaller elements of length l_2, which again are divided into the same number of still smaller elements of length l_3, and so on, until we reach the smallest elements, where $R_e \approx 3000$.† The energy of elements l_i is dissipated by turbulent friction and goes into the next smaller elements l_{i+1}. This dissipation (energy per volume and time) is

$$S_i = \tfrac{1}{3}\rho w_i^3 / l_i \qquad (4)$$

and the so-called "similarity hypothesis" yields $S_i = $ const and we arrive at the Kolmogoroff law,

$$w \propto l^{1/3} \qquad (5)$$

or, in our previous notation, $s_0 = 1/3$. If the turbulence is not supported (by a steady input of energy into the largest elements), then the velocities of the largest elements decay as

$$w(t) = \frac{w(t_0)}{1 + (w(t_0)/3l)(t - t_0)} \qquad (6)$$

No such theory exists for larger Mach numbers. It might be hoped that the above equations still are usable approximations as long as $M < 1$; but in the case of supersonic turbulence ($M \geqslant 1$), in which we are most interested, there must occur a new phenomenon, the shock front, which alters the whole picture completely.

Let us consider a plane velocity wave superimposed on an otherwise homogeneous medium (Fig. 1). During a short time t, the surrounding gas travels the distance $u_0 t$, but the top of the wave travels $(u_0 + w)t$. Thus the rear part of the wave gets flatter, while the front part has the tendency to steepen up, finally into a discontinuous shock front, if not counteracted by the increasing pressure of the compressed front part. A more thorough treatment shows that such waves always will build up shock fronts if the velocity differences w are larger than the velocity of sound in the undisturbed medium, which means if the Mach number is larger than one. Therefore, a gas in the state of supersonic turbulence *must* contain shock fronts in large numbers.

In the incompressible case, the energy was dissipated from larger elements into smaller ones, and so in a similar way for elements of all sizes. But shock fronts are able to dissipate directly into heat, and they even will radiate if hot enough. There is no reason for a similarity

---

† As described by an old poem:
　　The large whirls have little whirls to feed on their velocity,
　　The little whirls have smaller whirls and so on to viscosity.

hypothesis, and therefore no theoretical treatment of the supersonic case was possible.

We might try to guess the influence of shock fronts on the Kolmogoroff law. In the incompressible case, each moving element pushes the elements ahead of it, which yields a certain correlation of the velocities. But shock fronts travel faster than sound, there is no "warning" ahead of the front, and therefore the correlation must decrease. If shock fronts are the dominating phenomenon, one might consider $s_0 = 0$ as a working hypothesis.

Experiments. Experiments with supersonic, steady turbulence are not possible. The dissipated energy finally goes into heat and increases the temperature of the gas. In the incompressible case, the level of the thermal energy $(\sim v^2)$ is so much higher than that of the kinetic energy $(\sim w^2)$ that the increase of the temperature does not need much attention. This is completely different in the supersonic case, where the kinetic energy is higher than the thermal one. According to formula (4) we need only the time $3l/2w$ to dissipate all the present kinetic energy into heat. This means: If we have a container with gas and we stir the gas, say, two times with Mach two, then this gas becomes so hot that the velocity of sound will exceed the stirring velocity, and we again have $M < 1$.

Supersonic turbulence (in a steady state) is possible only if the dissipated heat is brought away quickly enough. There is only one mechanism known for this task—radiation. But the radiation of gases becomes appreciable only at, say, 10,000°, and as long as we cannot experiment with gases of this temperature, there will be no experiments with supersonic turbulence.

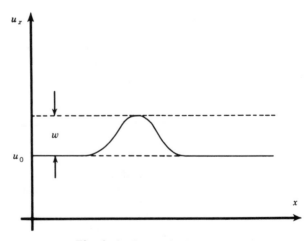

Fig. 1. A plane velocity wave.

Astronomical observations. Supersonic turbulence is one of the phenomena, like the degeneracy of matter, which cannot be handled in terrestrial laboratories but can be studied on astronomical objects. One method of doing so is to measure the radial velocities of a large number of points in a highly turbulent galactic emission nebula, to build the velocity differences of any two points, and to plot these differences as a function of the mutual distance of the two points. The conditions are here somewhat different from those leading to formula (3), because we observe only one component of the velocity, and we integrate over the line of sight within the nebula. But this integration can be treated mathematically. If we call $u(\Lambda)$ the rms difference of the observed radial velocities of two points at distance Λ, and R the geometrical depth at the optical-depth one (Fig. 2), the integration then yields

$$u(\Lambda) \sim \Lambda^s \tag{7}$$

with

$$s = s_0 \qquad \text{for } \Lambda \gg R$$
$$= s_0 + \tfrac{1}{2} \qquad \text{for } \Lambda \ll R$$

In the intermediate range ($\Lambda \approx R$) the function $u(\Lambda)$ is obtained numerically. The only object for which a large number of radial velocity measurements have been made is the Orion nebula. Wilson, Münch, Flather, and Coffeen have measured the radial velocities with a multislit spectrograph

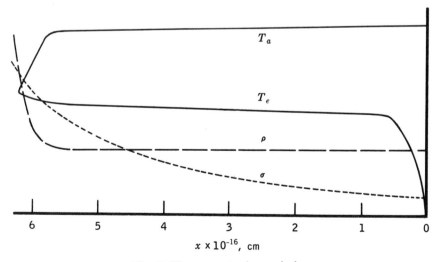

Fig. 2. The geometry in a nebula.

(30 slits) in three spectral lines, altogether a material of 40,000 velocities. In a preliminary analysis, Münch found good agreement with an analysis I had performed some years ago with a small number of older measurements. But the new material reaches to much smaller distances Λ, and this continuation could no longer be explained by the formula for incompressible turbulence with $s_0 = 1/3$. And the old discrepancy I had found in my first paper, that the observed line width was about three times larger than the one derived theoretically from the turbulence model, was still worse in Münch's analysis. I have the impression, however, that a model of the nebula containing shock fronts might be able to explain the observations.

A thorough analysis of the whole material is an extremely tedious task, but fortunately I got enough assistance in Green Bank to bring all of the material on punched tape. Up to now, all the necessary machine calculations of the analysis are finished. But quite a number of strange effects showed up, and at the moment I am not able to tell whether some striking differences between the center and the outer parts of the nebula are observational effects or whether they must be explained physically. I hope to continue on this subject until some reliable results can be told.

Teamwork on Strong Shock Fronts

The task. We have seen in the previous section that the state of supersonic turbulence is of extreme importance in astrophysics, but no satisfactory treatment of this state has been possible. A well-developed theory exists only about the incompressible case; this theory cannot be extended to the supersonic case mainly because of the appearance of shock fronts. Experiments with supersonic turbulence are not possible, because one would need strong radiation to bring the generated heat away quickly enough, which would demand extremely high temperatures. Astronomical observations might give some hints about this important state of motion, but observations alone, with no theory to compare them with, cannot tell very much in this case, not to mention the difficulties of their interpretation. Because of this situation, a team was started some years ago under von Weizsäcker to prepare the way for a theory of supersonic turbulence, beginning with the *details* of strong shock fronts and their interaction. The working program was the following:

1. The development of a single, strong, unstationary front, moving into a homogeneous region.

2. The radiation of the front and the effect on the distribution of temperature and velocity behind the front.

3. The influence of magnetic fields.

4. The interaction of two such fronts; to begin with, of fronts of the first type, later on, of fronts with radiation and magnetic fields.

5. Having solved the above details one should treat a field of statistically distributed shock fronts of all lengths and velocities, moving statistically in all directions, and interacting one with another. Given a proper input of energy, a stationary state will develop and should be described in statistical terms.

If it were possible to go successfully through this program until the last point, a theory of supersonic turbulence would be obtained. But, obviously, this is a very elaborate way to reach the goal, and the group working on it was dissolved before reaching it. But quite a number of single problems had been solved successfully and even a very rough treatment of the fifth question was tried. This group consisted of: von Weizsäcker, Crone, von Hagenow, Häfele, Hain, Hertweck, von Hoerner, Lüst, and Meyer. In a final paper [*Fortschr. Physik*, **6**, 375, 1958] I have given a summarizing report about 10 published and 5 unpublished papers of this group.

There are two reasons for again drawing your attention to this work. To begin with, some of our results might be useful but unknown to one or the other. But first of all, it is still to be hoped that the whole project might be taken up and completed by some other group which feels the need for understanding supersonic turbulence strong enough to do something about it. It is indeed a tedious amount of work, but certainly it would be worthwhile if successful.

The single, unstationary strong front (Hain, von Hoerner). Starting with arbitrary and very different initial distributions of velocity, temperature, and pressure behind a strong front, the Eulerian partial differential equations of motion were integrated by a method of characteristics. If no strong forces are pushing from behind, all of the different initial distributions approximate after a short time one and the same final distribution. This final *standard solution* is time-independent apart from its scale factors. Some examples are drawn in Fig. 3.

The most striking feature of this standard solution is the fact that the distribution of the velocity behind the front is almost linear over the distance x from the front. For all practical purposes, the following approximations can be used (capital letters = functions of time):

$$u(x, t) = A + Bx$$

$$p(x, t) = C\rho^{0.821} \qquad (8)$$

$$\rho(x, t) = D(1 + Bx/9A)^{-3}$$

Many other streaming processes also showed a strong tendency to approximate a velocity distribution linear in space. Therefore, the class of linear solutions of the Eulerian equations was investigated separately (von

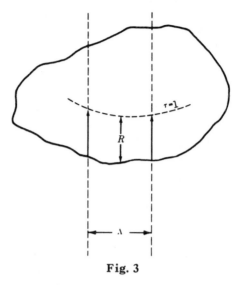

Fig. 3

Hoerner). The solution is obtained in analytical form and may serve as an approximation for many hydrodynamical problems.

In another approach, the problem of the standard solution was treated analytically (Häfele). It turned out to be a homology solution of the Guderley type. The velocity of the front decays according to

$$U_f(t) = \frac{\text{const}}{(t - t_0)^k} \tag{9}$$

where k is the so-called homology parameter. It turned out that only one value of $k = k_0$ leads to physically meaningful solutions. The value of k_0 was calculated for various specific heat ratios γ, with results as shown in Table 3. The velocity behind the front is *exactly* linear if $\gamma = 1.4$. Some

Table 3

γ	k_0
1.1	0.431
1.4	0.400
5/3	0.389
2.8	0.373

efforts have been made to prove the stability of this homology solution (Häfele, Meyer), but this should be continued.

Strong front with radiation (Hertweck). The loss of energy by radiation has been calculated and the results were applied to cosmical conditions. If, for example, the medium before the front has the parameters: density = 1 atom/cm³, temperature = 100°K, ionization = 1 per cent, and if the Mach number = 85 (front velocity = 100 km/sec), one gets the following result. Directly at the front (of a thickness of few mean free paths) the temperature of the atoms is $T_A = 240,000°K$; the temperature of the electrons is less by the mass factor m_H/m_e and amounts to $T_e = 130°K$. The more energy the electrons gain, the more they lose, until an equilibrium of $T_e = 21,000°K$ is reached at about 10^{16} cm behind the front. In the following region, the atom temperature drops very slowly and the electron temperature increases the same way; the density stays about constant, and the ionization increases exponentially. But at 6×10^{16} cm behind the front a very rapid change of all quantities begins over a thin compression region of about 10^{15} cm (500 mean free paths) (Fig. 4). A comparison of these calculated results with observations of the Cygnus nebula and with experiments in shock tubes gave satisfactory agreement.

The isothermal front (von Hagenow). If radiation plays a dominating role, the radiative exchange of energy tries to make the temperature alike at all places. The isothermal front therefore was treated as the limiting case for very strong radiation. In this case, one has not to care about

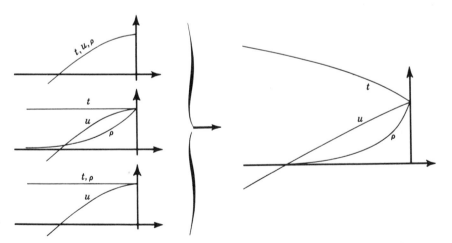

Three initial distributions ...approximate, after a short while, ...the same standard solution

Fig. 4. A strong front with radiation.

the details of the radiation, and the condition $T = $ const simplifies the calculation considerably. The development of some initial distributions has been calculated by a method of characteristics.

This investigation of the isothermal front was not completed. The preliminary results are: A time-independent standard solution does not exist (as it does in case of ordinary shock fronts) but there might exist a time-dependent one, varying as a function of the Mach number. The velocity distribution behind the front again is almost linear, and the logarithm of the density also is almost a linear function of the distance from the front.

For a complete treatment one should try to find out under which physical conditions the isothermal front becomes a good approximation, and one should include the influence of magnetic fields.

The stationary front with magnetic fields (Lüst). In the presence of a magnetic field, there are three different types of sound velocity in a plasma. These three velocities were calculated for all directions in fields of all strengths. According to the three velocities of sound, one might expect three different types of shock fronts. The equation for the density behind the front, for example, is of third degree and can have three real roots. But a discontinuous shock front can develop only if there is no "warning" ahead of the front, which means if the front velocity is higher than the highest of the three velocities of sound; and in this case there is only one real root. Therefore, probably only one type of shock front is actually possible in a plasma.

Interaction of two fronts (Hain). One of the most important questions with respect to the original task (supersonic turbulence) is the interaction of two fronts. One should calculate the interaction for fronts of all strengths and all directions, first without complications, later on with magnetic fields and with radiation, in order to find simple and general approximative descriptions of the results, descriptions which finally could be used for the statistical treatment of a field of fronts.

Only a first step was undertaken in this direction. A number of interactions (head-on collision and overtaking) were calculated for two plane, parallel, strong, unstationary fronts, and with various ratios of their front velocities. A short time after an overtaking collision, the resulting distributions approximate the standard solution. In case of a head-on collision, some general rules have been found but these would need further confirmation. In all cases, the created velocity distributions are again almost linear in space.

Statistical field of fronts (Crone). The investigations described above about the details of shock fronts are very far from being complete. Nevertheless, an extremely simplified model of a field of fronts was treated by a Monte Carlo method, in order to get a qualitative feeling about the way in which (and the conditions under which) this model will settle into an equilibrium, about the influence of the input of energy, and about the proper terms in which to describe the results.

This model was two-dimensional and contained three types of objects: shock fronts, discontinuities, and rarefaction waves. Each of these objects has three essential parameters: velocity (in the x direction), length (in the y direction), and age [t_0 according to formula (9)]. They are stored in a "list of objects present." The calculation process consists of the following steps: Two objects are chosen out of the list by chance (random numbers); the probability of their interaction is calculated according to their parameters; a random number is generated and is compared with the probability; if the number is higher, nothing happens and the next two objects are chosen; if the number is smaller, an interaction takes place; the resulting new objects and their parameters are calculated and are entered into the list; the two old objects are canceled from the list; the most probable time interval between the last two interactions is calculated and is added to the proper time of the model. In regular intervals, the distribution and the average are calculated for certain quantities as velocity, length, and energy. The input of energy was taken care of by putting long, quick new fronts into the list in statistical time intervals. If the Mach number of an object has decayed below 1.5, the object is deleted. If, by an interaction, an object is created below a certain minimum length, the object is deleted, too. This last point, in a very crude way, takes care of the disturbing influence of the edges in case of fronts limited in space.

This model contains a number of free parameters. The most essential one turned out to be the mean collision time divided by the age of the new fronts which take care of the energy input. If this ratio goes to zero, no aging takes place, all change is due to interactions, and only the objects below the minimum length are canceled from the list. If the ratio goes to infinity, no interaction takes place, all change is due to aging (decay of velocity), and only the objects with Mach numbers below 1.5 are canceled. A number of models with more realistic intermediate quotients have been calculated until a final equilibrium was reached and the influence of the free parameters on the equilibrium distributions could be studied.

Maybe there is a quicker way of obtaining a theory of supersonic turbulence. The way described above is very elaborate but has a fair chance of finally leading to success. I hope very much that this problem will be taken up by someone else.

Discussion

Dr. Lin: In connection with this stability problem you were discussing, I suppose you are aware of the work of David Butler (D. S. Butler: "The Stability of Converging Spherical and Cylindrical Shock Waves," ARDE Rept. (B) 18/56,

1956) and of Cathleen Morawetz (Ph.D. thesis, New York University) on the stability of a convergent shock [the Guderley solution (see Courant and Friedrichs, "Supersonic Flow and Shock Waves," Interscience, New York, 1948, pp. 419ff.), which is analogous to your case. This stability analysis presumably would bear on your problem.

Dr. von Hoerner: Guderley had spherical symmetry, and we had a plane case. Otherwise it was the same problem. I know that Häfele, who tried to solve our stability problem, had studied this one carefully and tried to make it similar to our case, and we believed it. Later on we found some reasons to doubt the result.

Dr. Lin: Another question is whether one could apply the Guderley solution (with some generalization) to the problem Dr. Kahn discussed this morning; maybe that will give stronger discontinuities and higher speeds, and perhaps tie up the solution with the point brought up by Dr. Spitzer.

Dr. Strömgren: I would like to return for a moment to Dr. Lin's question. Of course we cannot expect an answer here today. But I am sure that it should be further explored. If we look at the situation we are faced with now, in the field of application of the theory to the interstellar medium, then we have the approach that was discussed. We also have an approach that was inspired by the investigations of the structure and kinematics. After all, in our surroundings we have a good deal of information from the present state of interstellar matter, the clouds, their properties, and velocities. I am thinking of what began with Burger's investigations and continued with Kahn's work, not only the work he has reported today but also previous work, on the collisions of these idealized clouds. I am sure that further exploration of the question that Dr. Lin raised—of the relation of the two approaches—would be valuable.

Dynamics of bright-rim structures

S. R. Pottasch

Diffuse nebulae, or H II regions, are generally roughly spherical in shape, with a diameter of about 20 pc. Within these nebulae, or near their edges, are located the bright-rim structures, which have these common characteristics:

1. They seem to consist of dark matter, i.e., matter that absorbs the light from behind it.

2. They are bordered by a very bright rim on the side facing the exciting star.

3. These structures seem to "point" in the direction of the exciting star.

4. They have a characteristic size of about 1 pc.

An example of one of these structures, located in the diffuse nebula IC 1396, is shown in Fig. 1. The exciting star is located in the direction the rim seems to be pointing, and the bright rim is located on this side. Notice that there is a very sharp transition between the dark matter and the bright rim on the inner side of the rim. Probably the sharpness is as much as the seeing will allow, so that the transition region is smaller than several thousand astronomical units. On the other side of the rim the brightness falls off much more gradually until it merges with the general intensity of the nebula.

In addition it can readily be seen that the whole structure is blocking the star light from behind it. This absorption probably puts a lower limit on the density in these regions of about 10^5 atoms/cm^3.

These structures are associated with the exciting stars. If you draw a line through the axis of symmetry of this structure, in general this line

Fig. 1. Example of a bright-rim structure in the diffuse nebula IC 1396, taken with the 200-inch telescope at Mt. Palomar.

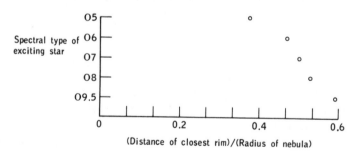

Fig. 2. The spectral type of the exciting star plotted against the position of the rim in the nebula.

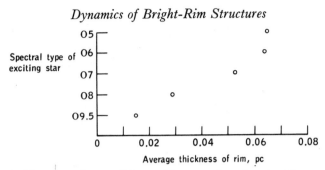

Fig. 3. The spectral type of the exciting star plotted against the average thickness of the bright rims.

will pass very close to the exciting star. This is the "pointing" effect which has been mentioned.

Other evidence that the bright rims are associated with the exciting star of the nebula is shown in Figs. 2 and 3, which summarize data for over 100 bright-rim structures in 17 diffuse nebulae. In Fig. 2 the spectral type of the exciting star is plotted against the position of the rim in the nebula, while in Fig. 3 the average thickness of the rims for each spectral type is plotted. There is a definite relationship. It is clear, I think, that the exciting star plays an important role in the development of these structures.

In order to further study the development of these objects, they were divided into five groups, according to their shape. The key to this division (or classification) is given in Fig. 4. The rim labeled *G* is very similar to the globules observed by Bok, and is the only one of the five categories where the structure appears to be "floating" rather than "anchored" to some larger mass.

Table 1 shows how the different shapes vary with the observed parameters. The flatter rims are located, on the average, much further from the exciting star than the more pointed rims. Likewise the thickness and the density in the rims indicate that the rims form a continuous sequence, with the pointed rims and globules being five times as dense as the flatter rims (the density has been determined from the extent of the ionized rim, the same consideration Strömgren used to determine the density in the H II region). The flat rims are also larger than the pointed rims. The most

Fig. 4. The key to the classification of the bright-rim structures referred to in the text.

Table 1
Properties of Rims

Shape	Number observed	Median distance from exciting star, pc	Median thickness of rim, pc	Average density of rim, cm^{-3}	Median length of rim, pc
1	21	8.9	0.057	206	2.85
2	30	6.4	0.049	360	2.26
3	28	3.9	0.034	660	0.95
4	12	2.9	0.034	1190	0.85
G	7	2.6	0.023	1235	0.44

pointed rims and the globules have very similar characteristics, which is reasonably good evidence that they are actually associated, and that these different-shaped rims form a single evolutionary sequence.

If these rims form an evolutionary sequence, and it is further assumed that the H II regions are in expansion with at least a modest velocity (1 km/sec), then it is clear that the most pointed rims are the oldest, because they are located closest to the exciting star (where the H II region first passed). This at least indicates relative ages for these objects. Absolute ages could be computed roughly if one knew the expansion rate accurately, but this is not known today.

Since it appears very likely that ionizing radiation plays an important role in the evolution of a rim, we must inquire into the effect of ionizing radiation on dark matter. This was discussed this morning by Dr. Kahn. In particular it seems likely to associate the D-critical condition with the bright rim (ionization front), for if conditions were not D-critical then either there is too little radiation to support this condition and the dark matter will expand until this condition is reached, or there is more radiation incident than is necessary to support the D-critical condition, but in this case conditions will remain D-critical at the ionization front and a shock wave will precede the ionization front into the dark matter. We can rule out the possibility of R-type conditions simply by noting that the ionizing radiation has more rapidly penetrated the rest of the H II region.

The question of actually proving that the bright rim is a D-critical ionization front is more difficult. The first attempts in this direction were discussions of the thickness of the observed rim and the falloff of H$_\alpha$ brightness from the rim. These discussions were made on the basis of the one-dimensional case discussed by Dr. Kahn in 1954. He considers the solution of the equations of conservation of mass, momentum, and energy. This last equation is difficult because it is necessary to take account of the cooling on both sides of the rim. Recently Dr. Spitzer has taken the position that it is not necessary to discuss the detailed mechanism of cooling, but merely to state that the temperature reaches equilibrium quickly, and then to assume values for an equilibrium temperature on each side of the rim. Such an approximation probably gives useful results.

Since the three-dimensional character of the rim is necessary for an adequate description, the one-dimensional solutions were adapted to the three-dimensional geometry. Then the predicted brightness as a function of distance from the edge of the dark matter can be calculated and compared with observation. Qualitative agreement is obtained, but the observations do not yet allow a quantitative comparison (the greatest difficulties are absolute calibration and separation of the H_α from the [N II] forbidden nitrogen lines).

One may try to predict the thickness of the rim and compare this with observation. We have assumed that the thickness will be measured when the brightness falls to 2/3 of its maximum value. This gives good agreement with the observations of the variation of thickness with the spectral type of the exciting star.

A more direct method of obtaining evidence that the conditions which obtain at the ionization front are D-critical is to actually observe the velocity of the ionized matter with respect to the dark matter; in the D-critical condition the ionized matter should be moving away with the speed of sound in the ionized matter.

We cannot measure the proper motion because the material is immediately replaced and the configuration of the whole structure changes only as the ionization front movesin to the dark matter with a speed predicted to be less than 1 km/sec, which is not observable at the present time.

Thus we must attempt to determine the motion by measuring the radial velocity. If we assume that the bright-rim structure is in the plane of the sky (and since it is observed at all, it is likely to be close to this plane), the shift of radial velocity should be observed in the material between us and the dark matter, moving away from the rim toward us. The light from the material on the other side of the dark matter is absorbed before reaching us. A systematic attempt to measure this velocity has been made by G. Courtès and Cruvellier of the Observatory of Marseille and myself in recent months.

What we have done is to take a picture of the rim through an interferometer. We can expect to observe a radial velocity shift by observing a shift in the interference ring when it crosses the bright-rim structure. It should be a deformed sine wave, and for the interferometer we have used, where the spacing between rings amounts to 70 km/sec, the maximum amplitude of the deformation should amount to 20 per cent of the inter-ring spacing.

We have found such an effect in the central regions of the diffuse nebula NGC 6611. Figure 5 shows a 200-inch picture of the object. When the nebula is observed with the help of the interferometer, the deformation of the rings, especially in the larger rim, is noticeable even

Fig. 5. The central regions of the diffuse nebula NGC 6611 show several examples of bright-rim structures.

to casual inspection. This effect was first noted by Courtès in 1954. Detailed measurements of the velocity shift bear out these first impressions in detail, as is shown in Table 2. The second and third columns of this

Table 2
Observed Velocities of the Ionized Gas Relative to the Ionization Front

Region	Velocity of deformation, km/sec	Velocity of surrounding region, km/sec	Velocity of ionized gas, km/sec
Large trunk	−0.8	13.0	13.8
Small trunk	−0.7	13.0	13.7
Large dark area	6.5	18.6	12.1

table give the absolute values of the radial velocity in the deformation (maximum value) across the dark matter and the velocity in the rings surrounding the dark matter. The last column gives the difference between these two velocities, which is the velocity of the ionized gas with respect to the surrounding matter. In all three areas measured the result is the same: The ionized material moves away from the rim with a speed of 13.2 ± 1.5 km/sec. This corresponds to a speed of sound at a temperature slightly greater than $10,000°$, and verifies that the situation at the bright rim is indeed D-critical.

If this is true, can one say anything about the further evolution of the rims? One can, at least, make a prediction of what the density of the neutral gas will be in the dark structure behind the rim. This depends on the radiation field, so we will assume an "average" exciting star with a temperature of $38,000°K$ and a radius of 10 solar radii. The radiation depends also on the distance from the exciting star, and we use the average distances of the five different rim shapes. The resultant densities are given in Table 3, the third column of which gives the density of the ionized matter at the rim and the fourth column the density of neutral matter in the dark structure.

These latter densities are consistent with the fact that light cannot pass through the dark structure. For comparison, column six of Table 3 gives the density for which an isothermal sphere is gravitationally unstable, assuming radii given in column five (from measurements of bright-rim sizes). Notice that the predicted density of neutral material in the rim is higher than that which is gravitationally unstable. This suggests that eventually the entire bright-rim structure "dissolves" by gravitational contraction.

Table 3
Predicted Densities in the Bright-Rim Structure

Shape	Distance from exciting star, pc	Density of ionized matter, cm^{-3}	Density of neutral matter (dark structure), cm^{-3}	R_c, radius of curvature, cm	Density for which an isothermal sphere is gravitationally unstable, cm^{-3}
G	2.5	1200	1.8×10^6	4×10^{17}	2.6×10^5
4	3	950	1.3	5	1.7×10^5
3	4	620	0.8	7.5	7.5×10^4
2	6	450	0.6	10.5	3.8×10^4
1	9	280	0.26	17	1.5×10^4

Discussion

Dr. von Hoerner: What are the masses included in these structures?

Dr. Pottasch: Between 50 and 500 solar masses.

Dr. Spitzer: While I gather that there are no computations along this line, I would be doubtful whether one could still get this agreement between theory and observation, which I think is really quite impressive, if one assumed that the initial magnetic field were 2×10^{-5} gauss. For example, the densities in the last column couldn't be anything like that large if the initial density before the shock went by was small. One would only get a very mild increase in density.

Dr. Pottasch: Clearly the observed densities in many cases are of this order, anyway—that is, from the fact that you can't see through the rim.

Dr. Oort: That gives only a lower limit, doesn't it?

Dr. Pottasch: It is only a lower limit. It must be greater than about 10^5 cm^{-3}.

Dr. Spitzer: Then this case can perhaps be regarded in almost the same category as the Zeeman effect measures in giving a rather good upper limit on the magnetic field intensity.

Dr. G. R. Burbidge: Can we decide what this upper limit is?

Dr. Spitzer: I am sure it can be done from these data.

Dr. Oort: Wouldn't the case be very similar to that of the dense clouds that were considered in the Zeeman experiments?

Dr. Spitzer: There I think the picture offered by Dr. Woltjer was that we had a magnetic field of 2×10^{-5} gauss but that it was in opposite directions along the line of sight. That possibility does not help here. One assumes that this density of 10^6 atoms/cm³ has been produced by the shock that has preceded the ionization front. If you make that assumption, and also assume that the magnetic field before was 10^{-5} gauss, you can't possibly compress the material by a factor of 10^4. That would give a magnetic field of a tenth of a gauss; the corresponding pressure would be out of this world as far as interstellar space is concerned.

Dr. Oort: It is the same with 10^{-6} gauss.

Dr. Spitzer: No. A field of 10^{-6} gauss is easy, because the gas pressure and the magnetic pressure are comparable. You don't violate equilibrium if you have regions in which there is no magnetic field, while with the field of 2×10^{-5} gauss you have to have a magnetic field everywhere to support the material, unless you somehow start off with a much higher density than we have been talking about. All these remarks are rather speculative. One ought to put in the numbers, which I haven't done.

Dr. Woltjer: If one argues that when star formation takes place in a certain region there arises a moment when the magnetic field can slip out, as is essentially assumed by Mestel and you, couldn't one then conceive that just in the process of star formation one creates a region in which there is a rather small magnetic field?

Dr. Spitzer: That may be possible.

Dr. Woltjer: Also in these regions there is very high interstellar absorption. One might think that ambipolar diffusion would be much more there than in any other region. Apart from the question of ambipolar diffusion, if you start out with a cloud with an irregular magnetic field it would compress along the field lines and force the gas to the same densities as considered here. So you would expect all kinds of curved structures.

Dr. Spitzer: If you had a uniform field would not the appearance of the clouds be different?

Dr. Strömgren: How large are the contraction ages of these regions once they have reached high densities?

Dr. Kahn: Of the order of $(4\pi G\rho)^{-1/2}$.

Dr. Strömgren: You also mentioned the time scale. How does that come out?

Dr. Pottasch: Then you have to make some assumption as to the speed of these regions. If you say they are moving at 5 km/sec then the ages of these things shouldn't be more than at the most 10^6 years, perhaps less.

Dr. Schwarzschild: What exactly determines the present density in the dark matter?

Dr. Pottasch: It is a pressure equilibrium between the ionized matter and the dark matter, effectively—of that order at least.

Dr. Schwarzschild: What is the guess of the origin of the elephant trunks to start with? Initial inhomogeneities or instability?

Dr. Pottasch: It is just a guess. I would say initial inhomogeneities, but it might be an instability. Assume an initial inhomogeneity. Consider what happens on a line connecting the source of radiation with the center of the region. The matter on the outer edge of the region nearer the star will be compressed toward the center until a D-critical density is reached, after which there will be no further large-scale motions of the gas. But on a line connecting the exciting star with points to the side of the center, the density of matter will not easily become great enough to effect the D-critical condition. Certainly at some distance from the center of the region, the density will never become great enough to allow a stable D-critical condition, and the matter at these points will remain in motion, with respect to the center of the region. This action can be thought of as an etching effect of the radiation, which will produce an elongated shape pointing in the direction of the exciting star.

Dr. Schwarzschild: Can one make an estimate of what fraction of the initial gas mass is now in these condensed trunks?

Dr. Pottasch: One per cent, I would say.

Dr. Blaauw: That is the lower limit. There may be regions where the star density is much higher; since star formation did take place in the region considered it is plausible that there are also densities intermediate between what is necessary for star formation and the values quoted.

Dr. Pottasch: Right. In other words the density originally might be 10^3, although now we only measure 10^2 or something like that. And in these inhomogeneities it might not have been much more than 10^3 or 10^4 originally.

Dr. Blaauw: Doesn't that mean that instead of 1 per cent you could get 10 per cent, or even more?

Dr. Strömgren: I take it that initially the inhomogeneity has to be high enough and the density sufficiently different from that of the surroundings for the structure to withstand the ionizing radiation.

Dr. Pottasch: Yes. I would say ten times the average density would be adequate.

Dr. Field: Could any of these objects be observed in 21-cm emission?

Dr. Pottasch: 100 solar masses? If you had a narrow-enough beam width I would imagine you could. Their angular width is of the order of a few minutes of arc.

Dr. Oort: All the hydrogen will probably be molecular, in these very dense things. If it condenses on the solid particles it will become molecular in a very short time at these densities. So there is no probability that you would observe anything in the 21-cm line. That is what happens in the dense Taurus clouds, for instance. You don't see any 21-cm radiation in the densest parts of these clouds at all.

Dr. Strömgren: With our present knowledge of these structures, if we have phenomena of this kind, would we always recognize them on good photographs of the bright rim?

Dr. Pottasch: If it was in or near the plane, perpendicular to the line of sight and passing through the exciting star, we probably would recognize it; although there is still a question of why you don't see things like this in the Orion nebula. I would say that if it was present in Orion we would notice it.

Dr. Blaauw: If you had a suitable background. You need a luminous background to see them.

Large-scale dynamics
of interstellar matter

The motion of gas in barred spiral galaxies

Kevin H. Prendergast

It is usual to make a number of simplifying assumptions about the physical state of the gas in ordinary spirals which may not be true for barred spirals. The most important of these are: (1) that the system is in a quasi-steady state, (2) that the underlying mass distribution is essentially axisymmetric, and (3) that the gravitational attraction of the whole galaxy is the dominant force acting on the gas. The pressure gradient, the force exerted by the magnetic field, and other complications are customarily neglected in the first instance. Then the rotational velocity of the gas is given by

$$\frac{V^2}{\varpi} = \frac{\partial \psi}{\partial \varpi} \tag{1}$$

where ψ is the gravitational potential and ϖ is the distance to the axis of symmetry.

The situation is certainly not so simple in barred spirals. In the first place, if a barred spiral is in a steady state at all it can only be so in a coordinate system rotating with the bar, and the bar must rotate with constant angular velocity. Then the galaxy will have the same three-dimensional configuration at all times, but it will be seen in different orientations. Also, there is no reason to believe that the gravitational field is even approximately axisymmetric in barred spirals: the light distribution, for example, is certainly not axisymmetric. As for the pressure and magnetic fields, it may still be true that they can be ignored in the first approximation. We shall assume, then, that the main difference between ordinary and barred spirals is that an ordinary spiral has an axisymmetric gravitational field, and a barred spiral does not. This is not to say that barred spirals are altogether devoid of symmetry properties. They certainly have a plane of symmetry, and it is also probable that $\rho(\mathbf{r}) \approx \rho(-\mathbf{r})$.

Under these circumstances the velocity of the gas with respect to a coordinate system rotating with the bar is governed by the equation

$$\mathbf{u} \cdot \text{grad } \mathbf{u} + 2\boldsymbol{\omega} \times \mathbf{u} = - \text{grad } \psi - \boldsymbol{\omega} \times (\boldsymbol{\omega} \times \mathbf{r}) \qquad (2)$$

where ω is the angular velocity of the bar. The first term in this equation is the usual inertial term, and the second, third, and fourth terms are the Coriolis, gravitational, and centrifugal forces, respectively. Since the gravitational field is no longer axisymmetric, we cannot expect to have purely circular motions; indeed, Eq. (2) has no such solutions.

Equation (2) may be put in the form

$$\mathbf{u} \cdot \text{grad } \mathbf{u} + 2\boldsymbol{\omega} \times \mathbf{u} = \text{grad } \Omega \qquad (3)$$

where

$$\Omega = -\psi + \tfrac{1}{2}|\boldsymbol{\omega}|^2 \varpi^2 \qquad (4)$$

may be thought of as the potential for the combined gravitational and centrifugal forces. The exact form of Ω depends on the mass distribution, but the surfaces $\Omega =$ constant have certain properties that are independent of the details of this distribution. Near the nucleus the gravitational force should be at least as large as the centrifugal force, and grad Ω should be directed more or less toward the center. At great distances from the system the centrifugal force dominates the gravitational force, and grad Ω is directed radially outward. Then for a system with the symmetry of a barred spiral there should be two points (X_1 and X_2, say) near the end of the bar where these forces balance, and the forces should also balance at two other points (O_1 and O_2) symmetrically situated on a line roughly at right angles to the bar. At X_1 and X_2, Ω has saddle points, and at O_1 and O_2, Ω reaches a minimum. There is a strong analogy between the surfaces of constant Ω and the Lagrangian surfaces for the restricted problem of three bodies; the points X_1 and X_2 have the same properties as L_2 and L_3, and O_1 and O_2 correspond to the "triangle points" L_4 and L_5.

It would certainly be very difficult to find an exact solution of Eq. (3) for an Ω of this complexity, but there is a method which allows us at least to estimate the speed and direction of flow at any point. The present problem has certain analogues in meteorology, where one is also interested in the flow relative to a rapidly rotating frame of reference. The gradient wind equation—a generalization of the well-known geostrophic approximation—has been developed to treat this problem. Consider the equations of motion in a coordinate system based on the streamlines.

The conservation of momentum in the direction perpendicular to the streamline requires that

$$\frac{u^2}{R} + 2\omega u = -\frac{\partial \Omega}{\partial s} \tag{5}$$

where u is the total velocity, R is the radius of curvature of the streamline, and $\partial \Omega / \partial s$ is the force perpendicular to the streamline. The equation for the conservation of momentum along the streamline can be integrated immediately to show that the quantity

$$E = \tfrac{1}{2}u^2 - \Omega \tag{6}$$

must be a constant along any streamline. Equation (5) states that the Coriolis force plus the centrifugal force due to the motion along the curved streamline must balance the applied force. Equation (6) states that the energy is conserved along a streamline, and may be regarded either as the Jacobi integral for the present problem, or as Bernoulli's theorem. Although these results are exact consequences of Eq. (3) they are not particularly useful, since R is generally unknown. However, let us now suppose that the flow is approximately parallel to the equipotentials; in meteorology, this amounts to assuming that the wind blows along the isobars. Then we can replace R by the local radius of curvature of the curves of constant Ω, and $\partial \Omega / \partial s$ becomes the total force. These quantities are known if Ω is known, and Eq. (5) degenerates into a purely algebraic equation for **u**, with the solution

$$u = -\omega R + \left[R^2 \omega^2 - R\left(\frac{\partial \Omega}{\partial s}\right) \right]^{1/2} \tag{7}$$

This solution has been evaluated at a large number of points for an Ω appropriate to a prolate spheroidal bar rotating end over end, and the flow pattern that emerges seems fairly reasonable. There are three main eddies in the flow: one about O_1, one about O_2, and a third which encircles the whole system. The sense of circulation is the same in each of these eddies and is opposite to the direction of rotation of the system. At large distances from the origin the velocity goes to infinity: This merely reflects the rotation of the coordinate system itself, since the velocity with respect to nonrotating axes approaches the Keplerian velocity appropriate to the mass of the bar, as it should. Near the origin the velocity may also be comparable to the rotational velocity of the coordinate system. Viewed from an inertial frame, the velocity on the axis of the bar is a linear function of the distance, but it drops sharply beyond the end of the bar. Something of this sort has been observed in NGC 7479, the only barred spiral for which an extended rotation curve has yet been obtained. It is particularly interesting to consider the streamlines that intersect the bar; if matter flows along them with the computed velocity they would look like trailing arms. Finally, it can be shown that the solution given by Eq. (7) satisfies Eq. (1) when ψ is made axisymmetric. This would seem to mean that the gradient wind approximation provides a natural generalization of Eq. (1) which can be applied to barred as well as ordinary spirals.

It is possible to compute the gas density in this model. The equation of continuity,

$$\mathrm{div}(\rho\mathbf{u}) = 0 \tag{8}$$

can be integrated to give

$$\rho\mathbf{u} = \mathrm{curl}(\chi\mathbf{k}) \tag{9}$$

where $\mathbf{k}$ is a unit vector normal to the plane of the galaxy and ρ is the gas density. The stream function χ can be shown to depend only on E, and E is known from Eq. (6) once $\mathbf{u}$ has been computed. Then the density follows at once from Eq. (9), and the computations show that ρ is relatively high near the ends of the bar. Furthermore, we may suppose that ρ is low on streamlines which do not intersect the bar, since Eq. (9) says nothing about the relative density on adjacent streamlines.

There are a number of difficulties with this simple model, of course. The solution given by Eq. (7) is exact only if the equipotentials are circles or straight lines. If the radius of curvature varies rapidly (as it does in certain parts of the system) then Eq. (7) can be misleading, and can even give complex values of $\mathbf{u}$. A more general objection is that a differential equation (3) has been replaced by an algebraic one (5), and there is no provision in the solution for fitting boundary conditions. The solution that has been found resembles the θ-type barred spirals, but not all barred spirals are of this type. Presumably the galaxies with very open arms can also be described by Eq. (3), but other solutions of this equation are not easy to find. Quite aside from the fact that Eq. (3) is nonlinear, we do not know the boundary conditions. There is a further difficulty—it can be shown by examples that even if we impose smooth boundary conditions on a smooth boundary curve, Eq. (3) may have no solution which is single-valued everywhere. Now a real fluid should certainly have a well-defined velocity at every point, and if Eq. (3) predicts that it does not it must be because one of the physical assumptions leading to this equation is wrong. The way out of this dilemma appears to be to restore the pressure gradient to the equations of motion; we should then expect a shock wave to intervene before the solution becomes multivalued. Unfortunately the relevant pressure in a galaxy is provided by the random motions of the interstellar clouds, and it is not clear what is to be taken for an equation of state in this case.

General References

Kevin H. Prendergast, *Ap. J.*, **132**, 162 (1960).
E. Margaret Burbidge, G. R. Burbidge, and K. H. Prendergast, *Ap. J.*, **132**, 654 (1960).

Discussion

Dr. Strömgren: I wonder if you would have any comment regarding a comparison of this approach and the approach of B. Lindblad to barred spirals, where he considered idealized orbits.

Dr. Prendergast: To answer this question I must explain the connection between the pressure-free equations and the particle-orbit picture. The equations of hydrodynamics without the pressure terms are parabolic; that is, there is only one family of characteristics, and these characteristics are just the orbits that particles would follow in the same gravitational field. To that extent, then, the two approaches are identical. But instead of solving the pressure-free equations exactly, I used the gradient-wind approximation.

There are genuine difficulties associated with the use of the pressure-free equations—for almost any set of boundary conditions, the solution will not be single-valued everywhere. This might be all right if the ambiguity in the velocity were only a few kilometers per second, but it might easily be hundreds of kilometers per second, and that would be intolerable. In reality, of course, the pressure prevents this sort of disaster from occurring.

Gravitational resonance effects in the central layer of a galaxy

P. O. Lindblad

I should like to describe here some experiments concerning numerical computations on the dynamics of the central layer of a galaxy with the aid of an electronic computer [1].

The models of galaxies used in these computations are two-dimensional and consist of a central field of force and a certain number of mutually attracting mass points moving in this field. Owing to the circumstance that the computing time increases as the square of the number of mutually attracting points, there is a definite practical upper limit to this number, and in the present program the number of mass points could not be more than 192.

As the central force we chose the force in the galactic plane of Schmidt's model, and this is stored in the machine as an interpolation table. This force will represent the main bulk of mass of the system, that is, population II and the disk population, which is supposed to remain throughout the computations in a stationary condition with axial symmetry unperturbed by the evolution in the plane.

The mass points, which will describe almost circular orbits, more or less correspond to population I. Owing to the heavy restriction on their number, they will possess masses that range from $16 \times 10^6 \ M_\odot$ to $64 \times 10^6 \ M_\odot$.

At the start of the computations, the mass points are generally placed along a certain number of more or less well separated circular rings with circular velocities. To initiate a development we shall introduce a deformation or density variation along one of these rings. This deviation from rotational symmetry will then travel along the ring with a certain angular velocity as a perturbing wave. We have started our numerical computations with strictly bisymmetrical variations from circular symmetry, first, because this for several reasons seems to be the most natural form of variation for the main body of a galaxy, and second, because it simplifies the problem very much, and the program can take twice as many mass points.

A massive ring in a central force field like that of the Schmidt model can carry two different kinds of bisymmetrical waves by self-gravitational action. The first kind to be treated here is connected with the concept of dispersion orbits, where a dispersion orbit is defined as the configuration along which a cloud of matter will be drawn out due to the differential rotation. We shall therefore enter briefly on the theory of dispersion orbits.

If R and θ are polar coordinates with the galactic center as the origin, we can write the first-order solution for the motion of a particle that moves in an almost circular orbit with radius R_0 in the field $F(R)$,

$$R = R_0 + c \cos \kappa(t - t_0)$$

$$\theta - \theta_0 = \omega(t - t_0) - \frac{c}{R_0} \frac{2\omega}{\kappa} \sin \kappa(t - t_0)$$

where

$$\omega^2 = \frac{F(R_0)}{R_0} \quad \text{and} \quad \kappa^2 = 3\omega^2 + \left(\frac{dF}{dR}\right)_{R=R_0}$$

Thus ω and κ vary with R_0. R_0, c, t_0, θ_0 are arbitrary constants. In a co-ordinate system with angular velocity ω' we have

$$\theta - \theta_0 = (\omega - \omega')(t - t_0) - \frac{c}{R_0} \frac{2\omega}{\kappa} \sin \kappa(t - t_0)$$

As c/R_0 is small we may write

$$R = R_0 + c \cos \frac{\kappa}{\omega - \omega'}(\theta - \theta_0)$$

We introduce $n = \kappa/(\omega - \omega')$ and obtain

$$R = R_0 + c \cos n(\theta - \theta_0) \tag{1}$$

This is the shape of the orbit in the coordinate system with the angular velocity

$$\omega' = \omega - \frac{\kappa}{n}$$

A cloud of particles with somewhat differing values of R_0 will disperse along a certain configuration due to the differential rotation. If we choose ω' such that n does not vary with first-order variations of R_0, i.e.,

$$n = \frac{d\kappa}{d\omega}$$

then Eq. (1) gives the shape of the dispersion orbit. Important cases are

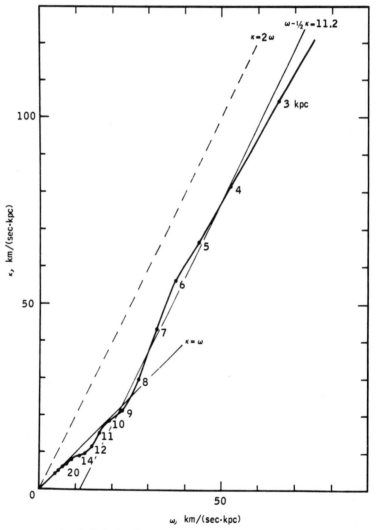

Fig. 1. Relation between ω and κ in Schmidt's model.

when n is an integer, i.e., the dispersion orbit closed and the matter thus trapped in the orbit.

The relation between ω and κ in Schmidt's model is shown in Fig. 1. The lines $\kappa = \omega$ and $\kappa = 2\omega$ that would be valid for a point mass and a homogeneous ellipsoid respectively are drawn in the figure. For large R the curve approaches the line $\kappa = \omega$ but for the inner region between $R = 3 - 10$ kpc it adheres closely to a line $\omega - (\kappa/2) = $ const. Thus n is close to 2 in this whole region and the dispersion orbits are ellipses with their centers in the center of the galaxy. Their apsidal lines all turn with the almost constant angular velocity $\omega - (\kappa/2)$.

Figure 2 shows an example of numerical computations of such a "dispersion-ring type" wave. The cross marks the galactic center and the ring consists of 48 points each with a mass of $16 \times 10^6 \, M_\odot$. The numbers in the upper-right corners give the time from the start of the computations in the unit 10^6 years. We see how the dots circle around the ring while the apsidal line turns with a much slower velocity. Owing to the law of areas we have maximum density at the vertices of the ring. After

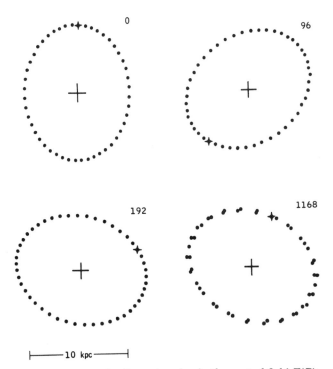

Fig. 2. Motion of a dispersion ring in the central field $F(R)$.

1168×10^6 years the ring is still well maintained. The points disperse and mix, but as the configuration is a dispersion ring, the dispersion mainly takes place along the ring that seems to possess a fairly high degree of stability, at least sufficient for our purpose.

We next ask what the influence of such a wave might be on other circular motions in the plane. A simple theoretical discussion shows that we have two cases of resonance where the perturbations will be large. One is in the region in which $\omega - (\kappa/2)$ equals the angular velocity of the wave, that is, throughout the main body of the system and especially for orbits intersecting the ring. This resonance case is of fundamental importance for the formation of such elongated dispersion rings. I shall not discuss this case here but it is treated in detail in a forthcoming paper by B. Lindblad [3].

The second resonance case appears in a region farther out in the system, where the circular angular velocity equals the angular velocity of the perturbing wave. Figure 3 shows the predicted first-order perturbations on a circular ring at that resonance distance. The direction of rotation is indicated, and the coordinate system rotates with the angular velocity of the apsidal line of the perturbing ellipse that is supposed to coincide with the vertical axes. The initially circular ring gets elongated in a direction differing 45° from the direction of elongation of the perturbing ring and with density maxima along the parts of the elongated ring where the

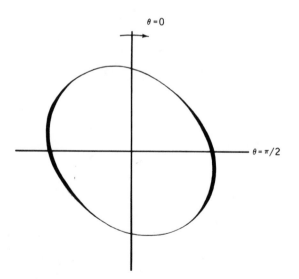

Fig. 3. Sketch of the first-order deformations of a circular ring perturbed by a bisymmetrical potential wave.

motion is outgoing in the direction of rotation. If we leave the case of maximum resonance in a direction toward the center, the angle between the apsidal lines of the perturbed and perturbing configuration gets smaller and the density maxima shift toward the ends of the major axis. If we leave the maximum resonance in the direction outward, the angle between the apsidal lines increases and the density maxima shift toward the minor axis.

This is confirmed by numerical computations (Fig. 18 in [1]). The maximum disturbance occurs around the resonance distance, which is 13 kpc from the center in this case. Possibly this region will in the end be swept clear of matter and an outer ring separated from the system. A comparison may be made with systems such as NGC 7217, in which the separation of an outer ring may be the result of a dispersion-ring type of wave in the inner region, or the surrounding ring of M 94 (cf. plates I and II in [1]).

We have also calculated the interactions between a massive ring carrying a dispersion-ring type of wave and outer massive rings, but I here want to pass directly over to the other type of waves, which can be maintained in a massive ring in a central force field of Schmidt's type.

These we shall call bar-type waves, as they probably are connected with the barred structure of spirals. The principal difference between these waves and the former ones are that they travel with an angular velocity fairly close to the circular velocity of the same region. A detailed theoretical discussion shows that two such waves are possible for one and the same ring—one with a velocity somewhat slower than the circular velocity and one somewhat faster. Owing to the law of areas the first wave will give an elongated ring with density maxima at the vertices, while the second one will give density maxima at the ends of the minor axis. To substantiate such a wave in our computations we have simply chosen a perfectly circular ring with exactly circular velocities and have then pushed the dots around the circumference of the ring slightly toward two opposite points. Two density maxima were thus created, where the density is about twice as large as at the minima. The result is that when the ring is let free it oscillates between a circular shape with uneven density distribution and an elongated shape with more even density distribution. This can be interpreted as an interference between the two waves described above, and so we have the two bar-type waves present at the same time. The action of this wave on other matter in the plane follows the same scheme as shown in Fig. 3, and the case of resonance, where the circular angular velocity equals the velocity of the wave, now occurs in the immediate neighborhood of the perturbing ring itself. Or, more exactly, the slower wave component, with density maxima at the ends of the major axis, will show resonance in a region somewhat outside the perturbing ring, and the faster wave, with density maxima at the minor axis, in a region somewhat closer to the center. As these effects now occur in the neighborhood of the wave-carrying ring itself, we get a counter-action from the perturbed region and a case of instability may be built up.

The effect of this will be seen in Fig. 4, prepared from one of the computations. This was a case where 116 mass points each of a mass of 64 million solar masses were distributed along three circles with radii 2, 4, and 6 kpc. The bisymmetrical wave is raised in the middle one. Above each configuration the time from the start is indicated in 10^6 years.

In Fig. 4 we see how the ring of 4 kpc (open circles) oscillates between circular shape with bisymmetrical density variation and elongated shape, owing to the interference of the two bar-type waves. The slower of these waves shows a marked influence on the outer ring that can be already seen clearly at 256×10^6 years. This ring gets elongated in a direction deviating $45°$ from the direction of the wave and shows concentrations of matter on the outgoing branches. This deformation in turn perturbs the ring with the initial density variation so that this gets enhanced, etc., and the whole configuration gets unstable. Around 400×10^6 years from the start the two rings join in their closest parts and break up, forming a pair of relatively long leading spiral arms. The relative motion of matter along these arms is toward the point of junction. Thus the arms get shorter until at 512×10^6 years they form two big agglomerations at both sides of the center. These agglomerations are again drawn out, owing to the differential rotation, and we get a pair of trailing arms that successively are wound up more and more. To make this clearer, the arms are filled in in the figure during this stage. At about 736×10^6 years the arms are drawn out so much that we have again a fairly continuous central layer. However, the velocity dispersion in this layer has increased.

At this stage the central ring starts to get elongated. This elongation causes a redistribution of the matter in the central layer. At first, matter collects in front of the vertices of the inner ring (832×10^6 years) and is then drawn out again as a pair of spiral arms (896×10^6 years). These spiral arms are rapidly drawn out in the field of differential rotation; the pattern gets smeared out and we end up with a model that has a fairly high velocity dispersion, where no further formation of well-defined spiral arms seems likely.

A case with a more continuous distribution of mass in the plane has been computed (Fig. 31 of [1]). We have here 5 rings with 192 mass points, which was the maximum number for this program. The mass of the mass points is half that of the preceding case, and the density wave is again introduced in the ring with radius 4 kpc. The actual perturbation is thus smaller in this case. The wave now spreads more rapidly inward and

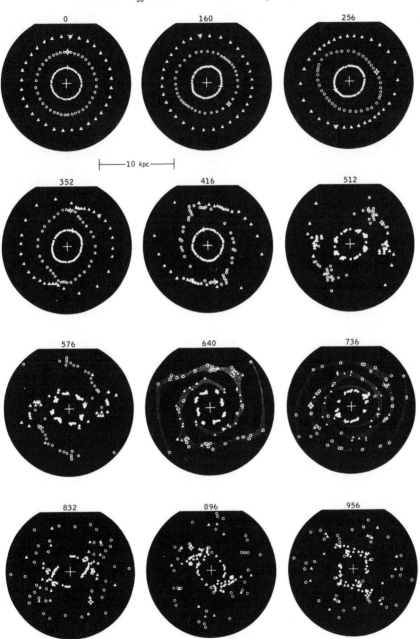

Fig 4. Evolution of a model galaxy.

outward in the system and the central layer again breaks up, forming what simulates a bar with spiral arms. These arms again are drawn into the ends of the bar and then drawn out again. We see clearly how the perturbations very soon have caused a bar-type of wave of the slower type in the innermost rings.

The picture given by these early gravitational computations may well be modified or changed by gas-dynamical or magnetohydrodynamic

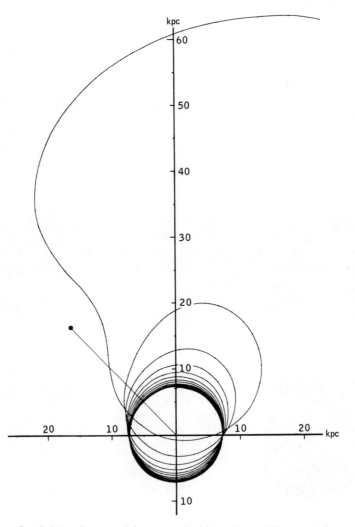

Fig. 5. Orbit of a particle in a double galaxy. The particle escapes from the system.

forces. However, it seems that the effects of gravitational resonance will play an important role and must be taken into consideration when we treat the problem of spiral formation and the evolution of galaxies.

I will just briefly mention a quite different case of gravitational resonance that we have investigated, too [2]. It concerns the possibility of ejection of matter from one component of a double galaxy, and the resonance case is the one where the angular velocity ($\omega - \kappa$) of the apsidal line of a Keplerian-type of orbit in one of the components equals the angular velocity of the components around each other.

We suppose that one component has a Schmidt type of central force field and that the other one is a point mass of the same total mass. In Fig. 5 the coordinate system turns in such a way that the point mass remains fixed at a distance, in this case of 23 kpc, from the center in the upper left quadrant. The computations show that it is possible to get an ejection of matter from a very narrow zone within the main body of the galaxy. In the orbit shown in Fig. 5 it takes 2.5×10^9 years for the particle to be ejected from an initially circular orbit. Ejections in the opposite direction also seem possible. In this way we would get a continuous stream of matter from one component in the direction of the other so that the bridge between the galaxies does not have to be stable in itself during a long time. The gas may be stripped from this stream during the passage through the ejecting galaxy, which could explain why these bridges seem to be formed of stars only.

Within the main body of a galaxy the angular velocity $\omega - \kappa$ of the apsidal lines of the Keplerian type of orbit is negative; i.e., they turn in the retrograde direction, which means that the components should revolve around each other in retrograde direction for this effect to occur. In the only case in which Zwicky and Humason have found it possible to determine the directions of motion of the bridge and the component galaxy, they actually seem to be opposite [4].

References

[1] P. O. Lindblad, *Stockholm Obs. Ann.*, **21**, 4 (1960).
[2] P. O. Lindblad, *Stockholm Obs. Ann.*, **21**, 3 (1960).
[3] B. Lindblad, *Stockholm Obs. Ann.*, **21**, 8 (1961).
[4] F. Zwicky and M. L. Humason, *Ap. J.*, **132**, 633 (1960).

Discussion

Dr. Kahn: With a slight perturbation in a uniform disk, could you get these structures formed?

Dr. Lindblad: Yes, I think so. The latter case I showed (Fig. 31 of [1]), where you have the more uniform distribution, is a step in that direction.

Dr. Prendergast: How large are the noncircular motions of this ring? About 10 to 20 km/sec?

Dr. Lindblad: You have almost circular motions all the time; the deviations actually are of that order.

Dr. Prendergast: May I ask if you have ever started a computation in which you have given each point an initial random velocity of a few kilometers per second? Does the pattern develop then or is it necessary to build in the phase relationships at the start?

Dr. Lindblad: In the program I have had you must start with a completely bisymmetrical configuration and perturbation. And I think that to study that random case I would need many more points than I can actually take in these programs, because 192 dots are still fairly few.

Dr. Lemaître: I should like to ask a question about the size of the "safety" sphere that you introduced at the beginning. I was somewhat uneasy to learn that the computation was very much dependent on the size of the "safety" sphere that you introduced.

Ed.: A long discussion followed on these "safety" spheres (regions around the point masses, where the inverse square law ceases to operate). Dr. Lindblad pointed out that they are necessary to avoid large random motions, which would otherwise result from the artificial distribution of mass in a small number of point masses.

Dr. Strömgren: How does the computing time go with the number of points, and how far would it be possible to go, increasing the number of points and reducing correspondingly the "safety" sphere that you are talking about?

Dr. Lindblad: The computing time increases as the square of the number of points. For 192 dots, one integration step, which will be about 8×10^6 years, takes about 20 minutes in the computer. So, for the second case I showed, this means a total computing time of the order of 20 hours. The 192 dots fill up the fast memory of the machine completely. To go to a larger number of points means a readministration of the whole program.

Dr. Oort: I think these computations are wonderful. It is most interesting to look at what happens if you introduce such a small irregularity. There is one thing that still worries me, and that is that most galaxies are much older than the 10^9 years at which you stopped, and still show spiral structure.

Dr. Lindblad: I think there you have two ways out. Either you have to find some mechanism, magnetic fields or such, that for some reason will make the spiral arms more permanent, or you will have to say that spiral arms are formed, destroyed, and formed again all the time; for this there was some indication in the motion picture.

Dr. Oort: But can you continue with that?

Dr. Lindblad: To be able to do this, I think you have to introduce some gas-dynamical forces, or friction, so that you can get rid of the velocity dispersion.

Dr. Oort: You also have to start new systematic irregularities in some way, presumably.

Dr. Lindblad: Yes, but I think they would perhaps be there all the time because I cannot see that you would have a perfect system.

Dr. Spitzer: I think these results are certainly most fascinating. I would assume that some of the details might be rather altered if one considered the dynamics of a gas rather than the point masses; in particular you would get damping of the motions by fluid dynamical effects. I am wondering if there is any chance that one might carry out similar integrations starting with the fluid equations. I would presume that there would be considerable similarities with what you get for the point masses, and yet there would also be large differences. But we have good reason to suspect that it is primarily the gas that gets concentrated in the spiral arm.

Dr. Lindblad: The initial configurations with which I started are more characteristic for the gas than for the older stars.

Dr. Spitzer: It would be very interesting if one could show that the dynamics of the spiral arms could be explained without any magnetic field; it is not impossible that this could be demonstrated.

Dr. Christy: If the spiral arms show up most clearly in the gas and the young stars, what is the estimated minimum age for the stars in spiral arms?

Dr. Oort: That is one of the problems that has never been studied well enough, really. But it should be one of the most urgent things in observational programs, I think.

Dr. Spitzer: You started out essentially with one Fourier mode excited. Could you in principle investigate the higher modes with your present program?

Dr. Lindblad: Yes.

Dr. Prendergast: I would like to make one remark as to whether or not the introduction of random motions would destroy the pattern. In our own galaxy, if you consider the terms in the equations of motion, other than the gravitational field of all the matter, then there are three: the random velocities, some sort of ordered magnetic field, and the self-gravitation of the gas. Unfortunately all three seem to be of the same order of magnitude. This clearly makes the problem very difficult. But the term that dominates in the end, for very large scale structures, even for low-density fluctuations, is the self-gravitation of the gas. Lindblad's model might work for that reason.

Dr. Woltjer: I noticed in your pictures that you have spirals rotating both with leading arms and trailing arms. There has, of course, been quite some argument from the observational point of view on how a spiral rotates and I don't want to go into that. But doesn't at least everybody agree that all spirals which have been observed are rotating either all with trailing arms or all with leading arms, and that it is not half of them one way and the other half the other way?

Dr. Lindblad: Yes. These structures you see depend to some extent on the very idealized initial configurations that you have. It might be that in the real situation one of these cases might be more concealed than the other.

Spiral structure

J. H. Oort

Spiral structure in galaxies is a remarkably general phenomenon. It seems that some sort of spiral structure has been formed in almost all galaxies which contain a reasonable amount of gas and which have evolved far enough for the gas to have contracted to a disk or to a bar.

As is well known, the spiral phenomenon presents itself in many very different forms. The arms can be very wide open and irregular (Sc); they can also be tightly wound and almost circular (Sa). The character is strongly correlated with the amount of old population II stars present. In the Sa spirals the regular, population II structure is very strong, in some Sc's it is almost absent, or at any rate it cannot be seen.

In systems with strong differential rotation, such as is found in all nonbarred spirals, spiral features are quite natural. Every structural irregularity is likely to be drawn out into a part of a spiral. But *this* is not the phenomenon we must consider. We must consider a spiral structure extending over the whole galaxy, from the nucleus to its outermost part, and consisting of two arms starting from diametrically opposite points. Although this structure is often hopelessly irregular and broken up, the general form of the large-scale phenomenon can be recognized in many nebulae. I am very well aware that there are many systems to which this general picture does not apply; you have seen quite a number of them in the account given by Mrs. Burbidge, and it is well to keep this, as well as the existence of the large class of barred spirals, constantly in mind. But at the moment I want to concentrate attention on those galaxies in which a more or less continuous pattern of the kind described can be discerned.

It may be practical, at least in the present stage of knowledge, to separate the problem into two parts: (*a*) How did the spiral structure originate? (*b*) How does it persist once it has originated?

With regard to (*a*), serious and interesting attempts have been made to explain spiral structure on the basis of stellar dynamics, mostly by Bertil Lindblad and his collaborators at the Stockholm Observatory. Recently these have been taken up in a novel way by Dr. Per Olaf Lindblad, who reported on them in the preceding paper.

They have elucidated a number of things that may be of basic importance for the origin of spiral structure. But in my opinion the occurrence of a more or less continuous and lasting spiral pattern extending over the entire system remains difficult to understand. Several of the observed phenomena appear to indicate that magnetohydrodynamical phenomena play a dominant part in addition to gravitation. But evidently we still know far too little about the evolution of a stellar system under gravitational forces to be able to assert with any certainty that magnetic fields are essential for the formation of spiral arms. We know even less about the evolution of a rotating gaseous mass of galactic dimensions, densities, velocities, and magnetic fields. We need not therefore be too surprised or worried about our inability to understand the origin of spiral and bar structures.

In this connection an important question is whether the arms in spiral nebulae consist principally of gas or of stars. We know from the 21-cm observations in the galactic system, as well as from numerous data on other systems, that the interstellar gas is concentrated in the arms. But we do not know with any certainty whether or not *stars* contribute in an important measure to the mass of the arms. This, however, is one of the few questions concerning spiral structure which could be answered by observations, viz., by photometry of spiral galaxies in different colors. As far as I know, no satisfactory answer can yet be given. An interesting thing was pointed out by Spitzer and Baade. In dense clusters of galaxies the proportion of spiral systems is very low; on the other hand, these clusters contain large numbers of S0 nebulae. These nebulae are as flat as spiral systems, but they show an entirely smooth structure, without spiral arms or any of the knotty appearance that is so characteristic of most spirals. Spitzer and Baade's attractive theory is that these systems are former spirals which, after they had assumed their flat shapes, lost their gaseous component through mutual collisions in the dense cluster, and that, with the gas, they lost at the same time the ingredient which seems to be a condition sine qua non for spiral or irregular formations.

Today I want to leave the problem of the *origin* of spiral structure and concentrate on that of the *persistence* of this structure. This is a problem that is much closer to us, and, because of that, it is a more urgent problem. The urgency becomes clear when we consider it numerically.

Let us first take the galactic system. We see arms spaced at about 2 kpc near the sun. We cannot observe whether they form a continuous spiral pattern. But, in view of what we observe in spiral galaxies such as M 81 and M 51, which in other respects seem to be very analogous, it is reasonable to assume as a working hypothesis that our galaxy has a similar spiral structure. A spacing of 2 kpc then corresponds to an average inclination of the arms of 6°.

For a numerical estimate of the rapidity with which the arms evolve we consider an arm running through the sun at S in Fig. 1. Assuming an inclination of 6°, we find that at a 90° higher galactocentric longitude (in the direction of the rotation) the arm would be at A, at a distance of 7.2 kpc from the center instead of the 8.2 kpc near the sun. At $R = 7.2$ kpc the angular velocity is 31.4 km/sec/kpc instead of the 26.4 found near the sun. The gas near A is observed to move away from that near the sun by this differential angular motion of 5.0 km/sec/kpc, or 5.0×10^{-3} rad per million years. In 3×10^8 years it will have doubled its angular distance from S, while 3×10^8 years ago it would have been on the same radius vector as S.

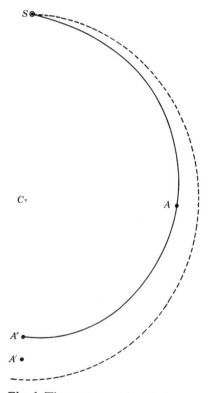

Fig. 1. The geometry of a spiral arm.

We see thus that, if the gas moved in circular paths, the spiral arm would radically change its structure in a time of the order of one revolution of the system. This would give a very unplausible picture. For the galactic disk has existed for at least 50 such revolutions. We can hardly imagine that the present spiral structure originated in the last 1 or 2 per cent of the life of the disk and that it is to be dissolved in the next few per cent of this life. It may be remarked in this connection that the total mass of the gas in the galactic system is only about 3 per cent* of its entire mass, so that a priori it does not seem likely that the gravitational attraction of the arms themselves could have helped to maintain them in a spiral pattern for such very long times as appear to be required for the permanence of this structure.

It is true that in the galactic system we have no absolute certainty from direct observations that the arms are really wound in a continuous spiral pattern. But the same direct observation of rapid differential rotation can be made in other galaxies, where there is no doubt about the continuous character of the spiral structure. The best observed galaxy fulfilling these requirements is M 81, where Münch has observed a fair number of emission knots in the arms. These observations show forcibly how the arms are being stretched out by differential rotation, with about the same rapidity as in the galactic system.

We are thus faced with a difficulty that follows directly from the observations, without recurrence to any theory whatever. I see three ways out of this difficulty:

1. The stretching is *not* a phenomenon that takes place continuously all along a spiral arm running through the entire nebula, but it is periodical in some such way as has been indicated by Dr. Lindblad. The entire arm structure should then be considered as something more or less periodical, renewing itself many times during the age of a galaxy. My feeling is that the observed large-scale spiral structures do not give the impression that such a thing is generally happening. But the possibility must certainly be kept in mind.

2. The stretching does not take place in the manner first suggested, in which the matter moved in circular orbits, but the gas streams along the spiral arms, the flow velocity being different at different R. This would require a flow that would be systematically inward or outward over large parts of the galaxy. The flow should be such that in a suitably chosen rotating frame of reference the spiral arms would be fixed structures.

3. The arms could retain their present spiral shapes if matter were

*In previous publications a lower estimate has been given, which was inaccurate. The above value is based on an improved computation by Mr. van Woerden; this gives 2.9×10^9 solar masses for the total hydrogen content (private communication).

constantly being added to their inner edges, while the outer edges would constantly lose matter. If this process would intensify with decreasing distance from the center, it is conceivable that in the time in which, relative to the gas at S, the gas at A would be moved by differential rotation to A', the differential growth process would bring the center of the arm in to A'' (again relative to S), so that the shape of the spiral arm would be conserved.

I should like to discuss briefly the consequences of (2) and (3).

Streaming along Spiral Arms

If the spiral structure is a more or less permanent one, we can always find a frame of reference rotating in such a way that the arms are stationary. We can picture the spiral arms as two long tubes having the form of the present arms. The gas flows through the tubes. The flow velocity must vary in such a way that the observed differential rotations are reproduced. The tube has an inclination of 6°.

In principle we could make the tube system rotate with an arbitrary angular velocity ω_t. But the observations we have on the galactic system put limits on the components in the R direction that we can admit.

Let us start by considering the picture we would get if the tubes were rotating with an angular velocity corresponding to that of the gas near the sun. In that case there would be no current through the tube in the latter region. Near the sun $\partial \omega / \partial R = -4.76$ km/sec/kpc, so that inside R_0 (the sun's distance from the center) the stream velocity through the tube would be directed inward (if the arms are supposed to be trailing). At $R = 7.2$ kpc the velocity in radial direction toward the center would be $7.2 \times 4.76 \sin 6° = 3.4$ km/sec. At $R = 4$ kpc it would become 10.5 km/sec.

These inward radial motions are relatively small, probably too small to be verified from observations, except possibly near the sun, where I believe that an "expansional" motion of this order would have been observed if it had been present. We are attempting further tests with our 21-cm receiver in the 25-m radio telescope in Dwingeloo, but without great expectations for positive results.

It may be asked whether we could also have a model in which the gas would everywhere be streaming *out*ward, as would seem more in line with the outward motions observed in the region within $R = 3$ kpc. However, this seems to me to be impossible. You would then have to take the rotation of the tube system equal to the angular velocity near $R = 3$ kpc or still higher. At $R = 3$ kpc, $\omega = 66.0$ km/sec/kpc. The gas near the sun would then have an angular velocity of 39.6 relative to the tube and a linear velocity through the tube of $8.2 \times 39.6 = 325$ km/sec. With a tube inclination of 6° this would give a radial motion away from the center of 32 km/sec, which certainly cannot be reconciled with observations.

According to a rough estimate the total amount of gas which, in the first model, would have to be transported inward through a cylinder with $R = 6.2$ kpc would be between 1 and 2 solar masses per year. This is of the same order as the amount estimated to be streaming *outward* from the *central* region of the galactic system.

These amounts are quite considerable; in order to maintain the present density we would have to assume a continuous exchange of gas between disk and halo, in such a way that the inward stream in the disk would be compensated by a net outward current through the halo. These streams would not necessarily extend over very large ranges in R; they might be broken up into parts which individually might extend only over an interval of the order of the separation of the arms. Only the vaguest conjectures can be made about the way the gas would flow from the halo into the disk or about the manner in which it would be ejected into the halo. It is conceivable that supernovae of type II would in some way be responsible for the latter (cf. the next section).

The systematic deviations from circular motion which occur when the gas is streaming through the imaginary tubes must be caused by large-scale magnetic fields, which, in order to produce such deviations, must have strengths of at least a few times 10^{-5} gauss. That the magnetic fields may have a large-scale influence on the motion of the interstellar gas is indicated by the large deviations from circular motion observed in the interstellar medium in the central part of the galactic system. Although no satisfactory theory has yet been developed, the most probable explanation is that the motion of the gas in this region is largely governed by magneto-hydrodynamical forces.

Although in the outer regions the magnetic forces are certainly at least two orders of magnitude smaller than the force of gravitation, there is some evidence that even here their influence may be observed. It has long been known that the velocity of the sun relative to A-type stars is considerably lower than its velocity relative to the gas and the B stars. From these data we find that in the direction of the rotation of the system the A stars have about 6 km/sec higher velocity. This might be interpreted as a velocity lag of the gas of the same amount, owing to magnetic pressure. However, this interpretation is very uncertain because of the great systematic streamings known to be present in the nearby A stars. But a confirmation may be obtained from the K giants, which on the average are considerably older and presumably also better mixed. These give a rotational velocity which is approximately the same as for the gas. But their rotational velocity must be smaller than the circular velocity corresponding to the gravitational force, because of the presence of a considerable density gradient. This causes a pressure gradient in the "stellar gas." The estimated correction to true circular motion is about 7 km/sec. This then would again give a lag for the gas of approximately the same amount.

Other Processes of Gas Transport between Arms

I now want briefly to discuss the possibility mentioned under (3) above, viz., that gas is being transported from an arm to the next outer arm and that the arms keep their present shapes without the action of magnetic fields.

If there are discrete gas clouds in the halo—and the scant observations that have so far been obtained give some indication that there are—it would seem probable that they have come from the disk. We do not know the mechanism by which they could have been expelled. It is conceivable that they could have been pushed out by the expanding shells of supernovae of type II. In this section we shall assume as a provisional working hypothesis that this is the case. It would require that a supernova shell is not a coherent shell but consists of filaments filling only a small fraction of its surface. For even under the rather too extreme circumstances of a shell of 10 solar masses ejected with a velocity of 5000 km/sec into a medium with an average density as low as 0.05 hydrogen atoms/cm^3, the velocity of a complete shell sweeping up the interstellar matter would decrease to 10 km/sec at a distance of about 100 pc, which is evidently far too small a distance for our purpose. However, the case of the Crab nebula indicates that supernova shells may be concentrated in rather narrow filaments, occupying a fraction of 1 per cent or less of a sphere. If the Crab nebula shell were expanded with its present velocity to a radius of 1000 pc and the filaments had at the same time expanded in width with the thermal velocities corresponding to their present observed temperature of about 10,000°, the surface covered by them would still be about the same small fraction of the sphere as in the present stage. If we assume that in the case considered above the fraction of the sphere covered by the expanding matter would be 1/1000, it could travel to a radius of the order of 1 kpc before being slowed down to a velocity of the order of 10 km/sec. In this case the cloud population of the halo could well be maintained by supernova explosions. A rough estimate made by Blaauw and myself indicates that an entire arm might "evaporate" in this manner in a time of the order of a revolution of the system.

We may now inquire what will happen to clouds that have been expelled from a spiral arm. In this reconnaissance, in which we shall be dealing mainly with high velocities, we shall neglect the influence of the magnetic field.

With the state of rotation and the form of the gravitational potential as observed in the system, there will be an asymmetry in the extent of the orbits of the expelled clouds—in this sense, that the clouds which obtain a certain additional velocity *in* the direction of rotation will move *out* further from their original orbit than clouds obtaining the same velocity in the opposite direction will move *inward* from their original position. For an example consider a star moving in a circular orbit with radius $R = 8$ kpc. If it is given a push of 20 km/sec in the direction of rotation it will move out to a maximum distance of 4.0 kpc beyond its original distance. With the push in the direction opposite to that of the rotation it will move in to a minimum distance differing only 1.7 kpc from the initial orbital radius. It is clear that if we consider gas clouds, the picture becomes very much more complicated, because the braking by the interstellar medium becomes a most important factor. If they are being expelled by means of supernova explosions, as suggested above, it would still seem possible to make gas clouds travel over a large range in R when pushed out under a considerable angle with the galactic plane, so that they would move mainly through the lower part of the halo. If the range is large enough, they will ultimately be absorbed by the next arm. As in the case of the star considered above, there will be an asymmetry: If we consider three consecutive arms A, B, and C, A being the innermost one, more gas will move from B to C than from B to A. For, if the expelled clouds do not reach A, they will have a tendency ultimately to come back to B if the region between the arms is sufficiently empty. Under the conditions described, the arm B will move inward, first, because it loses momentum by the asymmetric loss of the gas which is being caught by C; second, because B itself catches matter coming from A, which in general will have a lower momentum when it arrives at B; and third, because B will grow on the inside while it *looses* matter from its *outer* edge. It is quite conceivable that the effect of this kind of gas transport would become more important as we proceed toward the center and the spacing of the arms becomes less.

We would thus get a systematic inward displacement of the arms, the amount of which per unit time might increase with decreasing R. In this way we could get the same counterbalancing of the stretching of the arms by differential rotation as with the inward streaming along the arms which was considered in the preceding section. If the supernovae are the agents supplying the gas clouds in the halo, the amount of gas exchange between arms might possibly be of the right order.

It is clear that if this process of expulsion by supernova shells would really be important, the magnetic fields would be wound up in a very irregular fashion. However, this would not necessarily conflict with the observations of a magnetic field running parallel to an arm, because in the galactic plane the field lines would be constantly stretched along the arms by the effect of differential rotation.

This hypothesis of gas transport is still nothing but a vague possibility. I have elaborated it mainly to indicate that mechanisms other than a flow of gas through the arms are not entirely ruled out. It would, however, have to be discussed with much more care than I have yet been able to give to it before it could be regarded as a real alternative.

From the *observational* side the most promising direction of research for elucidating the mechanism of spiral structure would be the study of the distribution and systematic motions of stars of different, but not too old, ages relative to the gaseous arms in which they were born. If magnetic forces constrain the gas to the "tubes" considered above, the stars, once they are formed, would move away from these tubes and we could in principle compute where they should be after they reach a certain age. Partly because of the great irregularity of all spiral structures it is very hard observationally to get a satisfactory picture of this. And, so far, little has been obtained from which we have become really wiser.

It would evidently also be very important to observe whether the systematic inward streamings such as we were led to introduce actually occur. As I have already pointed out before, there seems to be little prospect to prove the presence or absence of these small motions in our own galaxy, but it is conceivable that it could be done in other galaxies, like M 81.

Discussion

Dr. Biermann: You mentioned the possibility, which has so often been discussed, that the arms are continuously being destroyed and reforming. In that connection I would like to ask the following question. Would it be possible that you have the same galaxies appearing for a part of their span of life as, say, spirals with very regular arms, and for another part as spirals with less regular arms— in such a way that you get a sort of mixture between phases which in some way might alternate? A spiral which today has irregular arms could then in, say, a few times 10^8 years look much more regular.

Dr. Oort: I don't know. You see, the amount of irregularity in the arms and the character of the arms seem to be correlated with the strength of population II in the galaxy, which probably would not change in the course of time. I have a feeling that the character of the arms is more a function of the type of nebula than that it could change with time, but I am not sure.

Dr. Kahn: In some of these models would you not have to transport angular momentum through the galaxy, and how would this be done?

Dr. Oort: In the second model you would have to transport it, of course. But one would suppose then that one would get it back again via the halo. I don't think there would be a problem in the third case. That would take care of itself.

Dr. Kahn: Is there ever any hope of seeing the gas in transit?

Dr. Oort: Yes.

Dr. Blaauw: We have the radio evidence of interstellar clouds coming toward us. All these are at intermediate and high latitudes and mostly at negative velocities. We may try to compute backward what their orbits have been. They now have velocities of, say, 50 km/sec, which must have been higher in the past. They have originated in the Perseus arm; just a rough estimate would indicate that that is about the sort of distance one would expect to find.

Dr. Lüst: I have one question concerning your third item—gas transport between arms. Would not the spiral structure be much more irregular if one had a supernova here and then there?

Dr. Oort: The times are long; you have 10^6 supernovae every revolution of the galaxy. So you have more than a thousand per kiloparsec arm length per revolution. And, after all, the arms *are* very irregular.

Dr. Woltjer: I am somewhat worried about the stability of the whole arrange-ment. If one supposes that by accidental circumstances one piece of the spiral arm has somewhat less gas than another piece, this lower density region will tend to grow less than the region in which there is a higher density. In this way once you have a region in which there is nothing, there will never be anything, so that you would break up the spiral arms very easily?

Dr. Oort: It may be. On the other hand, the number of supernovae is likely to go down as well if there is less gas. But I don't feel very safe about it, either.

Dr. Schwarzschild: What is you estimate in a typical Sb spiral of the mass that is in the spiral structure?

Dr. Oort: That depends, of course, on how much mass in addition to the gas you would put in the spiral arms. If you think of it as primarily gaseous, the mass would be quite small. In the case of our galaxy, the mass of the gas is only about 3 per cent of the total mass. In the Andromeda nebula it is 0.8 per cent. This is the fraction of H I. It may be that in the case of Dr. Lindblad's picture there would be many stars which follow these gravitational vibrations as well, and there might be considerably more stellar than gaseous mass. But I am afraid that you might still get into difficulties in the long run, because as Dr. Lindblad pointed out, if you want to keep this up for 10^{10} years you are likely to need gas-dynamical considerations as well. Also, we have the observation of Dr. Spitzer and Dr. Baade that spiral structure disappears in the long run if you have no gas, even if the systems are very flat and if originally they would perhaps have had spiral structure.

Dr. Schwarzschild: If one accepts these numbers, essentially what we are searching for here is the dynamics of a very small percentage of the total mass overlying the basic dynamics of the older stars.

Dr. Oort: The gravitational field is furnished by the older stars and does not change with time, and in the picture I drew the spiral is just a small, almost mass-less thing. In Lindblad's case this is different, however.

Dr. Lindblad: How far out from the center of our galaxy do you think this third mechanism would still work? Do you think you could explain the outermost arms in this way, too?

Dr. Oort: It looks difficult to fit the outermost arm into the same scheme.

Dr. Strömgren: In discussing item 3, would the phenomenon that Baade has pointed out, namely, that in some galaxies rather long sectors of spiral arm are almost dark, where star formation doesn't seem to be going on, be a factor in breaking up the structure temporarily? That would probably depend on the time scale of destroying the arms, when the mechanism is temporarily not operating, at such times when you might suppose, according to Baade, that you have inter-stellar matter but no star formation and no supernovae.

Dr. Oort: I must confess that I have not given enough thought to that.

Dr. Kahn: I would like to refer to your picture of the filaments making their way more easily through the interstellar matter and occupying less area. When you work out, for the case of great loop nebula in Cygnus, whether you can keep the filaments there alight, you find that the picture of a nebula consisting of filaments is rather unsatisfactory. You really have to take the view that it is a whole shell with a rather crinkly outer surface, and you see it bright when the line of sight cuts through this surface tangentially. That would give you a reasonable amount of surface area for pushing through the interstellar gas.

Dr. Oort: On the other hand, in the Crab nebula it is quite evident that you have a filamentary structure.

Dr. Kahn: Yes, but that is a rather young object.

Dr. Wares: Is there a possibility of mass transport of gas between arms in the at-present invisible form of molecular hydrogen?

Dr. Oort: That cannot be excluded, I think.

Ed.: Dr. Schwarzschild raised the question of whether there are galaxies in which one can follow the spiral arms well and at the same time establish the differential rotation. Dr. Oort and Dr. E. M. Burbidge indicated that M 81 and NGC 5055 are such cases.

Dr. G. R. Burbidge: I think it is worth pointing out that it is in the regions of constant angular velocity where you could maintain spiral structure that you generally don't see it.

Dr. Prendergast: I just want to make one comment about possible radial motions in galaxies. If the material moves radially and at all times stays fairly close to the local circular velocity, there is a dreadful problem of increasing the angular momentum of this material if it moves outward, or decreasing the angular momentum if it moves inward. There seem to be no obvious ways of doing this that are quantitatively convincing.

Dynamic effects of magnetic fields and the galactic halo

L. Biermann

The contents of this paper are essentially the same as those of the paper "Considerations Bearing on the Structure of the Galaxy" by L. Biermann and Leverett Davis, Jr., published in *Z. Ap.*, **51,** 19 (1960). Only the discussion of this paper at the conference is given here.

Discussion

Dr. Oort: I wonder what the observational evidence on the lag velocity V_1 is worth? You mentioned a paper by the Münchs on velocities of supergiants at somewhat larger distances from the sun. My impression is that the agreement with the 21-cm measures is all that could be wished for, and that one cannot from that derive any evidence for a difference between the stars and the gas. Moreover, the stars that they have measured were all quite young stars, and should be expected to move with the gas instead of showing this lag, even if it were there. The only observational evidence that I am aware of for V_1 is the evidence that I mentioned yesterday on the motions of the A and K stars near the sun. But that is rather weak, I think, because there are known to be other strong local deviations in the velocity field as well.

Ed.: A lengthy discussion followed on the state of motion of the halo gas. It was agreed that nothing is known about this at present.

Dr. Schwarzschild: Could we say that the analysis only shows that as long as we do not know more about the kinetic terms, there is space for a magnetic field of 2×10^{-5}?

Dr. Woltjer: That is saying it is weaker than it is—because the magnetic energy M you can debate, but the integral over the cosmic-ray pressure P you know, and the P in the picture is of the same order as the M. So even if M would be small it does not really alter things very much. You know how many cosmic rays there are near the earth.

Dr. Schwarzschild: Quite right, but we do not know the volume integral over P. If you say they are all through the universe, then this should not add at all. Isn't it as a matter of fact not so implausible a situation that the lowest energies are contained in the disk, the intermediate energies are contained in the halo, and the extreme energies are not contained at all? Then you have a complicated pressure falloff, the integral over which is still rather uncertain?

Dr. Lüst: If you make this assumption and say at least that the low-energy cosmic-ray particles are contained in the disk and halo, then this gives you all the pressure. The energy density in the higher-energy particles is only a very small fraction of that in the low-energy particles.

Dr. Spitzer: But the gravitational attraction on the mass of the halo would be enough to hold that pressure in.

Dr. Biermann: Yes, if something like one-third of the interstellar gas is in the halo.

Dr. Spitzer: You have an additional degree of freedom in what you assume for the regions near the galactic center, where you don't really have any observations. You would expect the lines of force to be pulling out, not at the solar distance from the center but much further in.

Dr. Woltjer: If you have a systematic field.

Dr. Spitzer: Any field. If you have the halo extending only out to a little more than 10 kpc from the galactic center, how can the lines of force produce a net radial force on the gas in the galactic plane at 10 kpc from the center? Close to the center, where nobody can check you anyway, conditions are most favorable.

Dr. Schwarzschild: Could we possibly ask Dr. Oort to make a personal sketch of θ_c and the rotation speed of the interstellar gas in the galaxy, just so that we can see whether he suspects any appreciable lag velocity in the inner portions of the spiral structure?

Dr. Oort: If we first get the circular velocity corresponding to the gravitational force only, then that goes up very steeply apparently, and reaches a maximum, say, around a hundred parsec. Then perhaps it goes down a little bit. There may be a secondary maximum. But that is unimportant. For the gas I would think that the evidence in the central part indicates that it would move more nearly like a solid body. What it does further out we do not know very well except for the 7 km/sec retardation near the sun. But the only evidence that is worth anything in my opinion is given by some bits of gas lying closer to the center than the 3-kpc arm, which do seem to fall far below the gravitational circular velocity curve.

Dr. Woltjer: But that gas does have a large radial component which also should be included in the kinetic energy term T?

Dr. Oort: Yes. So that may spoil the picture again to some extent. But it is difficult to say because you don't know what the space velocity is.

Magnetic fields and the dynamics of the galactic gas

L. Woltjer

We shall base this paper on the main conclusion of our preceding paper, namely, that the field in the central region of the spiral arms near the sun is about 3γ. We shall first investigate the equilibrium of the spiral arms.

If the field were parallel to the galactic plane the full Lorentz force connected with the field gradient in the z direction has to be compensated by the gravitational attraction toward the galactic plane. For the acceleration in the z direction near the sun we have from Oort's data [1] approximately

$$K_z = -9[1 - \exp(-0.003z)] \times 10^{-9} \text{ cm sec}^{-2} \tag{1}$$

for values of z smaller than a few thousand parsec. The hydrogen density may be represented for the present purpose by

$$n = n_0 \exp(-0.006z) \tag{2}$$

Then if the dynamic pressure of the gas were unimportant, we would have

$$\rho K_z = \frac{1}{8\pi} \frac{\partial B^2}{\partial z} \tag{3}$$

or

$$B^2 = 8\pi \int_\infty^z \rho K_z \, dz \tag{4}$$

With $n_0 = 1 \text{ cm}^{-3}$ and an average mass of 2.7×10^{-24} g per hydrogen atom, we have for $z = 0$, $B = 1.0\gamma$. In a spiral arm the density might be

247

somewhat larger than we have assumed here, and therefore K_z might also be increased somewhat; but our neglect of the dynamic pressure is more serious and means that we have overestimated the possible value of B. It is therefore clear that the spiral-arm field cannot be everywhere parallel to the plane. It has to be largely force free in the z direction. Thus the field lines should be helices around the arm axis. Since the width of the spiral arms is only a few hundred parsec it appears that this conclusion is not affected by the presence of matter high up in the halo.

Let us consider the configuration of the galactic field from the point of view of the tensorial virial theorem [2]. This generalized virial theorem is obtained by multiplying the i component of the equation of motion by x_k (instead of by x_i and summing over i) and then integrating over the volume of the configuration. The following symmetric tensors are introduced:

$$W_{ik} = \int \rho x_i \frac{\partial \Phi}{\partial x_k} d\tau \tag{5}$$

$$T_{ik} = \tfrac{1}{2} \int \rho v_i v_k \, d\tau \tag{6}$$

$$\mathfrak{M}_{ik} = \int \frac{1}{8\pi} B_i B_k \, d\tau \tag{7}$$

$$I_{ik} = \int \rho x_i x_k \, d\tau \tag{8}$$

For a closed configuration the theorem becomes

$$\frac{1}{2} \frac{d^2 I_{ik}}{dt^2} = 2T_{ik} - 2\mathfrak{M}_{ik} + W_{ik} + \delta_{ik} \left[(\gamma - 1) U + \mathfrak{M} \right] \tag{9}$$

where U is the thermal energy and $\mathfrak{M}$ the magnetic energy. In a configuration that is axisymmetric around the z axis, the tensors are diagonal, with two equal elements.

Our conclusion that the gravitational force in the z direction has insignificant effects if Eq. (2) is roughly right can also be expressed by stating that W_{zz} is negligible. Then if motions perpendicular to the galactic plane are also neglected and if U is taken to be the cosmic-ray energy, the zz component of Eq. (9) for a system in a steady state becomes

$$\mathfrak{M}_{zz} = \mathfrak{M}_{xx} + \mathfrak{M}_{yy} + \tfrac{1}{3} U \tag{10}$$

which shows that in the absence of much matter in the halo, or if the matter in the halo has motions that just compensate for the effects of the gravitational field, the z component of the galactic field should be the dominant one. It also proves that in this case the magnetic energy should be at least equal to one-third of the comic-ray energy if cosmic rays are to be confined. If U and $\mathfrak{M}$ were equal, we would have $\mathfrak{M}_{zz} = \frac{2}{3}\mathfrak{M}$.

If we should want to confine the cosmic rays by a much weaker field in the halo we have two alternatives. Either we consider all cosmic rays as intergalactic, which seems not very attractive, or we have to make W_{zz} approximately equal to $\frac{1}{3}U$, which means we have to add a large amount of matter in the halo ($n \simeq 5 \times 10^{-3}$ cm^{-3}). This matter may very well be in the halo, and then even a weak field could confine much of the cosmic rays. The stability of the arrangement would be doubtful, however. If the field is weak it would have no other function than to couple the relativistic particles to the ordinary gas; it would not have a direct influence on the equilibrium and stability. If it were twisted, the increase in magnetic energy would hardly change the total energy. Then the situation is not very different from the one in which a light fluid supports a heavy fluid in a gravitational field, and instabilities seem likely. Of course, with the values of B that we have adopted the situation is quite different.

If we consider the xx and yy components of Eq. (9) we come back to the results discussed by Biermann and Davis [3]. With our parameters we obtain a lag velocity, that is, the difference between the actual velocity and the local circular velocity of the gas, of 40 km/sec on the average, if no gas is assumed in the halo. Let us now consider an isolated spiral arm. The expression for the lag velocity ΔV is approximately

$$MV\,\Delta V = \tfrac{1}{2}(\mathfrak{M} + U) \tag{11}$$

where M is the mass of the gas. Let us consider the spiral arm as a ring. For a circular ring, rotating with $V = 200$ km/sec, with constant field and density inside the ring and nothing outside, we find from Eq. (11),

$$3.5 \times 10^{-15}\,n_{\mathrm{H}}\,\Delta V = B^2 \tag{12}$$

With $n_{\mathrm{H}} = 1$ and $B = 3\gamma$ we have $V = 2.5$ km/sec—quite compatible with observations. It is not obvious that it is possible, without a very artificial configuration, to change the magnetic structure in the arms so that the very large figure for the lag velocity required if the halo is coupled to the arm is produced. This should be studied in more detail, but the equilibrium problem for toroidal rings is mathematically quite difficult. It is not at all unlikely that considerations of this kind will show that additional mass in the halo is needed to obtain a probable equilibrium configuration.

As an alternative it might be supposed that the intergalactic matter around the galaxy might exert an effective pressure on the halo. This is only significant, however, if the pressure is ten times larger than the values given by Kahn and Woltjer [4], who still used a low value for the magnetic field intensity and did not include the cosmic-ray pressure. This could be done by increasing the temperature of the gas by a fairly large factor, which would mean that the gas could not be in equilibrium in the local group, but would pervade the whole universe. Or we could assume higher densities, which would make the total mass improbably large. We also could lower the temperature and make a mantle of gas around the halo. This could hardly be a permanent situation; moreover the motion of the galaxy through the gas would be supersonic and the results on the bending of the plane would have to be reconsidered. In the case of a higher temperature this is not so very serious. From the expressions given by Kahn and Woltjer it follows that, if the temperature is large enough to prevent much concentration around the halo, the difference in pressure between the stagnation points and the points of maximum flow is about M^2P, where M represents the Mach number at which the galaxy moves through the medium and P is the pressure in the medium. The required value for the pressure difference could, for example, still be obtained in a medium with $n = 3 \times 10^{-5}$ and $T = 10^8$. For various reasons connected with radio sources and other extragalactic evidence it might be useful to have such a medium, but about 3×10^{-30} erg/sec/cm^3 are needed to maintain it (about $10^{10} L_{\odot}$/galaxy).

At this point it may also be appropriate to discuss the addition of matter to a galaxy from the intergalactic medium. It is difficult to estimate how much gas could flow in the galaxy per year from this source. But it seems probable that if it were a significant amount, still more might be absorbed by the large elliptical systems, where the gravitational effects are larger and where the magnetic shielding may be less effective. Also the introduction of a significant amount of hydrogen would tend to increase the difficulties connected with the helium production in the galaxy.

The situation in the central parts of the galaxy is still quite confused. It is clear that if the arms trail, the motions cannot be explained by an outflow along the arms, even if the gas and the momentum were available. It has been argued by Wentzel [5] that if one has a plausible magnetic field, one can produce a Lorentz force in the plane which is directed outward. This does not help much. A stationary magnetic field can do no work. And if now we would let the arm expand as a unit, the field would soon be changed completely. This means that if the phenomenon is stationary, new arms would have to be formed on an embarrassingly short time scale. This then would seem to be the basic problem, much more fundamental than the questions about the origin of the gas.

As far as this last question is concerned, it is possible to consider halo models that condense in the central region, because cooling processes there are most effective. This is so because the gas pressure in the central region would be quite high. For example, in a nonmagnetic Spitzer halo, effects of this kind can be significant if the halo is cooled by heat conduction toward a large number of small ionized interstellar clouds of the kind considered by Münch and Zirin [6]. In such a model one might suppose that the matter acquires some momentum while falling down from the halo, then is directed out again by the magnetic field, and finally is stopped in some ringlike structure, where an appreciable part condenses into stars. Or part of it might be shot into the halo again during this star-formation process. On the basis of a model of this kind the circulation of gas would only involve the region within the 3-kpc arm. The only function of the magnetic field would be to change the flow direction near the galactic nucleus, that is, to prevent an inelastic encounter between the gas coming in from the north and south galactic poles. On the whole such a model seems rather unattractive.

The other possibility which could be considered is that the 3-kpc arm was originally in equilibrium with a mass larger that its present mass. Thus the magnetic forces (a volume force) balanced the gravitational and kinetic forces (force per unit mass). Suppose that now rather suddenly star formation took place over a rather large part of the arm, a possibility that receives some support from the observation of Westerhout [7] that there is a region of ionized hydrogen surrounding the 3-kpc arm. After the star formation has taken place, the equilibrium has been destroyed. The magnetic forces are the same but the other forces are decreased in proportion to the amount of matter used up in star formation. Quantitatively this might perhaps just be sufficient. Consider the ordinary virial theorem which for an expanding ring may be written

$$M \varpi \ddot{\varpi} = \mathfrak{M} + U + \Omega + 2T \tag{13}$$

In the original equilibrium the right-hand side is zero.

If one-half of the original mass (M) has, rather suddenly, been condensed into stars, the virial theorem applied to this new system gives

$$\tfrac{1}{2} M \varpi \ddot{\varpi} = \tfrac{1}{2} (\mathfrak{M} + U) \tag{14}$$

In the original configuration we obviously had

$$\mathfrak{M} + U < M \Theta_c^2 \tag{15}$$

where Θ represents the local circular velocity. Thus we finally have

$$\ddot{\varpi} < \frac{\Theta_c^2}{\varpi} \simeq 5 \times 10^{-8} \text{ cm/sec}^2 \tag{16}$$

Taking 10^7 years as a characteristic time scale the upper limit on the attainable velocity would be 150 km/sec. Of course this upper limit would

L. Woltjer

252

not be reached. The difficulty in a model of this kind is to understand how the star formation can be so sudden in a rather large region. It is clear that the basic processes which underlie the phenomena in the central region of the galaxy probably remain to be uncovered.

References
[1] J. H. Oort, *B.A.N.*, **15**, 45 (1960).
[2] S. Chandrasekhar, *J. Math. Anal. and Appl.*, **1**, 240 (1960).
[3] L. Biermann and L. Davis, *Z. Astrophys.*, **51**, 19 (1960).
[4] F. D. Kahn and L. Woltjer, *Ap. J.*, **130**, 705 (1959).
[5] D. Wentzel, *Nature*, **189**, 907 (1961).
[6] G. Münch and H. Zirin, *Ap. J.*, **133**, 11 (1961).
[7] G. Westerhout, *B.A.N.*, **14**, 215 (1958).

Discussion

Dr. Lüst: If you have that large a component of the magnetic field going from the disk into the halo, would you not get a co-rotating halo in a sense?

Dr. Woltjer: I would think that the spiral pattern as a whole, with the strong magnetic fields, may rotate as a solid body. This means that all these magnetic fields in the z direction, and thus eventually the halo itself, would co-rotate with the spiral structure.

Dr. Prendergast: The ordinary virial theorem that you have used holds for a system which conserves the mass in stars and the mass in gas separately. It is not obvious that the same virial theorem holds if gas is converted into stars.

Dr. Woltjer: It is schematically supposed that the star formation takes place instantaneously. Then the virial theorem is valid both before and after this instant, although it is of course applied to two different systems.

Dr. Field: If you account for this mass flow out of the center by a flow out of the halo, then isn't the halo going to be emptied rather quickly in a billion years or so?

Dr. Woltjer: Yes. You have to supply it either by supposing that matter comes into the halo through the boundary of intergalactic space or you have to get things straight by shooting matter up into the halo, and one comes again to the supernovae, or perhaps other mechanisms.

Dr. Strömgren: In estimating the flow from the center out, the value of one solar mass per year is derived on the assumption that the flow is stationary. Would you estimate what reduction could be expected in the last picture you discussed?

Dr. Woltjer: That could be a very large reduction, but to determine how large would involve an estimate of how long it takes to build up a spiral arm before it again breaks up into stars. I think it is not possible to make a reliable estimate. In this connection I should perhaps also point out another thing—that it is frequently argued from Münch's observations that there is evidence for an expansion in the central region of the Andromeda nebula also. From this one could argue that apparently this is not just an isolated phenomenon but something which happens continuously in many galaxies. I think this argument is not well founded. You may recall that Münch observed the λ3727 doublet in the central region of Andromeda, a region with a radius of 500 pc, and found some indication of an expansion velocity. Then he computed the total mass that would leave the center by assuming that the whole volume was homogeneously filled by a medium with a density of about 50 cm^{-3}. This figure was obtained from the doublet ratio. The difference in the doublet ratio between a density of 50 cm^{-3} and a zero density is extremely small and well within the observational and other uncertainties. Moreover, one can show that if a medium with a density of 50 was filling this space homogeneously about 100 times as much [O II] radiation would be emitted as is actually estimated. Thus either these emitting regions occupy only one hundredth of the volume or the density is 10 times lower; so this mass estimate is much too high.

Dr. G. R. Burbidge: I take it you are not questioning that the material is expanding from the center of Andromeda but that the rate is exceedingly uncertain?

Dr. Woltjer: I don't know whether one can really be convinced from observations that there is any expansion at all. There are large-scale irregularities.

Dr. G. R. Burbidge: There are considerable departures from rotation.

Dr. Oort: Shouldn't one really say that one doesn't know in the case of the Andromeda nebula because in the galaxy it is mostly neutral gas that we see expanding, and that could not be observed in the Andromeda nebula. So it might well be that further out there would be the same expanding features.

Dr. Schwarzschild: If I understand you correctly, in this tentative model of a large-scale magnetic field one is rather forced to make the whole magnetic field structure rotate like a solid body. Do I understand you properly then—that to make the observations of the rotational velocities of the galaxies come out correctly one has to go to the radial streamings that Dr. Oort discussed yesterday?

Dr. Woltjer: With these radial streamings one has quite serious difficulties with the angular momentum, as was remarked upon previously by Dr. Prendergast. I think this throws out many models that have been proposed. About the only way to resolve this, to my mind, would be to suppose that the gas flows only part of the time along the arm; for example, one could think of the connections one sees in external galaxies between various arms, and suppose that gas is there transported from one arm to the next. Alternatively one could suppose that the clouds have a certain mobility through the magnetic fields. I think it may quite well be possible that, even though the basic spiral structure would be represented essentially by a spiralling magnetic field, still the individual gas clouds would move in more or less closed trajectories.

Dr. Schwarzschild: Closed being, on the average, circular.

Dr. Woltjer: Being on the average circular, but not instantaneously circular.

Dr. Biermann: A high rate of mass exchange between gas and stars would also help in that direction.

Dr. Woltjer: Yes, but I would doubt whether the turnover from stars into gas is quick enough for that.

Dr. Oort: This would also disturb the magnetic field.

Dr. Spitzer: How does the gas get from one arm to the next in view of these strong magnetic fields and the wrapping fields around them?

Dr. Woltjer: In the first place, if one accepts the model of magnetic clouds, then it is possible that these clouds travel across the magnetic field lines.

Dr. Spitzer: If you aren't careful you will end up by getting these little clouds divorced entirely from the magnetic fields. You don't want that, either.

Dr. Woltjer: That depends essentially on what happens in the boundary layer between these clouds and the magnetic field. One would have to suppose on a model of this kind that it would be rather well coupled, but not coupled perfectly.

Dr. Blaauw: If you assume that the matter in the central part is supplied from intergalactic space, and you combine this with the intergalactic flow that you used to explain the distortion of the outer regions of the disk, would you expect any deviation in the central parts from the very flat galactic plane?

Dr. Woltjer: Not necessarily. That depends on the field structure there, because you would have to suppose that this matter flows in along a magnetic field line, and is subsequently deflected out into the plane. Because if you wouldn't have any magnetic field at all you would have streams of matter coming in from both sides, which would collide and essentially thermalize the systematic energy. Then there wouldn't be any matter transferred outward.

Dr. Lüst: You mentioned this spiral-arm field configuration where you have a B_θ field outside. Have you given any thought to the stability of such a configuration?

Dr. Woltjer: I am afraid not; it is not a very easy problem. In the first place, it is very hard to treat the equilibrium configuration exactly. To discuss its stability with gravitational effects included is even more difficult.

Dr. Lüst: Would it not be unstable for the long wavelengths?

Dr. Spitzer: That is true. If you idealize a spiral arm as an infinite cylinder, with a B_θ field encircling it, instability is present for a long-enough wavelength.

Dr. Woltjer: If you only have an infinite cylinder with toroidal field lines on the outside, then of course if you distort it you get an excess pressure that pushes the instability on. I wonder, if one considered for example a ring in the galactic plane, whether the same effect could happen, because then the matter has to flow through this instability. I can't quite see how this could be bent very far away from its original position due to conservation of angular momentum and energy. For perturbations perpendicular to the galactic plane, K_z provides a restoring force.

Dr. E. M. Burbidge: If one had a circulation of this sort, would you think that the dissipation of kinetic energy from the two flow patterns coming in, one from one side and the other from the other side, might be sufficient to maintain an electron temperature of 40,000°, which we suggested from the observations of the emission lines in other galaxies might be present?

Dr. Woltjer: I doubt it. Of course, it is easy to calculate. But, for example, I recall the calculation that if in the present filaments of the Cygnus loop, which move with a velocity of 50 or 100 km/sec, one maintained the radiation by collisional energy the whole shell would be stopped in a thousand years or so by its radiative losses. So I think that it would be difficult.

Dr. Kahn: In Mrs. Burbidge's case we would have to ask what intensity of the radiation she wants to maintain from the gas before you definitely throw out that suggestion.

Dr. Woltjer: If you have gas at 40,000° with a normal composition it is quite high.

Dr. Biermann: As to the early part of your discussion, there was a question about the stability of the arrangement in which you have essentially a considerable amount of mass and cosmic radiation in the halo, coupled together by a magnetic field. There was some disagreement about whether or not or under which circumstances this would be a stable arrangement. The point was made that the cosmic-ray particles could move relative to the gas in such a way that energy was effectively set free. Perhaps Dr. Spitzer would like to comment?

Dr. Spitzer: I have been thinking a little bit about the situation. It seems to me that if you start out with a small-scale field to begin with, rather than a steady field, then the situation is a little different. The instabilities would produce a looping of the lines of force up and out of the galactic place. This situation might well lead to an ellipsoidal distribution of magnetic field sectors that could explain the polarization in the spur. What the limiting factor would be in this process I don't know. You might actually increase the magnetic field to a point where an equilibrium configuration could perhaps result.

Dr. Biermann: Yes, you would probably get considerable amplification of the magnetic field.

Dr. Spitzer: But it would still remain small-scale.

Dr. Field: What is small-scale in this connection?

Dr. Spitzer: Some value much less than the diameter of the halo.

Dr. Woltjer: So this would produce, in your case, a field predominantly in the z direction.

Dr. Spitzer: Yes.

Dr. G. R. Burbidge: All these models suppose that the halo has a very regular structure and that the boundary layer between the halo and the intergalactic medium is fairly regular. The observations on the halo in M 31 suggest that it is rather irregular, and that there are large fluctuations in the continuum radiation in the region surrounding the M 31. Would this suggest that there was a strong connection between the halo regions and the intergalactic medium, or would one rather suppose that such an irregular configuration is essentially confined to the galaxy itself?

Dr. Woltjer: If one makes too strong a connection between the halo and the intergalactic medium it becomes difficult to see how you can keep the cosmic rays in the halo, because—at least if you do not accept the cosmological picture of cosmic rays—you have to suppose that the cosmic-ray particles can travel about a thousand times to and fro through the galactic system before they escape. Thus only about one in a thousand field lines could be really connected to a possible intergalactic field.

Dynamics of cosmic rays

R. Lüst

In discussing the dynamics of cosmic rays there is the difficulty that the theoretical situation seems to be even more complex than it was, for instance, 10 years ago. As I reported in my previous talk, a number of new observational facts could be obtained, but we still do not have enough evidence on the observational or the theoretical side to show that only one theoretical picture is possible to explain all the observations. As far as our topic here is concerned, the question is mainly: Must we take into account the cosmic rays in discussing the interstellar matter? One question, for instance, is whether or not the cosmic rays must be regarded as sink of energy of the interstellar matter. Furthermore: Are there other effects caused by the pressure of cosmic rays which cannot be neglected in discussing the motions of the interstellar gas, for instance?

It has already been mentioned by Prof. Biermann and by Dr. Field that the cosmic rays will give some energy to the interstellar gas mainly due to the ionization losses. For this the flux of the low-energy particles is of special importance. But, on the other side, the question arises if one must provide energy for the cosmic rays, for accelerating them in the interstellar space. This problem is ultimately connected with the problem about the origin. Therefore, I shall discuss first, very briefly, some of the problems connected with the origin and acceleration of cosmic rays to show to what consequences they may lead with respect to the motions in interstellar space. Finally I shall say a few words about other dynamical problems as far as the cosmic rays are concerned.

If we go back to the observations, one striking feature is the high degree of isotropy of the cosmic rays. To achieve this, magnetic fields have been invoked which should be responsible in some way for the observed isotropy. I shall discuss this point later. If we want in addition to store the cosmic rays in these magnetic fields, then the observed energy density might be used to get another estimate for the strength of the magnetic field by arguing that the energy density of the magnetic field should be at least not smaller than the energy density of the cosmic rays. This is not a very strong argument, but at least it may give us some further hint for the strength of the field. From this consideration a field of about 5×10^{-6} gauss follows.

The Origin of Cosmic Rays

The age of cosmic rays. The observational evidence of the relative abundance of Li, Be, and B shows that there is neither a fragmentation equilibrium with the heavier nuclei nor does the relative abundance correspond to the cosmical abundance. This leads to the consequence that the majority of cosmic-ray particles are not eliminated by nuclear collision with the diffuse matter of the storage region and may be explained by the following two alternatives: (1) there is a stationary state with the majority of cosmic-ray particles leaking out of the region in which they are stored, instead of being eliminated by collisions; (2) the storage is such that the storage time is only a moderate fraction of the time needed for establishing fragmentation equilibrium. In any case, the relative abundance of Li, Be, and B strongly suggests that the cosmic rays have traversed about 3 g/cm^2 since obtaining relativistic energies. This value gives an average age τ of the cosmic-ray particles:

$$\tau = 1.8 \times 10^6 \frac{1}{n} \qquad \text{years} \qquad (1)$$

n being the average particle density in the storage region (assumed to be protons).

Assuming that the cosmic-ray particles are stored in certain regions, three possibilities will be discussed: (1) the disk of the galaxy, (2) the halo of the galaxy, and (3) the local group.

Storage in the disk of the galaxy. In the original galactic theory it was assumed that the cosmic-ray particles should be stored in the disk of the galaxy. With an average density of 1 proton/cm^3 one gets from Eq. (1) an average age of the cosmic-ray particles of $\tau = 1.8 \times 10^6$ years. As far as the general energy supply is concerned, we may compare the lifetime of a light quantum with the lifetime of a cosmic-ray particle, since the energy density of the star light in the disk is about comparable to the energy density of cosmic radiation, namely, about 10^{-12} erg/cm^3. The light escapes in a time of the order of 10^3 years (the thickness of the disk in light years). This means that an efficiency of about 10^{-4} is needed for the energy of cosmic radiation with respect to the thermal radiation. The power that must be supplied to the cosmic rays is of the order of 1.7×10^{-26} erg/cm^3/sec.

But the assumption of storage in the disk leads to the difficulty that it seems impossible to store the particles with energies above 10^{17} ev, which have been observed and for which no anisotropy could be proved. In a magnetic field of 10^{-5} gauss, particles with an energy of 10^{17} ev have a Larmor radius of 30 ly, which is comparable to the substructure in the interstellar gas. For the highest energies that have been observed the Larmor radii are even comparable to the thickness of the disk itself.

Storage in the halo of our galaxy. Because of these difficulties, and since we have observational evidence for magnetic fields and relativistic electrons in the halo, it was proposed that all the cosmic-ray particles might be stored in the halo of our galaxy. The lifetime of the cosmic-ray particles will now depend on the average density of the halo and the disk. This number will not only depend on the assumed density on the halo but also on the size of the halo. For the following discussion we shall assume that the mass of the gaseous matter contained in the halo can be neglected, which might be justified if the size of the halo is not too large. The integrated mass of the gaseous matter in the disk has been estimated to be $1.5 \times 10^9 M_\odot$, or $1.8 \times 10^{66} m_H$. If one assumes for the halo a semimajor axis of 10 kpc and a semiminor axis of 5.4 kpc, which has been suggested by Biermann and Davis and which is comparable with the estimates of Mills, the volume of the halo is 2400 (kpc)^3 = 7.2×10^{67} cm^3, and therefore the total energy contained in cosmic rays is 7×10^{55} ergs. This volume leads, together with the above mass, to an average particle (proton) density of 2.5×10^{-2} cm^{-3}, and we get an average lifetime of the cosmic particles of 7×10^7 years. For stationary conditions, about 2.8×10^{40} ergs/sec are necessary. If we compare this number with the total luminosity of all the stars in the galaxy $L_g = 2.5 \times 10^{10} L_\odot = 10^{44}$ ergs/sec it turns out that again an efficiency of about 10^{-4} is required, as for the storage in the disk. The power density here would be of the order 4×10^{-28} erg/cm^3/sec. Assuming a magnetic field of 5×10^{-6} gauss in the halo, a cosmic-ray particle with an energy of 10^{19} ev will have a Larmor radius of 2.2 kpc, which is already a fifth of the assumed minor axis of the halo. Therefore, according to this picture, cosmic-ray particles with energies much greater than 10^{19} ev should not exist or at least cannot be stored in this volume.

Storage in the local group. The confinement of the cosmic-ray particles within the halo must be very good, since without magnetic fields a particle would cross the halo in a straight line in about 10^{12} sec, while the particles have to be confined for 2.3×10^{15} sec. This means that the reflectivity at the boundary of the halo must be quite high. These difficulties might be somewhat reduced if one assumes that the cosmic-ray particles are stored in the local group of galaxies, since between the galaxies magnetic fields might also exist. But the magnetic field strength cannot be too high, otherwise one would have difficulties with the virial theorem. Assuming that the magnetic energy is comparable to the gravitational energy, this would lead to a magnetic field of about 4×10^{-7} gauss, using the values for the local group as given by Kahn and Woltjer. But since the energy density of this field is only 7×10^{-15} erg/cm^3, only the corresponding energy density of cosmic rays can be stored. With the known energy spectrum this would mean that only the particles above 10^{13} ev would be stored in the entire local group. With a density of 10^{-28} g/cm^3 in the local group one would get an average age of 3×10^{10} years for this part of the cosmic rays. Concerning the energy supply, we have to deal here with about 6×10^{-33} erg/cm^3/sec, or 2.5×10^{40} ergs/sec.

Acceleration of Cosmic Rays

Invoking acceleration mechanisms one should keep two problems in mind: First, one has to show that it is possible to reach relativistic (or nearly relativistic) energies by this mechanism during the appropriate time; and second, one has finally to explain the observed power-law spectrum with the right exponent. Regarding acceleration mechanisms, the betatron effect, the statistical Fermi mechanism with a number of modifications, and microinstabilities (for instance, in shock waves as mentioned by Biermann) have been discussed. Furthermore, two alternative pictures may be proposed for accelerating the particles. In the first picture the particles may be accelerated and reach their final energy directly in the near neighborhood of the sources from whence they originated. One possible explanation in this way is that there exist different discrete sources, which contribute in different forms to the observed cosmic-ray spectrum. The particles with the lowest energies (up to 50 Bev) should come from relatively inactive stars like our sun, from which we know that cosmic rays with energies up to 50 Bev are occasionally produced. Particles with energies up to 10^3 Bev should originate from active stars, and particles with even higher energies should be generated in the shells of supernovae, while the most energetic particles should come from sources outside our galaxy. This eclectic theory has been proposed by Cocconi and Morrison, but it is difficult for me to see in which way the power energy spectrum can be explained, which seems to be fulfilled over the whole part of the observed spectrum with a nearly constant exponent. With these different sources for the different parts of the energy spectrum, one might expect more abrupt changes in the exponent. To overcome this difficulty, one may assume that there is only one kind of source which gives the main contribution to the observed cosmic rays. Ginzburg assumes that all cosmic rays originate in the shells of supernovae. As far as the power supply is concerned, this is not impossible. From the Crab nebula (a remnant of a supernova of type I) we know that 10^{48} ergs showed up in the form of relativistic electrons, and it seems not implausible that a comparable amount of energy had gone into ions, while the normal output of observable light of type I supernova is about 10^{49} ergs. The total energy of type II supernova is of the order 10^{50} to 10^{51} ergs. Assuming that a major fraction of this energy goes into relativistic particles and that one supernova occurs every hundred years, this gives about 10^{40} ergs/sec available for cosmic rays. This is approximately the amount needed for the storage in the disk as well as for the storage in the halo and also for the storage in the local group.

If the cosmic-ray particles are accelerated up to the actual energies directly in the neighborhood of the sources, the consequence is that the cosmic rays are not a sink of energy for the interstellar material as a whole but might provide a source of energy for the interstellar material, although no mechanism is known to convert the energy contained in cosmic rays into kinetic energy of the clouds. Just the contrary would be the case if the other alternative plays the major role, namely, that the cosmic-ray particles are accelerated by the sources only to very moderate energies and that the main acceleration takes place within certain regions of the interstellar space of the storage volume. Here we may call the first part of acceleration at the source the injection. But the injection energy must be in the relativistic range to overcome the losses (mainly ionization) during the main accelerating phase.

If we consider the statistical Fermi mechanism, it was originally proposed by Fermi that the cosmic-ray particles should be accelerated by separate and independently moving clouds of magnetic fields. In each interaction the energy change due to the particle is of the order $dw = \pm (v_p/c)(v_g/c)w$, where v_p is the speed of the particle, v_g is the random velocity of the cloud, and w is the total energy (including the rest energy) of the particle. But head-on collisions are more likely than overtaking collisions in the ratio v_g/v_p, so that the mean gain of energy is only quadratic in v_g/c, and the mean ratio of change of energy is given by

$$\frac{dw}{dt} = \left(\frac{v_g}{c}\right)^2 \frac{1}{t_1} w \qquad (2)$$

where t_1 is the time for a single interaction of the cosmic-ray particles with the changing magnetic fields. If the particles are injected at a constant rate, are accelerated according to the above picture, and are stored with the time constant τ (that means that the probability of escape out of the accelerating region in the time dt is dt/τ), all parameters being independent of w, then the power law spectrum results with the exponent

$$\gamma = \frac{t_1}{(v_g/c)^2 \tau} \tag{3}$$

The observations show that γ is approximately 1.6. The difficulty is now to find regions in the interstellar space in which the parameters are such that the observed exponent can be explained and where sufficient power is available in the gas motion.

If we assume that the acceleration takes place in the galactic disk, then $\tau = 1.8 \times 10^6$ years. With a random velocity $v_g = 8$ km/sec, we need an interaction time t_1 of the order of 2.1×10^{-3} year, which is implausibly short. Therefore, the necessary velocities should be much higher. If we assume that the acceleration also takes place in the halo, then $\tau = 7 \times 10^7$ years. Here the velocities might be of the order of 100 km/sec, which would give $t_1 = 1.8 \times 10^1$ years. As Biermann and Davis pointed out, the conditions for the Fermi mechanism were very probably much more favorable during the early stages of the evolution of the galaxy, since with a much greater density of bright stars the gas velocities should have been relatively high and the power supply should have been higher. Therefore, the particles of highest energies, which might be very old, are stored in the halo, where the conditions might not have been so difficult.

On the other hand, the required conditions are considerably less extreme if one accepts one of the modifications of the Fermi mechanism. Davis showed, for instance, that $(v_g/c)^2(t_1/\tau)$ could be higher by a factor of 30 to 100, while the same γ would result. Furthermore, Fermi offered an alternative choice, proposing that the cosmic-ray particles may be trapped between two approaching hydromagnetic waves, so that all the reflections of the particles from the waves are head-on. Then the mean rate of change of energy is given by

$$\frac{dw}{dt} = \alpha \frac{V_w}{c} \frac{1}{t_1} w \tag{4}$$

and, therefore,

$$\gamma = \frac{1}{\alpha} \frac{t_1}{(V_w/c)\tau} \tag{5}$$

where V_w is the velocity of the waves, t_1 the mean time between collisions, and α is a factor of the order of 1. Also, for the so-called gyrorelaxation mechanism (heating by compressional hydromagnetic waves) the energy gain would be linear in V_w/c. Applying Eq. (4) for γ and assuming a wave velocity of 50 km/sec (magnetic field of 2×10^{-5} gauss) in the disk, one gets $t_1 = 4 \times 10^2$ years. For storage in the halo with a magnetic field of 0.5×10^{-5} gauss, we end up with $t_1 = 4 \times 10^4$ years.

The observed isotropy should be restored, according to Fermi, by scattering of the cosmic-ray particles on hydromagnetic shock waves. In earlier times objections were raised that this mechanism should not work, since the thickness of the shock waves should be of the order of the mean free path of the thermal particles, which is large compared to the gyro-radius of the cosmic-ray particles (with the exception of the highest energies). But the shocks can only scatter cosmic-ray particles from one helical trajectory to another and thus contribute to the cosmic-ray isotropy gyroradius, if the shock waves have a thickness that is small compared to a cosmic-ray gyroradius. But theoretical work indicates that such hydro-magnetic shocks might have at least a fine structure in which there are substantial changes in the magnetic field over a distance of the order of the gyroradii of the thermal particles, which are of course small compared to those of the cosmic-ray particles.

Possible Influence of Cosmic Rays on the Motion of the Interstellar Gas

Finally, I want to discuss one point that might be of some importance for the motions of the interstellar gas, namely, whether or not the cosmic-ray particles are effectively accelerated in interstellar space. As we have seen, the energy density of the cosmic rays is of the order 10^{-12} erg/cm^3. This energy density corresponds to a pressure of 10^{-12} dyne/cm^2. On the other hand, the normal gas pressure in the H I region is of the order of 1.4×10^{-14} dyne/cm^2, assuming a density of 1 proton/cm^3 and a temperature of 100°K. In the halo, with $N = 10^{-2}$ cm^{-3} and $T = 10^4$°K, the pressure is the same. Therefore, the pressure of the cosmic-ray particles is very large compared to the pressure of the ordinary gas. Since there are magnetic fields, the cosmic-ray pressure may not be neglected in such cases. We may regard the cosmic-ray particles as atoms of an extremely hot gas embedded in a very cool gas, which may interact with the cool gas through the magnetic field. A compressional hydromagnetic wave perpendicular to the magnetic field must not only compress the ordinary gas but also the cosmic-ray gas. For the H I region, one might think the ambipolar diffusion would prevent coupling of the ordinary gas and the magnetic field. But it can easily be shown that this is not the case, since the ambipolar diffusion velocity is normally much smaller than the wave velocity. We can express the estimate of the ambipolar diffusion velocity V_D in the following way:

$$V_D{}^2 = \frac{\lambda}{L} \frac{B^2}{4\pi\rho}$$

where λ is the mean free path for a neutral atom and L is the wavelength. Therefore, only if the wavelength is comparable to the mean free path will the ambipolar diffusion velocity be of the same order of magnitude as the Alfvén velocity, which is the speed of the compressional hydromagnetic wave. Therefore, for these cases, the cosmic-ray pressure should be taken into account—for instance, in calculating the sound velocity, which would become much higher. This will also have some influence on the dissipation of such pressure waves, since these waves will not steepen and become shock waves as fast as they will without the cosmic rays.

But of course this coupling does not exist along the magnetic field lines, since in this direction the cosmic-ray particles can move essentially freely, and their mean free path in this direction is very long. Therefore, the influence of the cosmic-ray particles due to their high pressure is, on the whole, not very simple to estimate, but I think one should at least keep this in mind for any particular problem with which one is concerned.

General References

L. Biermann and L. Davis, *Z. Naturforsch.*, **13,** 709 (1958).
L. Biermann and L. Davis, *Z. Ap.*, **51,** 19 (1960).
G. Cocconi, *Ap. J. (Suppl.),* **4,** 417 (1960).
L. Davis, *Nuovo cimento (Suppl.),* [X]8, 444 (1958).
V. L. Ginzburg, "Progress in Elementary Particle and Cosmic Ray Physics," Vol. 4, Interscience, New York, 1958.
F. D. Kahn and L. Woltjer, *Ap. J.*, **130,** 705 (1959).
E. N. Parker, *Rev. Mod. Phys.*, **30,** 955 (1958).

Discussion

Dr. Christy: This energy source of approximately 10^{-3} of the luminosity of the galaxy that you require for the cosmic rays is quite serious. Do you think that there is a single source or a combination of sources that you have named that adequately accounts for this?

Dr. Lüst: I agree completely that this factor 10^{-4} or 10^{-3} is really very severe. I would think that supernovae, active stars, and things like this together might make up this energy balance; also, if you just count the very luminous stars and take a factor of 10^{-4} efficiency, this would bring you to the same order.

Dr. Spitzer: I believe there is a fourth possibility here. If you could assume that the magnetic field is essentially weak and tangled, you come out with a situation in which the cosmic rays are not confined; they are proceeding throughout the universe. One then gets around Dr. Christy's problem by essentially assuming they were created with the universe. You then are probably required to explain the amount of beryllium and boron. The uncomfortable thing is that you have to assume that the heavy elements were created originally. If you did assume that you needed 3 g/cm^2 along the particle path, this would give you an intergalactic density of 3×10^{-28} g/cm^3. I don't know how this compares to the relativistic estimates.

Dr. Lemaître: Of course that seems rather high, 10^{-28} g/cm^3; as far as I see there is no need for an intergalactic density higher than 10^{-30}. That, of course, would give 2×10^{12} years for the time. It is not quite impossible that the cosmic rays would be of primary origin.

Dr. Biermann: One sees that there is a theoretical possibility to make all the cosmic rays in the local group of galaxies. If we would say that nothing escaped into the true intergalactic space, the energy density that would emerge is within the limits imposed by the magnetic field, accepting the Kahn–Woltjer figures for the possible magnetic field and energy density of cosmic radiation which could be sustained by that.

With regard to the universal picture, we have a point already raised by Morrison; if we assume that the average density of matter condensed into stars is of the order of 10^{-31} g/cm^3, we would have to transform all of this into helium to obtain 10^{-12} erg/cm^3. And this energy would have been converted with something like 100 per cent efficiency to cosmic-ray energy. I think that pretty much rules out the possibility that the production of cosmic rays can be understood by a picture of this sort. If one accepts a universal theory, it must be a fundamental theory in the sense that it must be connected with something that is outside the laws of ordinary physics, including nuclear physics.

With regard to this efficiency of something like 10^{-3}, which was commented upon by Dr. Christy, this is, I think, not so improbable as it might seem at first sight. We know, for instance, solar flares in which cosmic-ray particles are accelerated. In these events the fraction of cosmic-ray energy, or energy of relativistic electrons, when compared with the energy present in lower quality form, ultraviolet light or so, is of the order of 1 or 2 per cent. For a general discussion of these questions, I may perhaps refer to an article by Dr. Lüst and myself in Volume VI of "Compendium for Astrophysics." If one makes a rough guess that about 10 per cent of the over-all energy produced thermally in our whole galactic system is due to stars that are active in some sense, and that of this 10 per cent again something of the order of 1 per cent is used to give energy to cosmic rays, then one would, without any particular effort, have this efficiency of 10^{-3} or a reasonable fraction thereof. So I don't feel it is a quite unreasonable proposition to argue this way.

Dr. G. R. Burbidge: I would like to make a comment about this calculation of the storage based on the number of grams of material the cosmic rays have traversed. It seems to me that a point which cannot be excluded, and is often not discussed, is that if one supposes that the cosmic rays originate in active stars and in supernovae, there is also the possibility that a good bit of the spallation which gives rise to lithium, beryllium, and boron takes place in the stellar atmosphere or in the shells before the material gets into the interstellar medium. So unless one can make some very careful estimates of how large a contribution this can be, I think that the storage times one gets in this way can be misleading and in fact too high.

Dr. Spitzer: That would increase the power problems.

Dr. G. R. Burbidge: If the observations that were mentioned previously on the production of tritium are good, we have some evidence that this kind of effect does take place in the sun, presumably.

Dr. Woltjer: I would like in the first place to comment on this possibility which Dr. Burbidge brought up. There is an opposing factor there—namely, that if a large part of the interstellar matter is locked up in magnetic clouds, it may very well be that interstellar matter is to a certain extent shielded, at least for the low-energy cosmic rays. One doesn't know how much this could be, but it could be an important factor. The second point is something that has been raised, of course, many times, but which now becomes particularly acute, and that is the question of the values of the exponent when one assumes the Fermi acceleration mechanism. One sees that in almost all nonthermal radio sources the exponent—

at least of the electron spectrum—is always the same in a very narrow range; and it seems very hard to explain this on the basis of the two noncorrelated time scales of the Fermi theory.

Dr. Oppenheimer: This has always been really unsatisfactory.

Dr. Lüst: To your last point, I think there you are right, that this is one of the real difficulties—that the exponent always comes out in this order of magnitude. The only possible hint might be that if the energy needed for acceleration of cosmic rays is really an essential part, so that the dissipation of cosmic rays has to be taken into account, for instance, in the motion of the interstellar clouds, it might be that the exponent adjusts itself in such a way that dissipation is minimized.

Dr. Woltjer: I don't think that that has to do directly with the exponent. This could have something to do with the approximate equality between the cosmic-ray energy density and, say, the energy density of motions in interstellar space. But if what you say is right, the exponent would also be determined, for example, by the number of injected particles.

Dr. Lüst: Yes, but if the exponent would be much lower, much more energy would be contained in the high-energy part and maybe you would run into difficulties. On the other hand, if it would be much higher, so that the energy spectrum would be much steeper, the dissipation would be much too low.

Dr. Biermann: Davis has discussed this much more carefully than we can here. I don't recall the details, but I do recall that he convinced us—we originally also were of a different opinion—that you might have a sort of reaction between the production of cosmic-ray particles and the hydromagnetic processes, which has the effective result that you very often should expect something of the order unity for the exponent, if you get a sizeable amount of energy converted into cosmic rays at all and if that draws an essential fraction of the available energy.

Dr. Kahn: If you introduce the cosmic-ray pressure and thereby increase the velocity of sound, you may reduce the frictional dissipation of energy, but aren't you in danger of radiating away the kinetic energy of motion of the gas to the boundary of the galaxy? The energy probably would be radiated in hydromagnetic wave motion rather than in electromagnetic waves. Wouldn't you be in as bad a situation then as you were before?

Dr. Lüst: Possibly. But this would depend also upon the structure of the magnetic field. For instance, if cosmic-ray particles are caught in some region, and if you increase the magnetic field, you may increase the energy density of the cosmic-ray particles in the whole volume and it would not really lose energy.

Dr. G. R. Burbidge: I would like to ask a question about the cosmic-ray particles of highest energy. If one contains the cosmic rays, let us say within the local group, and if one says that the Fermi mechanism within the galaxy and within the halo is not a very effective mechanism, can one really explain the acceleration of these particles within supernova remnants and things of this nature, or are energies of 10^{18} ev and greater really too high?

Dr. Lüst: I personally feel it would be very difficult to get to such high energies in the direct neighborhood of a supernova, but I am not sure.

Dr. G. R. Burbidge: Wouldn't you think, therefore, that at least this is one argument which might suggest that there is some small extragalactic component of very high energy cosmic rays?

Dr. Woltjer: In extragalactic space it is also becoming difficult with the large radius of curvature for energies of 5×10^{19} ev.

Dr. G. R. Burbidge: I don't think this can be done in the local region, but I think it can be done in other clusters.

Stellar evolution phases
with mass ejection

M. Schwarzschild

For the purpose of this conference, we are to consider stellar evolution only in two specific aspects, the consumption of interstellar matter by the birth of stars, and the replenishment of interstellar matter by mass ejection from stars. Let us start with the first of these two aspects.

It seems to me that there is only one item related to star births that is really important for the study of interstellar matter—the over-all rate of mass consumption by star births. This rate we can estimate by the following argument, first developed by Salpeter: For the solar neighborhood, we know the luminosity function, $\phi_{MS}(M_{\mathrm{vis}})$, i.e., the number of main-sequence stars of a given visual magnitude per cubic parsec. From the theory of the early evolution phases, we know the main-sequence lifetime, τ_{MS}, of a star as a function of its brightness or mass. If we divide the luminosity function by these lifetimes, we obtain the birth-rate function, $\psi(M_{\mathrm{vis}})$, i.e., the number of stars of a given visual absolute magnitude born per year and per cubic parsec. If, finally, we multiply this birth-rate function by the masses of the corresponding stars and integrate over all magnitudes corresponding to stars that have lifetimes shorter than the galactic time scale, we find

$$\int_{+3}^{\infty} \psi \, \frac{M}{M_{\odot}} \, dM_{\mathrm{vis}} = 0.01 \, \frac{M_{\odot}}{(\mathrm{pc})^3 (\mathrm{billion\ years})}$$

This represents the rate of mass consumption by the birth of upper main-sequence stars. To this we should add the corresponding number for

266

lower main-sequence stars which we can estimate, under the assumption that the presently observed lower main-sequence stars were formed, more or less evenly, throughout the past 15 billion years; it is

$$\frac{0.05\ M_\odot/(\text{pc})^3}{15\ \text{billion years}} = 0.003\ \frac{M_\odot}{(\text{pc})^3 (\text{billion years})}$$

The sum of these two values gives us our estimate of the over-all rate of mass consumption by star births in the solar neighborhood.

We feel sure that this consumption rate must be more or less balanced by the rate of mass ejection from dying stars since, otherwise, we would find an uncomfortably short exhaustion time for the observed interstellar matter in the solar neighborhood. If we accordingly assume, more or less, a steady cycling of mass from the interstellar matter into stars and back, we can now estimate the turnover time for this cycling by dividing the mass consumption rate we just derived into the observed mass per cubic parsec of the interstellar matter in the solar neighborhood, which gives us for the turnover time,

$$\frac{0.02\ M_\odot/(\text{pc})^3}{0.013\ M_\odot/(\text{pc})^3 (\text{billion years})} \approx 1\ \text{billion years}$$

The accuracy of this value for the turnover time is terribly hard for me to judge. To be really cautious, one might have to say that a correction of a factor 10 in either direction is not excluded, although I myself would be very surprised if the final correction will turn out to be that large. The main uncertainty, I feel, arises from the bolometric corrections that are needed in the derivation of the birth-rate function. The bolometric corrections are greatly uncertain for O- and B-type stars, but it is just these spectral types which give the main contribution to the over-all mass consumption rate. As soon as we know the bolometric correction for the O- and B-type stars more certainly from satellite or rocket measurements, we shall be able to give the turnover rate with much more accuracy.

We shall now turn to the second aspect, the replenishment of the interstellar matter by mass ejection from stars. That such a process is actually going on as a general phenomenon in the solar neighborhood is suggested by three separate arguments. The first one runs as follows: Stellar evolution computations show that stars in the mass range in question here (3 to 30 solar masses) burn on the average only about 30 per cent of their total hydrogen store while they are in the main-sequence band. Furthermore, they do not seem to burn more than an additional 5 per cent in the subsequent evolution phases. This is shown by the observed fact that the total energy output of all the stars away from the main sequence in the solar neighborhood amounts only to a modest fraction of the total energy output of the main-sequence stars. It appears, therefore, fairly certain that these heavier stars, on the average, burn only about one-third of their entire hydrogen store during their active lifetime. It seems to me hard to imagine how a star could manage to die with two-thirds of its fuel left, except by ejecting the outer fuel-rich portion of its mass.

The second argument is based on the circumstances that we cannot see how white dwarfs can come about except as the end result of stellar evolution; but a white dwarf has a mass far lower than the average dying star. Accordingly, if a white dwarf is to be the final state of a dying star, the latter has to get rid of a large fraction of its mass.

Last, but not least, there is direct spectroscopic evidence of mass ejection, at least from super giants, as Deutsch has shown.

Altogether then, it looks to me entirely plausible that a typical dying star ejects something like two-thirds of its mass and that this process largely balances the consumption of interstellar matter by star births.

This completes our discussion of the main cycle by which matter seems to go back and forth between the interstellar state and the stellar state, with a turnover time of the order of 1 billion years. I would now like to turn to two auxiliary cycles which do not involve ordinary main-sequence stars, and therefore are not included in the main cycle. I shall ignore the supernovae throughout this discussion, since they contribute little to the total cycling in mass, although they do play a decisive role in the transmutation of the elements. This is a topic that will be discussed in detail by Dr. Christy.

The first of the two auxiliary cycles refers to mass ejection from stars that are still in their initial contraction phase. In the Hertzsprung–Russell diagram of very young clusters, the bright stars lie just where we expect them, namely, on the initial main sequence with a slight turning off at the very brightest stars. However, the faintest stars, which are presumably still in the initial contraction phase, do not behave as expected. Theoretical predictions would have placed them on a fairly horizontal, narrow, sparcely populated line in the Hertzsprung–Russell diagram. Instead, we find them occupying a large area stretching from the theoretical line toward fainter magnitudes, with some extreme stars being more than four magnitudes fainter than expected. The observational data are not yet too strong; particularly, there have been lively arguments recently regarding the possibility that many of the stars in question might not be members of the associations under discussion. However, the unexpected phenomenon I have described is clearly shown, even if you consider only the T Tauri stars, whose membership can hardly be doubted.

The only explanation of this unexpected phenomenon which I am aware of, and which seems to me reasonable, is one suggested by Dr. Spitzer. The discrepancy between theory and observation may be caused by the earlier assumption that each star goes through its initial contraction phase with a more or less constant mass. Under this assumption, the faintest stars have hopelessly longer contraction ages than the age of the association as judged by the brighter stars. If, however, the faintest stars went through most of the contraction phases with masses substantially higher than they seem to have now, and if they then lost a large fraction of their initial mass during the last portion of their contraction phase—for example, by some form of rotational instability—they may well have arrived at their present observed position in the Hertzsprung–Russell diagram in a time equal to the age of the association as a whole. To fit the observations by this explanation, it is required that a contracting star commonly loses about one-half of its mass before it settles on the main sequence. An additional argument for Dr. Spitzer's suggestion is given by the spectroscopic peculiarities of the T Tauri stars, which long ago were tentatively explained in terms of mass ejection.

Another pleasant consequence of this picture is the following: The T Tauri stars appear to be generally rich in lithium, while main-sequence stars are poor in this element. By whatever process the lithium in the T Tauri stars may have originated, we are sure that no lithium can exist in the bulk of the interior of the T Tauri stars because of the very fast transmutation rate of lithium at temperatures above 2.5 million degrees. If the T Tauri stars eject a good fraction of their total mass, including the lithium-rich outer shell, they are bound to end up as lithium-poor main-sequence stars.

If we then accept the picture of strong mass ejection in the last portion of the contraction phases, we have to assume a mass distribution for the protostars substantially different from the mass distribution of main-sequence stars; on the average the protostars must be about twice as heavy as the main-sequence stars. This suggests that the mass consumption of the birth of protostars may be higher than the value we discussed earlier by perhaps a factor 2, and that half the consumed mass goes through the main cycle while the other half goes through this auxiliary cycle. It seems doubtful, however, that this auxiliary cycle has any substantial consequences for the interstellar matter; the energy supplied by the auxiliary cycle to the interstellar gas can hardly be large, since the main nuclear-energy sources are not being tapped at all in this process.

May I then turn to the second, highly speculative, auxiliary cycle. It has long been suspected that the upper limit for stellar masses is set by the occurrence of the pulsational instability in excessively massive stars through an indirect effect of the radiation pressure. Indeed, recent detailed calculations indicate that stars of more than about 65 solar masses should be pulsationally unstable. Double star observations seem to show that stars of about 90 solar masses do exist. But, on the other hand, spectroscopic observations seem to make it plausible that all the heavier stars, say above 65 solar masses, may show shell emission of the P Cygni type. It appears, therefore, possible that all stars above 65 solar masses are pulsationally unstable, but that this instability takes a fatal form only for stars above, say, 100 solar masses.

Now this pulsational instability for excessively massive stars is energized by the effects of the pulsation on the hydrogen burning in the core. Accordingly a star of say 200 solar masses, which is still in the initial contraction phase and hence does not burn any hydrogen, cannot show this instability. It seems, therefore, not implausible that protostars of such very high masses might be born, might go through their entire contraction phases, and might then blow up the moment they start hydrogen burning. Such a process would represent another cycling of matter between the interstellar and stellar state. Since this cycle taps nuclear-energy sources, it could, in principle, act as an appreciable energy source for the interstellar matter. But I do not know any method by which we could, at present, estimate the mass consumption rate of this auxiliary cycle. The extrapolation of the observed birth-rate function for stars with stable masses into the range of hypothetical overmassive protostars is far too uncertain to show whether this additional process could make any substantial contribution to the other cycling processes or not.

I should now like to leave the auxiliary cycles and return to the main one, with the aim of reviewing the various consequences that this cycle might have for the interstellar matter.

Without any doubt, the most important consequence for the interstellar matter is the change in composition caused by nuclear transmutations in the stellar phase of the cycling. This topic will be covered in detail by Dr. Christy, and I will, accordingly, skip it here entirely.

As a second consequence of the cycling, you might think of the destruction of dust grains by the heating of the matter during the contraction of protostars. However, our main cycle appears to be rather too slow to be of importance in this connection. Other processes that destroy dust grains and the balancing processes that reform them are presently estimated to have a time scale of the order of 10^8 years, i.e., to be 10 times more effective than our main cycle, with a turnover time of the order of 10^9 years. Hence, only if it should turn out that we have grossly underestimated the turnover speed of the main cycle or the relative importance of the auxiliary cycles could all these processes be of any importance for the interstellar dust.

As a third consequence of the cycling you might consider the possible gain of the interstellar matter in macroscopic kinetic energy by the mechanisms that cause the ejection of mass from stars on the return trip to the interstellar matter. If this process is to be of any importance, it appears from Dr. Biermann's discussion that it should provide a rate of energy gain of at least 10^{-4} ergs/g/sec, since otherwise it would not compete with other energy-providing processes.

It is easy to compute that to provide this rate of energy gain with a turnover time of 1 billion years, the mass ejected from stars must, on the average, have a velocity of about 30 km/sec. This velocity seems to me uncomfortably high. As far as I know, it distinctly exceeds those indicated by the spectroscopic evidence for red giants or for the T Tauri stars. As it stands, therefore, it seems to me that one cannot make a strong argument for the mass ejection from stars as a major source for the macroscopic kinetic energy of the interstellar matter.

As the last item, I should like to mention the possible consequence of the cycling for the interstellar magnetic fields. During that part of the cycle in which interstellar matter goes into stars, i.e., during the formation of stars, the physical situation presumably must permit the separation of the matter from the magnetic fields, and that may occur through the process investigated by Spitzer and Mestel. On the other hand, what may happen with regard to the magnetic fields during the return trip, i.e., the ejection of mass from stars, seems far less clear. It appears not implausible, however, that the ejected mass may be prevented from regaining a position on the lines of force of the general interstellar magnetic fields, since the ejection process does presumably not go through sufficiently cool phases in which the movement of mass across magnetic field lines would be relatively easy. Even though I feel on very unsafe grounds here, it does not seem to me implausible that the cycling we have discussed might have very essential effects on the interstellar magnetic fields.

Discussion

Dr. Lüst: If one could treat the outflow as a hydrodynamical problem, would it not be conceivable to get the higher velocities at large distances, since the gravitational field acts somewhat like a channel, as shown for the corpuscular radiation?

Ed.: A discussion followed on the mass-loss question in connection with Deutsch's results. Dr. Biermann noted that the steady component of the solar corpuscular radiation has indeed a high value, although there the mass flow is negligible. For a further discussion of these questions the reader is referred to the proceedings of the Fourth Symposium on Cosmical Gas Dynamics held at Varenna in 1960.

Dr. Schwarzschild: If we are permitted to extrapolate the solar case to the red giants at a fixed velocity but enormously higher density, then this ejection process would become a major source of energy for the interstellar matter. But it still is true at the moment that direct evidence does not seem to exist.

Dr. Kahn: On your last point: It may be hard to get matter out of the magnetic field, but I think it is even harder to keep ionized matter confined by the magnetic field. Suppose you try and set up a boundary. You usually find that it is rather unstable.

Dr. Spitzer: Isn't this different? You have a material with one magnetic field and a different material with a different magnetic field hitting it.

Dr. Kahn: But the magnetic field with which it comes along isn't anything much compared with the interstellar magnetic field.

Dr. Spitzer: That is right. And you will get flutes of one material going into the other. But will you ever get really detailed mixing?

Dr. Kahn: At what stage is it mixed? How fine must the flutes you want be?

Dr. Spitzer: Fine enough so that on a macroscopic scale the material experiences a different flux per unit area than it had before.

Dr. Kahn: The finer you make the flutes surely the more we have to worry about dissipative processes which will mix the material and the field together.

Dr. Spitzer: The question is: Is it reasonable to believe that the flutes will be small enough? After all, the longer the wavelength, the more rapidly these things grow. There is a certain wavelength of maximum rate of growth. The small ones haven't grown much, perhaps. I think it is not obvious whether or not really complete mixing will result.

Dr. Kahn: Whenever one considers matter in such situations it always seems to be unstable.

Dr. Lüst: In which stage would this mass loss from contracting stars usually occur?

Dr. Schwarzschild: The star must not become fixed in mass so early that from then on the fixed mass contraction time is substantially too long. Thus in the case of the fainter stars, the star, after the ejection, must land more or less where you observe it now; any reasonable rate of evolution at this low luminosity is just too slow.

Dr. Lüst: Thus the trouble with the angular momentum would start much earlier.

Dr. Christy: You mentioned the problem that one doesn't see the luminosity corresponding to the burning of a large fraction of the hydrogen. Has there ever been any suggestion that we were losing a lot of luminosity in the infrared?

Dr. Schwarzschild: Yes, there have been such suggestions. If you go to very faint stars, I don't know of any arguments that can limit the luminosity. But if you go into the giant region, I really think a large infrared luminosity is doubtful. Just the phenomenon that we have a band of unstable stars (irregular and long-period variables) which seem to terminate the observed HR diagrams makes me feel a little skeptical as to whether there is any chance of getting substantial infrared light.

Dr. E. M. Burbidge: One used to think that this rather puzzling constancy of the mass function in a number of clusters would give information on the fragmentation process when the protostars formed. On this new picture it should rather give information on the statistics of the mass-loss process.

Dr. Schwarzschild: If this new picture is true, the mass function observed on the main sequence is the product of the original process determining the mass function for the protostars, and the reduction of mass during the contraction stage. So I think we cannot get a clear answer to either one or the other.

Dr. E. M. Burbidge: Unless we assumed the initial mass were very large and that the process did not particularly depend on the exact value of the mass.

Dr. Schwarzschild: Right, If you swing to the other extreme and start with protostars that are all really large. But observations do not force us to accept tyis.

Dr. Strömgren: Returning to the question of the estimate of the turnover time and the uncertainty of this estimate if one looks at your $\psi(M_{vis})$ curve, the right part of it is the one that is not too much affected by the bolometric-correction uncertainty. Thus, one can derive an upper limit to the turnover time. When we compare with the theoretical predictions that Dr. Christy is going to discuss, it would certainly be necessary to know it better than to a factor of 10. Perhaps one could reduce the uncertainty somewhat by this kind of argument. From your curve it looks as if one-half of the computed rate of change is certain.

Dr. Schwarzschild: Right. I think you cannot go below one-half of my number for the mass consumption rate if you believe the theoretical main-sequence lifetimes for the early B stars which give the main contribution.

Past distribution of the interstellar gas

B. Strömgren

Dr. Schwarzschild has discussed problems of the exchange of matter and energy between stars and interstellar matter. I should like to consider briefly the question of what we can learn from studies of the properties of stars regarding interstellar matter at previous phases of evolution of our galaxy.

Dr. von Hoerner has already given a general discussion of this subject. I wish to refer to Dr. von Hoerner for the background of the discussion today, and in particular also to the volume "Die Entstehung von Sternen durch Kondensation diffuser Materie," with contributions by G. R. Burbidge, F. D. Kahn, R. Ebert, S. von Hoerner, and St. Temesvary [1].

If for a star we can determine the chemical composition, the space velocity, the orbit through the galaxy, and the age, then we can derive a corresponding piece of information concerning the past history of the interstellar medium of our galaxy.

Ideally, one would determine on the basis of the space velocity and the age of the star its place of formation, and then one would know that at a certain time and location the star formed out of the interstellar medium, and had such and such chemical composition.

In very few, if any, cases can we carry out this ideal program. However, for very young stars that are still in associations we have a situation that approaches the ideal, and for the young high-velocity stars that Dr. Blaauw has discussed we have a similar situation, since they can be traced back to the associations to which they used to belong.

When we go to considerably older stars, we find that the uncertainty of the data, in particular of the space velocities and ages, are such that we generally do not get useful results from individual stars. Nevertheless, statistical studies of the results pertaining to a large number of stars yield very valuable information regarding the evolutionary history of the interstellar gas of our galaxy.

In particular, investigations of the correlation between ultraviolet excess determined from photoelectric UBV photometry and space velocity, by N. G. Roman, H. L. Johnson, O. Eggen, A. Sandage, and others, have yielded important results. Wallerstein and Carlson [2] and Wallerstein [3] have carried out a calibration for late F and G stars of ultraviolet excess, in terms of the atmospheric chemical-abundance ratio Fe/H as derived from quantitative analysis based on high-dispersion spectra, and they have studied the relation between chemical composition and space velocity in further detail.

Referring to this general background I should like to discuss in somewhat more detail a few specific questions. I shall describe, first, a method based on photoelectric photometery in bands of intermediate width (200 A) for determination of absolute magnitude for stars in the spectral range A2–G0 and of luminosity classes III, IV, and V. The precision obtained is fairly high (probable errors $\pm 0^{m}_{.}1$ to $0^{m}_{.}2$). and the absolute magnitudes are therefore satisfactory for the following purposes: (1) determination of space velocities of relatively high precision, and (2) high-accuracy determination of location in the Hertzsprung–Russell diagram and, correspondingly, a satisfactory division of the stars under consideration into age groups. Next, a method of deriving an index of chemical composition (atmospheric Fe/H ratio) for F and early G stars, from photoelectric photometery of the type just mentioned, will be discussed. Finally, I would like to report briefly on a few results pertaining to the problem of correlation of age, chemical composition, and space velocity which have been obtained using the methods referred to.

The photoelectric photometry in question is four-color photometry in wavelength bands as specified in Table 1.

The u band is isolated with a composite glass filter, the three other bands with the help of interference filters. The magnitudes u, v, b, and y

Table 1

	Central wavelength, A	Half-width, A
u	3500	300
v	4110	190
b	4670	180
y	5470	230

corresponding to the intensities measured consecutively through the four filters are combined to yield three indices, as follows:

$b-y$ a color index that is relatively insensitive to chemical-composition effects because the effect of absorption lines is about the same for the b and y magnitudes.

$c_1 = (u-v) - (v-b)$ a color difference that is a measure of the Balmer discontinuity (cf. Strömgren [4])

$m_1 = (v-b) - (b-y)$ a color difference that is a measure of the total intensity of the metal lines in the v band, i.e., a metal-content index (cf. Strömgren [5])

The relation of this four-color system to other color systems, in particular the UBV system, the six-color system of Stebbins and Whitford [6], and W. Becker's four-color system [7], is discussed in some detail by Strömgren [8]. We may note that the u–band is located practically in its entirety, below the Balmer discontinuity.

In the spectral range A2–G0 and for luminosity classes III, IV, and V, the combination of the indices $b-y$ and c_1 yields absolute magnitudes of very satisfactory accuracy. Calibration of the $c_1 - (b-y)$ diagram in terms of visual absolute magnitude M_v has been carried out on the basis of somewhat more than 100 M_v values derived from trigonometric parallaxes and cluster parallaxes (for members of the Hyades cluster, the Coma cluster, and the nucleus of the Ursa major stream). The residuals obtained in the calibration process indicate that M_v can be determined from $b-y$ and c_1 with a probable error of $\pm 0^{m}_{.}1$ to $0^{m}_{.}2$.

The absolute magnitudes were corrected according to the value of the metal-content index m_1 to allow for the effect of variations in chemical composition; i.e., the classification is actually three-dimensional. However, the corrections in question are fairly small.

It should be emphasized that the $c_1 - (b-y)$ method of classification is sensitive to the effects of interstellar reddening, contrary to the case of the $c_1 l$-method of two-dimensional classification (cf. Strömgren [4]). However, in all the applications of the method considered here, the stars in question are within 90 pc, in the great majority of cases in fact within 50 pc, and it can therefore generally be assumed that the effects of interstellar reddening are negligible.

Distance and space velocities derived on the basis of visual absolute magnitudes with a probable error of $\pm 0^{m}_{.}1$ to $0^{m}_{.}2$ have quite satisfactory precision. Also the corresponding accuracy of location in the Hertzsprung–Russell diagram permits adequate subdivision of the stars into age groups. For the width of the main sequence of hydrogen-burning stars is 1^{m} to 2^{m} for the spectral range in question, and when the absolute magnitude is determined with an accuracy of $0^{m}_{.}1$ to $0^{m}_{.}2$ we would expect that the age can be estimated with an accuracy of, very approximately, 10 per cent of the main-sequence lifetime of the star.

Let us consider next the derivation of the Fe/H ratio from the metal-content index m_1. For the F and early G stars a standard relation between m_1 and $b-y$ was derived from the observation of member stars of the Hyades cluster. The deviation Δm_1 of a measured m_1 value from the standard value is then an index of the difference in metal content (i.e., the Fe/H ratio, since most of the stronger metal lines in the 4100 band are Fe lines) between the star in question and the Hyades cluster stars. We define Δm_1 in such a way that a positive Δm_1 indicates that the metal content is lower than for the Hyades stars.

The photometric probable error of a Δm_1 value determined from two observations is about $\pm 0^{\text{m}}005$. For the late F and early G stars a calibration of Δm_1 in terms of the abundance ratio Fe/H was carried out on the basis of Wallerstein's determinations of Fe/H ratios (cf. [3]). The nature of the correlation is seen from Table 2.

Table 2

	$\log\left(\dfrac{\text{Fe}}{\text{H}}\right) - \log\left(\dfrac{\text{Fe}}{\text{H}}\right)_{\text{sun}}$ according to Wallerstein	Δm relative to the Hyades stars
Group 1 (average values)	0.22	$0^{\text{m}}010$
Group 2 (average values)	−0.39	$0^{\text{m}}062$
Group 3 (average values)	−1.88	$0^{\text{m}}172$

A linear relation const $-\ 13\Delta m_1$ is found to reproduce the $\log(\text{Fe}/\text{H})$ values quite well. In fact the scatter in the relation suggests that $\log(\text{Fe}/\text{H})$ can be predicted from Δm_1 with an accuracy of 0.1 to 0.2, comparable with the accuracy of the values determined from the high-dispersion spectra. However, it should be kept in mind that the material on the basis of which this conclusion is drawn is still small, and the actual uncertainty may well be somewhat larger. Nevertheless, it is clearly possible with the help of the m_1 indices to segregate not only the extreme population II stars of group 3 from stars of Hyades composition, but also stars that differ in composition from the latter by a factor of, say, 3 to 4.

Photoelectric *uvby* photometry has been carried out in collaboration with C. Perry for approximately 1200 A2–G0 stars (Harvard classification) brighter than apparent visual magnitude $6^{\text{m}}5$ and between declinations $-10°$ and $+65°$. The observations were made with the 20-inch reflector at

Mount Palomar Observatory and the 36-inch and 16-inch reflectors of the Kitt Peak National Observatory. Reductions have been completed for about 40 per cent of the stars, and the following discussion is based on the photometric data available for these stars. A discussion based on the complete material will be published elsewhere.

From the observed values of $b-y$, c_1, and m_1 the absolute magnitude, the distance, and the quantity Δm_1 were derived as described above. For the F and G stars distances were combined with proper motions and radial velocities where the latter were available (as is the case for the great majority of the stars in question) to give the space velocities. In what follows we shall limit ourselves to results obtained for F4–G2 stars of luminosity classes IV and V, i.e., to stars generally older than about 1 billion years.

If the stars are plotted in an $m_1 - (b-y)$ diagram it is seen that the corresponding chemical compositions range from Hyades composition to a composition in which the Fe/H ratio is down by a factor of about 5. Among the stars brighter than apparent visual magnitude 6^m5, the extreme population II stars, with Fe/H ratios down to two orders of magnitude are not represented at all.

Let us consider, first, certain general features of the correlation between age—as indicated by location in the Hertzsprung–Russell diagram—and metal content. For the spectral range in question it is found that stars within a few tenths of the zero-age line generally have Fe/H ratios that do not differ much from that of the Hyades cluster stars. Among the stars that have evolved away from the zero-age line one finds stars of Hyades composition—even for the latest types included in the discussion, i.e., G1 and G2—as well as stars with Fe/H ratios down by factors up to about 5.

An attempt was made to segregate through the location in the Hertzsprung–Russell diagram a group of stars of approximately the same age as the galactic cluster M 67. For these stars the average value of Δm_1 was found to be $+0^m025$, indicating that the average Fe/H ratio is down by a factor of about 2 in comparison with that of Hyades members. The scatter in Δm_1 for these stars is considerably larger than for a comparison group of earlier (and younger) F stars.

The conclusion reached by Greenstein, Sandage, Oke, O. Wilson, and others—that stars of nearly the same chemical composition as the Hyades stars have been formed out of the interstellar medium of our galaxy through a period of considerable length, presumably longer than 4 billion years—is thus confirmed. There is evidence for some scatter in the chemical composition of stars formed at the same epoch, but it should be emphasized that further investigations are necessary before more detailed conclusions can be drawn regarding this point. In particular, a better calibration of the Hertzsprung–Russell diagram in terms of age is required—a calibration that takes into account the effect of differences in chemical composition.

Next, we shall consider certain aspects of the correlation between age, as estimated from the location in the Hertzsprung–Russell diagram, and space velocity. The material of late F and early G stars was subdivided into three groups according to the color index $b-y$ and the absolute magnitude M_v. The first group consists of stars within $0^{\mathrm{m}}5$ of the zero-age line. The second group consists of stars located in the Hertzsprung–Russell diagram in the region occupied by stars of the old galactic cluster M 67, i.e., for the color range in question $0^{\mathrm{m}}9$ to $1^{\mathrm{m}}2$ above the zero-age line. The third group contains the stars that are $1^{\mathrm{m}}3$ to $1^{\mathrm{m}}7$ above the zero-age line, with ages smaller than that of M 67 and larger than the age of NGC 752.

From the available material of space velocities it was found that the average speed $\underset{\sim}{Q}$ relative to the local standard of rest (computed excluding high-velocity stars) was as follows for the three groups: 26, 37, and 29 km/sec, with probable errors in each case of about ± 1 km/sec. We see that the average speed is definitely higher for the oldest group than for the two others. For the latter the average speed is indeed very close to the value found for groups of younger stars such as late A stars, early F stars, and Hyades–Praesepe type K giants, i.e., for stars in the age range from 2×10^8 to 1×10^9 years.

These results suggest that the average speed $\underset{\sim}{Q}$ is nearly the same for all stars in the age range from 2×10^8 years to about 2 to 3×10^9 years. At the age of M 67 a definite increase in $\underset{\sim}{Q}$ has occurred. On the basis of the present material it is not possible to indicate more precisely how $\underset{\sim}{Q}$ increases with the age of the group of stars considered. However, it appears that such more detailed information can be obtained if the observational material is enlarged, and when the satisfactory age calibration of the Hertzsprung–Russell diagram just referred to is available. On the basis of more material it should also be possible to carry out a corresponding analysis of the velocity components at right angles to the galactic plane.

Finally, let us consider the correlation between chemical composition as indicated by Δm_1 and the average speed $\underset{\sim}{Q}$ (excluding high-velocity stars). The material was again subdivided into three groups, with Δm_1 less than $0^{\mathrm{m}}015$, between $0^{\mathrm{m}}015$ and $0^{\mathrm{m}}035$, and in the range $0^{\mathrm{m}}035$ to $0^{\mathrm{m}}060$, respectively. The mean speeds $\underset{\sim}{Q}$ were found to be 28.5, 32, and 36.5 km/sec, again with probable errors of ± 1 km/sec for each value. There is thus an increase in $\underset{\sim}{Q}$ with decreasing metal content. This corresponds to the finding of N. G. Roman that $\underset{\sim}{Q}$ is larger for weak-line than for strong-line stars of late F or early G spectral type.

With regard to the high-velocity stars in our material (i.e., disk-population high-velocity stars) it is found that the average Δm_1 is positive, about equal to that found for the stars in the M 67 age range. However, a considerable fraction of these high-velocity stars have Δm_1 values, indicating the same chemical composition as the Hyades stars.

In concluding, I should like to mention that it is planned to extend the program of photoelectric four-color observations of the type described for F8 and G0 stars (Harvard classification) between $-10°$ and $+65°$ to apparent visual magnitude 8^m. This program should yield a sample of approximately 2000 stars of luminosity classes IV and V and in the color index $B-V$ range $0^m.45$ to $0^m.65$. A material of this size could be subdivided into a fairly large number of subgroups, according to age and chemical composition, so that rather a detailed analysis of the correlations between age, chemical composition, and space velocity would become possible.

References

[1] G. R. Burbidge, F. D. Kahn, R. Ebert, S. von Hoerner, St. Temesvary, "Die Entstehung von Sternen durch Kondensation diffuser Materie," Berlin, Göttingen, Heidelberg, 1960.
[2] G. Wallerstein and M. Carlson, *Ap. J.*, **132,** 276 (1960).
[3] G. Wallerstein, unpublished. The author is grateful to Dr. Wallerstein for the communication of a preprint.
[4] B. Strömgren, in D. J. K. O'Connell (ed.), "Le Problème des populations stellaires," Pont. Ac. Sc., p. 385 (1958).
[5] B. Strömgren, in D. J. K. O'Connell (ed.), "Le Problème des populations stellaires," Pont. Ac. Sc., p. 245 (1958).
[6] J. Stebbins and A. E. Whitford, *Ap. J.*, **102,** 318 (1945).
[7] W. Becker, *Veröff. Univ.-Sternwarte Göttingen Nr.* 79–82, 1946.
[8] B. Strömgren, in K. A. Strand and S. Sharpless (eds.), "Stars and Stellar Systems," Vol. 3, Chap. 9.

Discussion

Dr. Blaauw: The percentage of the younger stars that have high velocities seems quite small. If one sees how quickly the percentage goes down from the O types already among the early B's, it would seem that the fraction is less than 10^{-3}.

Dr. Strömgren: In view of this it is hardly necessary to take into account the very small fraction of F- and G-type high-velocity stars that might be young stars. The kind of variation of the metal index that has been found for F and G stars, if it really persists in a larger material, would be an indication of the variations of chemical composition at the same age in samples from different parts of the galaxy.

Dr. Oort: How about these F-type high-velocity stars that are in Miss Roman's catalogue? Are they stars that have high velocities parallel to the galactic plane, or in radial direction, but have at the same time a large ultraviolet excess?

Dr. Strömgren: The ultraviolet excess and the metal index are quite parallel. If you know the absolute magnitude from other information you may use the ultraviolet excess and apply a correction dependent on the absolute magnitude. Among the high-velocity stars certainly some have normal composition and no ultraviolet excess.

Dr. Blaauw: Is that computed from the Hyades? They have a fairly high space velocity. From how far inside the galaxy do they come?

Dr. Strömgren: I tried to look at that, and found that they came from the arm that is inside our arm, between 1 and 2 quadrants away, but a more accurate investigation with a revised age might lead to a different conclusion. With regard to the question about high-velocity stars, there aren't many in this material. There will be more when we do next year's observations and go to $8^{m}.25$ for the F and G stars. Already there is another program on high-velocity stars, that of Whitford and Sears, which should contain a lot of information. They carried out six-color photometry for the high-velocity stars in the available catalogues, and they should have very good data both on the ultraviolet excess and on the behavior of the violet.

Dr. Oort: But you don't think the available photometries indicate a difference in metal content between Miss Roman's high-velocity stars with big ultraviolet excesses and, say, common weak-line stars?

Dr. Strömgren: If you exclude the halo stars such as HD 19445, then the range of chemical composition according to the ultraviolet excesses as well as the metal indices is approximately, from Hyades composition to a metal content, down by a factor of 4 or 5. When you have three indices you can segregate the absolute-magnitude effect and the chemical-composition effect. I should qualify this by saying that of course the indices should in every new range that we go into be calibrated by results of quantitative analysis on the basis of high-dispersion spectra. In other words, the ultraviolet excess is easy to interpret when you know from other sources that you are very close to the main sequence. If the range of absolute magnitude is considerable, then with UBV photometry only you can't distinguish between the absolute-magnitude effect and the chemical-composition effect.

Nuclear evolution in the galaxy

R. F. Christy

Recent Developments

In the last year Reynolds [1] has reported an anomalous abundance of Xe^{129} in the Richardton meteorite, presumably arising from the decay of I^{129} (mean life $= 2.5 \times 10^7$ years) that was in the parent body. The size of the anomaly suggests that of the order of $10T \simeq 2$–3×10^8 years elapsed since the last process of generation of I^{129} and the formation and trapping of the I^{129} in the meteoritic body. This discovery was important in that it demonstrated that element formation had occurred as recently as $\sim 0.3 \times 10^9$ years before the formation of the meteorites, which is taken to be about 4.6×10^9 years ago. Thus elements were formed not long before the formation of the solar system.

It was also pointed out, however, by Wasserburg, Fowler, and Hoyle [2] that this observation did not restrict the duration of the period during which elements were formed but merely determined the time that has elapsed since the last newly formed elements were admixed to solar-system material. It is this period that they estimate to be $\sim 2 \times 10^8$ years.

In a recent paper by Fowler and Hoyle [3] it is shown how measurements on the abundance ratio of U^{235}/U^{238} and of Th^{232}/U^{238} can lead to estimates of the period during which element formation has taken place. Here, $R_1 = (U^{235}/U^{238}) \approx e^{-t/1.22 \times 10^9 \text{years}}$ is a fairly rapidly decreasing function of time whereas $R_2 = (Th^{232}/U^{238}) \approx e^{t/9.63 \times 10^9 \text{years}}$ is a slowly increasing function of time. The measurement of R_1, which should be reliable, and of R_2, which is less so, are then coupled with the theoretical estimates of the relative production ratios in each case to give information on the period of element production.

282

Such calculations for R_1 will determine the ratio of recent element production to total element production. R_2, on the other hand, is less time-sensitive and tends more to determine a mean age of elements. This mean age is quite sensitive to errors in R_2 or in the theoretical production ratios of the elements; it is of the order of 10×10^9 years and could range from 6 to 16×10^9 years measured from the present. The R_1 determination unambiguously demands some recent production, even as I^{129} does. It permits the initial element production to be as long as 16×10^9 years.

Further, more detailed estimates of the duration of element production demand attention to questions astrophysical. All the isotopes discussed above would be expected to be made in a process of rapid neutron capture. It has been customary to attach this process to the most violent natural objects—supernovae. It is essential to know whether the supernovae in question are massive compared to the sun and therefore underwent their explosion a short time (compared to 10^9 years) since their origin, or whether they have masses comparable to that of the sun and may have been born 10^{10} years before their explosion. I shall discuss this question later.

From astrophysics, we know something about recent star formation. For this discussion we need to know about star formation at least 5×10^9 years ago and perhaps 20×10^9 years ago. This clearly involves us in the question of the evolution of the galaxy. Estimates about these questions have been made, and lead Fowler and Hoyle to attach an age of $15^{+5}_{-3} \times 10^9$ years to our galaxy if they assume that our galaxy is isolated in its matter content. They also mention the possibility that the solar element content is related to extragalactic material. I shall not pursue this question here.

My conclusions regarding these recent discussions of the age of the elements is that they lead readily to a minimum age that is only slightly longer than the age of the solar system, i.e., about 6×10^9 years. An upper limit on the earliest significant element production in our galaxy is far less certain but tends to be in the neighborhood of 20×10^9 years. In between these values the various theories involved have sufficient flexibility to accommodate themselves to more definite knowledge of the history of the galaxy and of stars when it becomes available.

The Relation of Element Generation to Stellar Activity

It has been known for some years that nearly all the energy generated in stars is associated with the conversion of hydrogen into helium. This means that from the luminosity of any normal collection of stars we can deduce the rate of generation of helium. Thus a luminosity equal to that of the sun results in the generation of 0.095 solar masses of He^4 in 10^{10}

years. We shall see that this basic relation leads to by far the most definite and precise conclusions about the matter in our galaxy. Other nuclear reactions undoubtedly take place in stars but lead to much less clear conclusions.

For example, after hydrogen is exhausted in the stellar core, the evolutionary models of F. Hoyle and M. Schwarzschild show that He^4 burning to produce C^{12} and heavier elements becomes important. This process undoubtedly becomes important in the region near the tip of the giant branch of stellar evolution. Since, presumably, all heavier elements that are made by stellar activity pass through this stage of He burning, we could calculate the amount of heavy elements Z if we could relate the extent of He burning to observable stellar features. Our knowledge of stellar models does not yet show us this connection in any manner that permits real conclusions. The formation of all the carbon and up has been accompanied by only about $\frac{1}{2}$ per cent of the energy evolved in He formation.

Beyond this stage of He burning the energy available is so small that further nuclear processes are essentially instants rather than phases of stellar evolution. The formation of the iron group involved only about 10^{-4} of the He burning energy. The further relation of these processes to stars must then depend on a detailed picture of the later stages of stellar evolution. Various proposals of stellar evolution have been made in this connection but none are clearly established.

Nuclear evidence has suggested the formation of heavier elements by several processes. Neutron capture on a slow time scale may be involved in red giant stars where Tc and other abundance anomalies have been observed. However, there seems no way at present to determine from the stars how much of this activity has taken place. In addition to this slow neutron process there is nuclear evidence for a rapid neutron process and for a high-temperature equilibrium process. Both the freezing of this high-temperature equilibrium and the rapid neutron process seem to require violent stellar conditions and have been related to supernovae. These phenomena, by their very violence, are also observable, so that it becomes possible in this way to relate these processes to stellar activity. We shall discuss this later. Apart from those stars which suffer catastrophe in the form of supernovae we are unable at present to relate the nuclear processes beyond He formation to stellar activity. This is so because an unknown amount of activity takes place, and of that which takes place, an unknown amount is returned to the interstellar medium. It is conceivable that large amounts of heavy elements are buried in white dwarfs, which are the presumed remnant of evolved stars. At present we do not know what fraction of the elements made in the interior are ejected and what fraction end up in the dwarf core.

Supernovae

In a recent paper, Hoyle and Fowler [4] point out two different types of instability that may lead to stellar explosions and identify them with the two kinds of supernovae. Type II supernovae are supposed to involve massive ($> 10 \, M_\odot$) stars and become unstable because of an endothermic transformation of iron into helium at sufficiently high interior temperature ($> 6 \times 10^9$). This leads to the collapse of the center and free fall of the surrounding material. The subsequent rebound is accompanied by detonation of nuclear fuel and leads to the stellar explosion.

Type I supernovae are supposed to involve the emergence of a new nuclear fuel by evolution of a degenerate core. Heating of a degenerate core does not produce expansion, so that the nuclear reaction is not self-controlling and a runaway explosion may occur. Such a tendency has already been seen in model calculations of Schwarzschild. In order to involve degeneracy it is necessary that the star be not too massive ($M \approx M_\odot$).

Other views, involving much greater central densities, have been proposed by Cameron to explain supernovae. It is probably not possible yet without much more detailed knowledge of evolutionary models to accept any picture of supernovae as complete.

We have been led to attach two types of element formation to supernovae—the Fe group and the r process. We shall now explain the relation of these production processes to supernovae.

The total of the Fe group elements is about 1.7×10^{-4} (as given by Goldberg, Müller, and Aller [5]) of total, or about 5×10^{-4} of He. If the $L_G \approx 6 \times 10^9 \, L_\odot$, the He production rate is $\approx 0.06 \, M_\odot/\text{year}$, so we require $3 \times 10^{-5} \, M_\odot$ of Fe per year. Alternatively the total Fe may be $\approx 7 \times 10^{10} \times 1.7 \times 10^{-4} \approx 1.2 \times 10^7 \, M_\odot$. To make this in 2×10^{10} years requires $6 \times 10^{-4} \, M_\odot$ of Fe per year. A guess of the amount in the Crab [6] is $\approx 0.1 \times 2.5 \times 10^{-4} \approx 2.5 \times 10^{-5} \, M_\odot$, and at 1 per 400 years is insufficient. On the other hand, in $20 \, M_\odot$ at 2.5×10^{-4} we have 5×10^{-3}, and at 1 per 400 years we get $1.2 \times 10^{-5} \, M_\odot/\text{year}$. In other words, a supernova in 400 years needs to have $\approx 10^{-2} \, M_\odot$ of Fe. This is reasonable for a massive one $\sim 20 \, M_\odot$ but not for $1 \, M_\odot$. It therefore seems reasonable to look at massive supernovae as the source of Fe.

The total r-process elements are $\approx 10^{-2}$ of the Fe group and the heavy ones ($A > 70$) amount to $\approx 10^{-3}$ of the Fe group. These could be made in either type of supernova as far as the required masses are concerned. To make 10^{-2} of the Fe group means $2.5 \times 10^{-7} \, M_\odot$ of r process per year now, or 6×10^{-6} on average. At 1 per 400 years requires

$10^{-4}\,M_\odot$ per supernova. This may just be possible in the Crab. Observation of unusual abundances in supernovae remnants would be interesting.

Supernovae—the Light Curve

One additional observable relation between astronomy and nuclear physics has been proposed. This is the suggestion that the type I light curve is due to a radioactive decay. Proposals include Be^7, Cf^{254}, and Fe^{59} [7], [8]. This proposal is so definite that it permits immediate deduction from the light curve of the amount of material involved.

Taking a magnitude of -18 for type I supernovae we find the exponential part of the light curve to involve 3×10^{48} ergs (assuming a normal photographic spectrum). This requires $2 \times 10^{-3}\,M_\odot$ of Cf^{254} or $\sim 10^{-1}\,M_\odot$ of Fe^{59}. In either case, at least $10^{-1}\,M_\odot$ of heavy elements are required. Both these numbers seem to violate observations on the Crab, assuming it to be a type I supernova.

In addition, we can calculate the total element production of 1 SN per 400 years for 2×10^{10} years $= 5 \times 10^7$ SN and find in the Cf case that $10^7\,M_\odot$ of r-process elements $= 10^{-4}$ of total, which is too much by ≈ 1000. In the case of Fe^{59} we get $5 \times 10^6\,M_\odot$ of Co^{59}, which is $\approx 10^{-4}$ of the total. This is about 40 times too much. Thus each of these cases seems to violate both observation on the Crab and on the solar-system abundances.

It should be pointed out however, that the r-process elements and the e-process elements that we now observe in solar-system abundances cannot have been exposed to the neutron flux of the S process. We must suppose therefore that the present abundances of these are just that fraction that has survived further evolution. This may, depending on the model, effectively reduce the time during which they can have been formed by as much as a factor of 10, depending on the model for star formation.

A further essential point about the light curve is the question of how the energy of radioactive decay might be fed into light. In view of the rapidly changing physical conditions associated with the expanding gas, it seems very difficult to feed a constant fraction of the decay energy at each instant into the light without any hold up comparable to 50 days or any reservoir to fill or empty. Certainly no reasonable physical model that is able to account for the light curve and spectrum has yet been made, and doubt about the possibility of doing so remains.

My conclusion here is that it is unlikely that the hypotheses which relate the light curve directly to nuclear decay can be correct. It is, however, still possible that radioactivity plays some role in some part of the light curve of one or the other type of supernovae, but probably the part is a minor one or becomes prominent only after a long time.

Helium Evolution

Various authors (Salpeter [9], Schmidt [10]) have considered models of the stellar birth-rate function and its comparison with observation in our galaxy. I do not intend to repeat these discussions here. Instead I shall discuss some of the features of the problem as Burbidge [11] has done already.

For these purposes I shall suppose that we can talk about two populations—a young and an old one. The young one is characterized by a median mass of order 3 or $4 M_\odot$. This is defined as roughly that mass such that half of the light is from brighter and half from fainter stars on main sequence. The old population is defined as one that has lost its main sequence at magnitudes less than about 4 or 3.5. It is relevant for our estimates that most of the light in each of these populations arises from stars whose life expectancy is short compared to the age of the galaxy. As a result we can immediately relate the luminosity to the stellar death rate.

For the purpose of argument, we shall divide the galaxy as follows. We assume an old elliptically distributed population of mass $\approx 6 \times 10^{10} M_\odot$ and luminosity $\approx 3 \times 10^9 L_\odot$ and a flat young population of mass $\approx 7 \times 10^9 M_\odot$ and luminosity $4 \times 10^9 L_\odot$.

For the old population we then calculate that $0.03 M_\odot$/year of He are produced and therefore about $0.04 M_\odot$/year of stars are dying at a rate of 0.03 star/year or 1 star/30 years. Another estimate of the number of stellar deaths of old stars has been made by Woltjer, who took an estimate of 1.7×10^5 RR Lyrae stars in the galaxy coupled with an RR Lyrae lifetime of 8×10^7 years to obtain one RR Lyrae death per 500 years, which corresponds to an estimate of the type I supernova rate. We see that there is a significant discrepancy between these estimates and presume that the incidence of RR Lyrae stars in the old population we are discussing is quite different from that in globular clusters. It is, of course, generally agreed that the galactic old population is not as metal-poor as the globular cluster population. This may well be significant for the RR Lyrae group—direct observational evidence on the incidence of RR Lyrae stars in the old galactic population would be of interest. We also see from the above that the usual type I supernova rate of 1 per 400 years is not consistent with the death rate of old stars. It is more nearly consistent with a guessed death rate of extreme population II stars.

For the young population we find that about $0.04 M_\odot$/year of He is being generated and if stars die with 30 per cent conversion to He (about $1 M_\odot$ of He), then the mass death rate is about $0.13 M_\odot$/year and the stellar death rate is ≈ 0.04 per year or 1 per 25 years. This rate is also in excess of the type II SN rate of 1 per 400 years. The latter rate would correspond to the death rate of massive stars of masses greater than 15 $M_\odot$. It is interesting that the mass of gas found to be emerging from the center of the disk, $\approx 0.5\ M_\odot$/year, considerably exceeds the death rate in the same region and in fact exceeds the death rate for the whole galaxy. Salpeter's birth rate puts about 25 per cent of the mass in young stars. Thus the gas leaving the center of the galaxy can account for all the gas used up in stellar births. This casts some doubt on the details of the models that have been computed for the evolution of the galactic gas.

Finally we can estimate the total He production from the galaxy at present as $\approx 0.07\ M_\odot$/year. In 10^{10} years this would give $7 \times 10^8\ M_\odot$ of He, whereas the actual mass is presumably greater than $10^{10}\ M_\odot$. We must presume that, if all the He has been formed by stellar activity, that activity was on the average about 10 times what it now is.

No attempt has been made in this paper to provide authoritative numbers in connection with the properties of our galaxy. Rather the numbers are intended to illustrate the ways in which a comparison can be made between the observations on stars and the calculations on energy sources.

References

[1] J. H. Reynolds, *Phys. Rev. Letters*, **4**, 8 (1960).
[2] G. J. Wasserburg, W. A. Fowler, and F. Hoyle, *Phys. Rev. Letters*, **4**, 112 (1960).
[3] W. A. Fowler and F. Hoyle, *Ann. Phys.*, **10**, 280 (1960).
[4] F. Hoyle and W. A. Fowler, *Ap. J.*, **132**, 565 (1960).
[5] L. Goldberg, E. A. Müller, and L. H. Aller, *Ap. J. (Suppl.)*, **45** (1960).
[6] L. Woltjer, *B.A.N.*, **14**, 39 (1958).
[7] E. M. Burbidge, G. R. Burbidge, W. A. Fowler, and F. Hoyle, *Rev. Mod. Phys.*, **29**, 547 (1957).
[8] E. Anders, *Ap. J.*, **129**, 327 (1959).
[9] E. E. Salpeter, *Ap. J.*, **129**, 608 (1959).
[10] M. Schmidt, *Ap. J.*, **129**, 243 (1959).
[11] G. R. Burbidge, *Publ. Astron. Soc. Pacific*, **70**, 83 (1958).

Discussion

Dr. G. R. Burbidge: I suppose I should say something about the comments that Dr. Christy has made. As far as the amounts of the heavy elements produced by the supernovae are concerned, our ideas have changed. Of course, one does find that by taking uniform rates of supernovae one tends to get too much. Probably the difficulty lies in the idea that one is dealing with a uniform rate. We know, or we think we know, from the composition of old stars that the chemical composition has not changed very much in the last 10—maybe more than that—billion years, and so we have to put the major phases of element synthesis back to a very early stage. If you do that, then I agree that you push it back into an unknown region. However, you can no longer make estimates concerning rates of supernovae based on estimates from a whole range of galaxies, which is the only way we get them today.

As far as the Californium hypothesis is concerned, I think we have all realized that it is difficult to reproduce the light curves. I still am personally a little more optimistic than Dr. Christy. As far as Fe^{59} is concerned, one has to have a process that adds very few neutrons to Fe^{56} and has to cut this process off after three neutrons have been added. This seems an awkward point from the straight nuclear physics of the problem. As far as using the Crab is concerned, I just don't know. Of course, one cannot believe that the data derived from the Chinese observations are really very good. So I would not even like to say that the Crab was originally a supernova with an exponential light curve; and we certainly know that only some of the supernovae do give rise to such light curves. This is clear, I think, from more recent work and also from some of the old work, which has never been properly calibrated.

Dr. Christy: I take it then that you are still hopeful that the light curves and element production can be related to the type I supernova.

Dr. G. R. Burbidge: I think that it is still possible, yes.

Dr. Lüst: Did I understand you correctly—you imply that the supernova frequency in earlier times was smaller than today?

Dr. G. R. Burbidge: The supernovae that give rise to the elements. This is the crucial point. As Dr. Christy pointed out, we don't know enough about the evolution of the stars to know exactly how all these supernovae will go. Therefore, they were recently divided into two groups by Fowler and Hoyle, so that type II produced the iron group and type I the *r*-process group. One can certainly think of evolutionary stages where we will get nuclear explosions, but perhaps the process doesn't go in quite the same way. So we may not get elements from every supernova; we may not get these quantities of elements. You could, for example, argue that in the early stage the composition of the stars that gave rise to supernovae was quite different. There is no reason to believe that the evolution would go in the same way as it has gone in more recent years.

Dr. Woltjer: This figure of 10^{-1} solar masses of heavy elements is, of course, troublesome, but perhaps you can argue it away. I would think that the much more serious question is that to produce these heavy elements you have to have a neutron source which usually involves quite a bit of mass. With the recent increase in the luminosity of the supernovae the masses you need are just too large to make a process of this kind very well possible unless you are prepared to assume a neutron core in the central region.

Dr. Christy: It is very difficult. But it seems to me that that was not quite as clear an argument as just the amount of material.

Dr. Woltjer: A large fraction of the elements that are produced could remain in the remnant.

Dr. G. R. Burbidge: This is always possible. I don't know if the mass that is needed is so large if you go to a neutron core. We originally did not use a neutron core and therefore the neutron production was low. One now thinks in those terms. It is perhaps not too difficult to get enough neutrons. There are other difficulties. I don't think we have ever been persuaded that we understood exactly how a star would get right to the neutron configuration.

Dr. Woltjer: Without becoming a supernova.

Dr. G. R. Burbidge: This was always the difficulty. In fact, all the work that has been done on neutron stars has been done on the assumption that they can be treated as gigantic stable nuclei, and the evolution to this stage has not been discussed.

Dr. Biermann: Reference was made during this conference to a much simpler possibility for the type II supernovae, a model proposed by Dr. Blaauw—that a very heavy star of something beyond 60 or so solar masses might explode because of internal instability not involving nuclear action. It has been known I think for about 30 years that the simplest kind of instabilities, radial instabilities, grow with increasing mass, so that beyond some limiting mass of the order of not quite a hundred solar masses, you would expect that without any additional disturbance the star, at some stage, might explode and then, of course, nuclear reactions might be coming in.

Dr. Christy: If it really explodes there is a strong tendency for a shock wave to form which gets more violent in the outer parts of the star and, therefore, automatically tends to make conditions favorable for nuclear reactions.

Dr. Burbidge: Of course, this would not demand that you have such a high degree of chemical evolution. You would suddenly detonate the hydrogen in the outer parts. In fact this would give you supernovae without the production of heavy elements, if you are worried about producing too much.

Evolution of galaxies

G. R. Burbidge

I have been asked to talk about the evolution of galaxies. This is a subject about which we know little, except in a very speculative sense. It seems to me that one can draw a parallel between the attempts to talk about galactic evolution at the present time and the attempts to understand stellar evolution before the sources of energy in the stars were understood.

Therefore I would like to discuss briefly all the factors on which the evolution of galaxies probably depends, and to discuss the time-scale problem associated with the evolution of different types of galaxies. This means that one has also to say something about the cosmological models. Then I would like to discuss the information that we have on the masses and mass-to-light ratios of galaxies. The mass-to-light ratio is one evolutionary parameter that can be measured. Finally I would like to show some pictures and discuss some rather peculiar galaxies which one suspects may be quite young in evolutionary terms.

There are three possibilities in considering the way in which galaxies initially condense. First, it has been common to suppose that the era of galactic formation was in the remote past, at a very early time, soon after the initial expansion in an evolutionary cosmology, or during the long period when the universe was in a quasi-stationary state, according to the model of Dr. Lemaître. Second, we can consider within the framework of an evolutionary cosmology a situation in which not all the galaxies formed at an early time. That is to say, protogalaxies might form and to some extent condense, but if bright stars do not form and evolve, then the evolutionary rate can be very slow. Thus even with this type of cosmological model some galaxies could be young in evolutionary terms if star formation was delayed until a time much later than the origin.

On the other hand, within the framework of the steady-state cosmology, the third possibility, we have to assume that the galaxies are forming and evolving continuously, so that we necessarily have to see young galaxies and much older galaxies together.

One might expect to get some idea about the evolutionary rate by considering the relative frequency of different types of galaxies. However, I do not think this is in general possible, because the selection effects are very considerable and one is not looking at a fair sample of the universe when one looks at galaxies that can be classified. That is, classification systems break down at distances small compared with those required to include a fair sample of the galactic population. For distant galaxies there is a tendency to lose the outer regions of low surface brightness, and hence we may classify as faint elliptical systems those which may be, for example, spiral systems with very bright nuclei and relatively faint arms.

From the theoretical standpoint we can list the factors on which the rate of formation and form of the evolution of a protogalaxy can be expected to depend, although I do not believe that we understand the relative importance of these. They are:

1. The angular momentum per unit of mass of the initial condensation after the Jeans criterion has been fulfilled and the protogalaxy has been separated from the surrounding medium.

2. The initial density in the medium.

3. The initial temperature in the medium.

4. The initial turbulent velocity.

5. The initial magnetic field.

These physical parameters must together determine the way in which the first stars will condense, and the form of the initial mass function. This in turn probably to a large extent governs the rate at which the successive generations of stars can condense and form. This is an important point in the context in which it is supposed that the bulk of the elements apart from hydrogen are formed in the stars.

As was mentioned earlier by Professor Schwarzschild, the chemical composition at an early stage of the galaxy is almost certainly a very important factor in considering whether or not the system can cool after it has been heated by the first stars, so that new stars can form. If there are a lot of metals, cooling will be hastened. On the other hand, one has to start with a considerable abundance of hydrogen and, depending on one's viewpoint concerning the origin of the elements and the cosmological model, either a small admixture of the heavier elements or none at all, so cooling will be slow until the material has been enriched in the heavier elements.

All the parameters listed above are important, but only in the case of the angular momentum has there been any discussion of its importance in general galactic evolution. The work in which the rate of star formation has been related to the gas density has been restricted to a limited region in our own galaxy.

With the data now becoming available it should be possible very soon to calculate the angular momentum per unit mass for a number of galaxies. However, at present we can only make qualitative statements, as follows. Spiral galaxies are highly flattened and rotations extending up to about 300 km/sec relative to their centers have been measured in some casse. Thus they have considerable amounts of angular momentum. On the other hand, elliptical galaxies are much less flattened, many are spherical, and it is generally believed that they have little rotation. Of course, the observations required to detect such rotations are exceedingly difficult, and I think it is fair to say that observationally we are not sure of this. However, there are, perhaps, theoretical arguments which can be adduced to suggest that if there is rotation it is small. Because of this it is thought in general that the discrimination between the spirals and the ellipticals is mainly due to the initial angular momentum.

The initial magnetic field may also be an important factor in determining whether a protogalaxy will evolve into a spiral or an elliptical. We have already discussed the problem of the magnetic field in our own galaxy. For galaxies other than our own we can get only a very indirect estimate of the magnetic field by considering the conditions in the galaxies which are radio sources. These may be peculiar in many ways, but it is of interest that if one does make these estimates one finds that in many systems the magnetic fields probably lie in the range 10^{-5} to 10^{-6} gauss.

This does not say anything about the initial values for the magnetic fields in the protogalaxies. If the galaxies were all produced in a very early phase of the universe, when the universe was highly condensed, the conditions were quite different from those prevailing if protogalaxies condense from the intergalactic material today. In this case we can neither use the estimates we make today for the relevant parameters listed above nor can we use the estimates we make today for the conditions in the intergalactic medium.

Thus all the fundamental parameters that one has to deal with here remain undetermined observationally, and I am not aware of any detailed theoretical work on the formation of galaxies other than work some time ago by Dr. Lemaître, and more recently by van Albada, who has considered the formation and the dynamical evolution of a cluster of galaxies (the Virgo cluster) within the framework of an evolutionary cosmological model. Some ideas about the way in which new galaxies may form in the presence of other already existing galaxies, arguments which are required in steady-state cosmology, have been developed by Sciama. Some tentative ideas have also been expressed by Hoyle and Gold.

It is well known that galaxies can be broadly classified into irregular systems, barred spirals, normal spirals, S0 galaxies, and ellipticals. It may be that the initial values of the parameters listed above uniquely determine the form of a galaxy so that we cannot suppose that a galaxy will go through successive phases in which it can be identified at different stages with a particular galactic type. However, the sense of the evolution through the sequence of galactic types in the order listed is fairly obvious, if we base it on modern ideas of star formation and stellar evolution. Hubble, in his original classification, specifically stated that there was no attempt there to write down an evolutionary sequence. I think that Shapley was the first astronomer to point out that the probable sequence would be in the sense irregular–spiral–elliptical.

Qualitatively one can understand such a sequence quite straight-forwardly. The first thing that will happen in a protogalaxy is that stars of comparatively large mass will form, because their contraction times are very much shorter than stars of lesser mass which may have started to form at the same time. The only possible flaw in this argument is that perhaps only stars of small mass might start to form first, and sufficient time might elapse for them to reach the main sequence before stars of large mass, which might condense later. If large-mass stars form first, they will have high luminosity and will irradiate the uncondensed gas and ionize much of it, thus making further star formation more difficult. The first stage that one might expect to see, therefore, is a system containing pre-dominantly high-luminosity stars and large H II regions. Many irregular systems certainly do show just these features.

After the system has settled down and reached a symmetrical con-figuration, the turbulence in the system will decay and the system will flatten to whatever extent is indicated by its initial angular momentum. This, and the initial density distribution, may determine, for a spiral, the relative importance of the disk and central bulge. The density of stars in the halo will probably depend on the rate at which the decay in the turbulence goes on, as compared with the rate at which the stars can form.

So one can in principle suppose that there are different degrees of concentration of material in the disk and in the halo regions in different galaxies. But eventually the material in the disk will evolve, through successive generations of stars, into a population of comparatively low-mass stars with a steadily decreasing amount of gas. Superposed on this disk and defined by the gas is the spiral structure. I think that at the stage where we see most normal spiral galaxies, the spiral structure is nothing more than a tracer element contained in a fairly uniform disk of material. As we have heard already, this is probably related to the magnetic field in the disk.

If we follow this evolution through, then provided the galaxy conserves its mass (except for that part of the mass which is converted to radiation and escapes, or is used for heating up the gas), there will come a point at which there is insufficient gas for further stars to form. There is, of course, a continuous ejection of gas from evolving stars, but the fraction of mass in the form of gas will get smaller and smaller, and if the time scale is long enough the final result will be a galaxy consisting predominantly of white dwarfs. At this point the galaxy will steadily fade. It may be that no galaxy has yet had sufficient time to reach such a stage. Whether or not this is the case depends on which cosmological model best represents the universe. In the steady-state universe many galaxies must have reached this state. If they have, then such configurations could contribute to the density of nonluminous material in the universe.

The evolution of barred spiral galaxies is not even qualitatively understood. It is possible that the formation of the bar is a result of the initial conditions and that later the bar gradually becomes less of a dominating feature and the galaxy evolves into a normal spiral.

We have little understanding of the way in which protogalaxies evolve to become ellipticals. It is possible that in these cases the initial star formation and the turnover rate between gas and stars was very rapid. If a large fraction of the gas was initially condensed into stars of comparatively low mass, this would slow down the evolutionary rate very considerably once the large-mass stars had disappeared, since the time scale for evolution of stars of solar mass and less is equal to, or greater than, 15×10^9 years. The light from elliptical galaxies comes in large part from K giants, which probably have arisen from the region of the main sequence around solar type. Within the framework of an evolutionary cosmology all the elliptical galaxies can be very old. However, if the steady-state model is accepted, we must ask which young galaxies that we see now will evolve into ellipticals. This question remains unanswered at present.

It is appropriate here to mention the characteristic time scales. The ages of galactic and globular clusters in our own galaxy range up to about 25×10^9 years, while the age of the elements in the solar system is of the order of 12×10^9 years. On the other hand, the inverse of the Hubble constant is currently thought to be about 13×10^9 years. The age of the universe in many cosmological models is less than the inverse of the Hubble constant, while for Lemaitre's model much longer times are possible. I do not think that it is too meaningful at present to enter into a discussion of the fact that the age of the galaxy, from star clusters, appears to be greater than the age of the universe given by the Hubble constant for some cosmological models, because of the uncertainties involved. In an evolutionary cosmology, then, we have a time scale of 10 or 20 billion years in which the galaxies must evolve to their present forms, unless there is an earlier epoch of undetermined length, as Lemaitre's model would allow.

Within the framework of the steady-state cosmology, although we do not have time-scale problems of this nature, there may be other time-scale problems. For example, the average age of a galaxy in the steady state is $\sim \frac{1}{3}H$ which, according to the current value, would be about 4 billion years. Thus for this model our galaxy is about five times the average age. This puts us in a rather privileged position.

Another point of interest is the question of whether or not the mass of a galaxy is conserved during its evolution. It can gain mass by accretion processes since it is moving through an intergalactic medium of very low density. This gain of mass is easily calculated from the normal accretion formulas. For reasonable values of density and relative velocity it is extremely small, so that a galaxy in a period of about 10^{10} years will probably only gain 10^7 solar masses. This is, as far as I am aware, the only mechanism by which a galaxy can gain mass. On the other hand, it can certainly lose mass, and the most efficient way of doing this is through collisions between galaxies. A number of years ago Baade and Spitzer considered this question in an attempt to understand the S0 galaxies, and they pointed out that in rich clusters of galaxies (where there is a high frequency of S0 types) one could well imagine the situation in which galactic collisions were quite frequent. In such collisions the gas in the galaxies would be swept out but the stars would remain. Baade and Spitzer at that time worked out the rate of collisions and showed that it was quite high in a rich cluster. Since this was done, the distance scale has increased by a factor of between 2 and 3; on the other hand, the effective cross sections of the galaxies have also increased, and the net result is that the process is a little less efficient than was originally thought. But it is still quite an important process for rich clusters.

It should be mentioned in passing that there are many S0 galaxies which do not lie in rich clusters. Some other mechanisms must be invoked to account for the forms of these galaxies, since collisions in the general field are exceedingly rare.

Another mechanism for mass loss in the galaxy is that of supernova explosions. It is fairly clear that supernova explosions are so violent that the material achieves very high velocities—perhaps 5000 km/sec. These velocities are far in excess of the escape velocity in a galaxy. Provided the material is not slowed down by interacting with nearby gas in the galaxy, it will certainly escape. The so-called Seyfert galaxies are a class of galaxies in whose nuclear regions there is evidence for exceedingly high velocities.

It is probable that in these galaxies material is escaping from the nuclear regions. However, it appears unlikely that such a process would go on for very long in terms of galactic time scales. It is therefore difficult to believe that such mass loss, in general, is an important factor in galactic evolution, although possibly, perhaps at an early stage, it is significant in some cases.

The general conclusion is that in the majority of galaxies mass is conserved through their evolutionary history. However, I would like to discuss one galaxy, NGC 3646 (Fig. 1), in which the mass is probably not conserved. This galaxy was studied by us because it was thought to be an extremely large Sc galaxy. It has a recession velocity of 4100 km/sec. There is very little evidence for spiral structure in the outer parts. It consists, roughly speaking, of two concentric ellipses, surrounding the central nucleus. The galaxy has been observed spectroscopically and we have found a very surprising result.

If one considers the inner region, one can get a satisfactory interpretation of this as being a normal stable system with a mass of about 2 or

Fig. 1. NGC 3646.

$3 \times 10''$ solar masses. (The velocity rises to about 400 km/sec with respect to the center about $27''$ out from the center.) However, the measured velocities in the outer ring suggest that this ring is not stable. There are velocities in the apex in the lower part which are far below the Keplerian velocity on the assumption that the mass is about 2 or $3 \times 10^{11} \ M_{\odot}$. The details of this investigation have been published elsewhere [1].

I have been talking about the problem of the conservation of mass because it seems to be significant in considering galactic evolution, since if galaxies can evolve from one form to another, and if they conserve mass, then we would expect that the masses of galaxies of different types would be approximately the same within the dispersion.

This leads me to the question of masses and the mass-to-light ratios in galaxies. The mass-to-light ratio conventionally measured in solar units is an important parameter describing galactic evolution. In Tables 1 and 2 are given masses and mass-to-light ratios for the systems for which data are available. These are based on material from a number of sources, including work by the Leiden group, Minkowski, Münch, Mayall, Hodge, Aller, Page, de Vaucouleurs, Prendergast, Fish, and ourselves. In deriving these results no account has been taken, except for M 31, of the effect of internal absorption, so that the intrinsic mass-to-light ratios in spirals and irregulars are probably smaller than the values given in Table 1.

Table 1

Galaxy	Type	$M/M_{\odot} \times 10^{-10}$	M/L, solar units
M 82	Irr.	1.5	7.4
NGC 55	Irr.	~4	~6
NGC 3556	Irr.–Sc	1.4	1.4
Large Magellanic cloud	Irr.	1.3	1.9
NGC 3646	Sbp–Scp	> 20–30	> 2.5–4
NGC 2146	Scp	1.8	3
M 33	Sc	1.8	11
NGC 157	Sc	6.0	1.9
NGC 3504	SBb	0.3–0.9	0.9
NGC 5055	Sb–Sc	5.5	2.8
NGC 2903	Sb	4.9	> 4.2
M 101	Sc	1.4	13
NGC 5005	Sb	9	6
M 81	Sb	15	20
M 31	Sb	34	23–10
NGC 3623	Sa–Sb	20–30	10–20
S + Irr.	Average from pairs	2	1

Table 2

Galaxy	Type	$M/M_\odot \times 10^{-10}$	M/L, solar units
Sculptor dwarf galaxy	dE	~ 0.0002	2–4
Formax dwarf galaxy	dE	~ 0.002	2–4
M 32	E2	0.18	13
NGC 3379	E0	10	12
NGC 4486	E0	~ 100	~ 60
NGC 3115	S0–E7	11	19
NGC 4111	S0	1.2	13
E + S0	Average from pairs	50	70

At an early stage in galactic evolution the mass-to-light ratio will probably be quite small. If there are many high-luminosity stars, M/L will be small. However, there may be a lot of uncondensed gas which contributes to the mass and not to the luminosity. Thus it is not clear how small this ratio should be. On the other hand, when a galaxy reaches a late

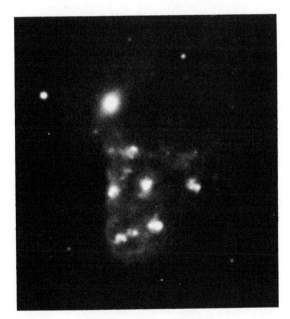

Fig. 2. NGC 2444–2445.

stage of evolution it will fade in brightness and the mass-to-light ratio will become large.

For a long time it was thought that there were very significant differences between the mass-to-light ratios for spiral and irregular galaxies, on the one hand, and elliptical galaxies on the other. The irregular and Sc galaxies apparently do have a smaller M/L ratio than the others. However, if one puts together the spirals of all types, the results for single galaxies do not show a large effect of this kind, although the results of Page for double galaxies do.

The mass-to-light ratio as an evolutionary parameter perhaps does not tell us too much. There are many ways to make up a mass-to-light ratio, because the gas, the stars, and the white dwarfs or evolved stars all contribute to the mass, but the light contributions come predominantly

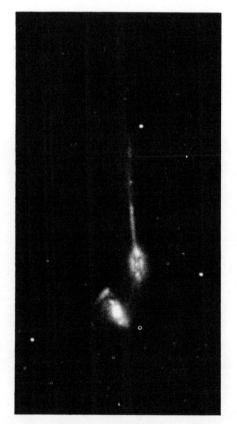

Fig. 3. NGC 4676.

from stars on the main sequence or on the giant branch. Thus, considerable variations in the ratio can be expected as the relative amounts of gas and dust, main-sequence stars and giants, and evolved stars change as a galaxy evolves.

As a possible evolutionary parameter one might also consider the color of an elliptical galaxy. In an elliptical galaxy the light that we see comes to a large extent from K-type giants and the color indices lie in the range 0.8 to 0.9. Hoyle and Crampin have made a recent investigation related to the evolution of ellipticals. They took a population of stars corresponding to the initial population in the galactic cluster M 67, and they let evolution proceed onward down the main sequence. They then computed the integrated color index as a function of time, and found that one quite soon reached the stage where the color index changed extremely slowly for very long time intervals. Thus color differences of the order of one-tenth could be explained by a time spread of anything from 15 to 30 billion years. The important point that comes out of this investigation is simply that the color index is not a very sensitive criterion of evolutionary age. Further, one is clearly making a considerable assumption in supposing that the population of stars in elliptical galaxies is similar to that in M 67. However, it is clear that the spread in the colors of elliptical galaxies could be explained in part by an evolutionary effect of this type.

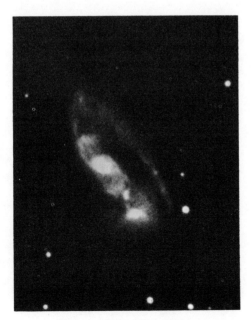

Fig. 4. NGC 6621–6622.

Finally, I would like to discuss observational evidence for the existence of systems which are apparently very young in an evolutionary sense. As was stated in the earlier part of my talk, the first stages of galactic evolution are probably represented by the irregular galaxies. In addition to the well-known irregular galaxies, Vorontsov-Velyaminov has searched the Palomar Sky Atlas and found a large number of peculiar multiple systems, many of which are irregular galaxies. In Figs. 2 through 5 we show some examples of these. NGC 2444–2445 consists of a number of bright H II regions, perhaps a protogalaxy, physically connected to an elliptical galaxy. NGC 4676 has two bright nuclei with strong emission and long tails or plumes. It is 3° from the center of the Coma cluster and has a redshift very close to that of the mean for the Coma cluster. Thus it may be a member of the cluster. Detailed discussions of both of these systems are given in [2] and [3]. The two other systems also have strong emission features in their spectra and have configurations which suggest that they will evolve on a time scale of the order of 10^8 years. It is impossible as yet to estimate the frequency of occurrence of such systems. They are probably not intrinsically bright, but no photometry is yet available. Without detailed investigation with large reflectors it is not possible to tell what many of the systems are.

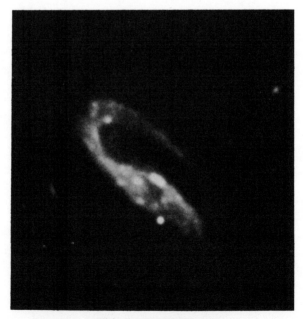

Fig. 5. NGC 3509.

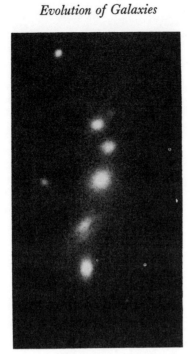

Fig. 6. V-V 172.

Figure 6 shows a chain of galaxies which was discovered by Vorontsov-Velyaminov. Probably this configuration is also not stable and has a short time scale associated with it.

Another interesting object is the Hercules cluster of galaxies, which consists predominantly of spiral and irregular galaxies. Its geometrical configuration and the fact that its members do not satisfy the virial theorem suggests that it is disrupting on a time scale of the order of 10^9 years. In this region of the sky we are perhaps seeing new generations of galaxies forming.

References
[1] E. M. Burbidge, G. R. Burbidge, and K. H. Prendergast, *Ap. J.*, **134**, 237 (1961).
[2] E. M. Burbidge and G. R. Burbidge, *Ap. J.*, **130**, 12 (1959).
[3] E. M. Burbidge and G. R. Burbidge, *Ap. J.*, **133**, 726 (1961).

Discussion
The discussion of this paper was postponed until the general concluding discussion.

Concluding session

Summary

B. Strömgren

In preparing this introduction to the discussion I found that it would probably be difficult and perhaps not fruitful to try to summarize all the papers that have been given here. We have covered a lot of ground, and what we have heard is still in our minds. I intend instead to make some introductory remarks that might serve as a framework to which some of the questions that will be brought up could be related.

My introduction will be concerned with the observational part and will be followed by Dr. Woltjer's introduction, which deals with the theoretical questions. It is clear that there will be some overlap.

Our topic has been the interstellar medium of our galaxy and of other galaxies. Most of the discussion has been concerned with our own galaxy. However, in the interpretation of the data we have very frequently been referring to results obtained for other galaxies. On previous days we have heard from Dr. Osterbrock and Mrs. Burbidge on results regarding the interstellar medium in external galaxies. A wide range has been covered, including questions of chemical composition and motion of the gaseous component. Today Dr. Burbidge has discussed the wonderful variety of regular classes of galaxies as well as irregular objects that all form part of our subject.

In the discussion we might proceed in a similar way, i.e., take our own galaxy as the starting point but relate the problems to the whole background of knowledge obtained from the study of other galaxies.

The direct observations deal with the present phase of distribution and motion of the interstellar medium. Let us refer to this as phase 3, and let us define an intermediate phase—phase 2—through the conditions that most of the stars (in terms of mass) had not yet been formed at this phase, while the medium had already condensed to a disk not more than, say, 2 to 3 times thicker than the present disk. Finally, we refer to the early, or halo, stage of the interstellar medium as phase 1.

Let us begin, then, with a discussion of observations pertaining to phase 3. The inventory of components of the interstellar medium in phase 3 includes the gaseous and the particle component, the cosmic rays, and the magnetic field. In discussing the gaseous component we started out by listening to Dr. Oort, who gave an account of the results obtained through the 21-cm work regarding the large-scale structure of the disk. Here perhaps the most striking feature is the very high degree of flattening and the pronounced regularity, with relatively very small deviations from flatness, up to distances from the sun somewhat larger than that of the sun.

The most striking large-scale structural feature is that of the spiral arms. To our knowledge of this we can now add a considerable amount of information regarding the structural properties of the central region.

As we go from the disk into the halo we encounter, as both Dr. Oort and Dr. Blaauw discussed, regions of well-measurable density a few hundred parsec above or below the galactic plane. In the outer regions we find features that indicate considerable deviations from the flatness that is so striking within, say, 8000 pc from the center.

When the structures are examined in greater detail, in particular with regard to the fine structure of the spiral arms, it becomes clear that the 21-cm observations made in the galactic plane do not yield sufficient information. However, as Dr. Blaauw's discussion showed, observations taken a few or several degrees away from the galactic equator are adequate for the purpose, since the lines of sight here pass through a suitable number of clouds. Much information has already been gathered regarding density variations in the spiral arms and the pattern of cloud motions. Questions pertaining to the relation between clouds and cloud complexes which had already been raised in connection with the work in the optical region can be studied further with the help of 21-cm observations.

During our discussions the problem of the motions of the gas in the spiral arms was brought up several times, in particular the question of the relative motion of the interstellar gas and local stellar centroids. We have been reminded of the typical differences between motion of the gaseous masses and motion of the stars that have condensed out of these masses.

As we discussed the patterns of motion further, the central regions played a large role. The facts that have been gathered regarding the structural and kinematical properties of the central region evidently tell us something quite important regarding the large-scale motions of the interstellar medium in our galaxy.

As was emphasized, the amounts of matter that stream outward in the expanding spiral arm located a few thousand parsec from the center are very large. This observational fact was the starting point for our discussions of questions of the circulation pattern and of large-scale mixing of the interstellar medium, of spiral-arm structure, and of star formation.

Questions of the chemical composition of the interstellar medium as determined through the combination of optical and 21-cm studies have been considered also. In particular, the importance of the H_2 problem was emphasized again.

A large part of our discussion of the observational data was devoted to the particle component of the interstellar medium, the cosmic-ray component, and the galactic magnetic field. The picture of the present phase 3 was completed through presentations covering problems of star formation and of the interaction between evolving stars and the interstellar medium.

Dr. Biermann and Dr. Schwarzschild discussed problems of the mass, energy, and momentum balance of the interstellar medium in phase 3 as it interacts with the galactic star system. In particular, the role of the high-luminosity stars and the supernovae of type II was discussed in some detail. This whole discussion connected naturally with that of problems of secular change of the interstellar medium and with the questions of comparison of phases 3, 2, and 1.

It was emphasized many times in our discussion that in a galaxy such as ours the amount of matter in the entire interstellar medium in phase 3 is small compared with that in all the stars. On the other hand, when our galaxy went through phase 2 (approximately 1×10^{10} years ago), most of the mass of the system was presumably in the form of interstellar matter. Since the volume of the galactic system was only a few times larger in phase 2 than in phase 3, the average density of interstellar matter must have been higher by a very considerable factor (10, or larger) in phase 2 as compared to phase 3.

With regard to the chemical composition of the interstellar medium in phase 2 we cannot be so sure. However, the information derived from discussions of the chemical composition of old disk-population stars such as we find them in M 67 and NGC 188, as well as in the sample of nearby stars, suggests that the chemical composition in phase 2 was not radically different from that in the present phase 3. The abundance ratio metals-to-hydrogen may have been lower in phase 2 by a factor of, say, 3 or 4.

When we compare the state of motion of the interstellar medium in phases 2 and 3 we are again led to the conclusion that the difference was not very great. Average turbulence velocities as deduced from the evidence of the space velocities of old disk-population stars were somewhat, but

B. Strömgren

not very much, larger in phase 2 than in the present phase 3. The main difference is that of average density.

With regard to the gradual transition from phase 2 to phase 3 it is clear from observational results referred to in our discussion that the changes in the properties of the interstellar medium have been quite small during the last 2 (possibly even 3) billion years. This conclusion is compatible with the inferences from the discussion of the mass, energy, and momentum balances of the interstellar medium in phase 3 that I referred to before.

As we go to the early phase, which we have called phase 1 (approximately 2×10^{10} years ago), the principal basis for any conclusions is, of course, the existence of the extreme population II, the halo stars, characterized as far as we can see by a very low heavy-element content. In phase 1, when the system of the interstellar medium was not very much flattened, the volume was, as has been emphasized in our discussions, so much larger than in phase 3 that the average density of the interstellar medium was a good deal lower than in phase 2, and in fact not very different from that in the present phase 3.

With regard to the total mass of the stars formed during phase 1, the investigations of the extreme population II stars now observable suggest that it amounted to only a few per cent of the total mass of the system (even allowing for the size of the halo volume throughout which these stars are found). However, it must be kept in mind that we do not possess direct evidence concerning the total mass of the relatively massive stars formed during phase 1.

If we try to draw further conclusions we shall have to base them on investigations that will be covered by Dr. Woltjer's summary, and I should therefore like to stop at this point.

Summary

L. Woltjer

It would be very nice if at the end of a conference one could write on the blackboard a number of points that have now been solidly established, but this would be quite a rare exception among astronomers. Therefore I just want to mention a number of points discussed here which appear to be of some importance and which would seem to deserve further study.

Magnetic Fields

One of the topics during this conference that has been put perhaps more clearly than before is the question of how important the magnetic forces are in galactic gas dynamics. There have been two schools of thought: one which feels that the field is very strong, and one which feels it is very weak, strong and weak meaning essentially that the magnetic energy density is dominant or negligible in the energy densities we encounter in the interstellar medium.

Let me summarize in the first place some points which, if they were by themselves, one would be inclined to accept as evidence for a strong field.

1. From the cosmic-ray electrons near the earth and the galactic radio emission one would certainly infer the high field.

2. The confinement of the cosmic rays also points to a fairly strong field. It seems somewhat difficult to get stable confinement of the cosmic rays with a magnetic field that has an energy density which is much less than that of the cosmic rays.

311

3. If one supposes that magnetic fields have something to do with the expanding arms observed in the central regions of the galaxy, it is obvious that these fields should be strong; the same conclusion would, although with less cogency, follow from other dynamic phenomena, such as the fairly large deviations from the circular velocity which one also observes in the outer regions of the galaxy.

Let us now turn to the indications for a weak field.

1. There are, as Dr. Spitzer has shown, difficulties in connection with problems of star formation in a strong field, and perhaps even more so in connection with the bright rims one sees frequently around dark regions near young stars.

2. The Zeeman effect measurements indicate a very low value of the magnetic flux in interstellar clouds.

3. Finally we have the problem of the origin. I have put it last, but it might very well be the most important argument for the low field. It is indeed much easier to conceive of a mode of origin for a field of a few times 10^{-6} gauss which could be produced by random motions than for a field of 3×10^{-5} gauss. It may be that if one assumes the high field value there is little alternative but to suppose that the field was there when the universe in its present aspect began, although there may also be other possibilities. For example, Dr. Biermann has suggested that in the early phases of the galaxy, when the gas density was much higher and the random motions much larger, a fairly strong field could have been produced. And of course once a field is produced in a galaxy it is very difficult to get rid of it.

Let us now consider some points which eventually may give additional evidence on the magnetic field, but which have not yet been studied well enough. I think that one of the most important points is the question of the Faraday rotation in interstellar space, which one can measure both for features in the halo and, perhaps even more profitably, for extragalactic radio sources. For example it has recently been indicated that the radiation from Vir A is polarized. By measuring the total Faraday rotation for this source one could obtain an estimate of the total Faraday rotation in the galactic halo. As remarked by Dr. Spitzer on the model of the weak tangled field, one would expect the Faraday rotation to be low, while on the basis of the more systematic field the rotation might be higher.

A second point is the question of the matter in the halo. Again at the moment we know very little about this. If in the course of time it will appear that there is quite a bit of matter in the halo with a velocity dispersion that would be insufficient to maintain it there, one could consider that as an indication that magnetic forces are apparently quite important. Similarly, we have the questions of the lag velocity which have been discussed by Dr. Biermann. Again, if we are able to measure the difference in the velocity of the gas and the velocity of the stars better, we might get an impression of how strong the magnetic forces actually are.

Finally there is a point which we have not discussed but which may give at least some indication of the field strength, and that is the question of the shapes of supernova shells, H II regions, and features of that kind. If a supernova, for example, explodes in a region of systematic magnetic field, one would expect that this would produce a certain oblateness, which would depend on the field strength.

In the discussion of the magnetic field we have to consider also the question of the structure and the size of the halo, which are quite important in the interpretation of the observed cosmic-ray electrons. If we suppose that the halo consists of an assembly of sources, then we would have to say that the observed electrons have very little to do with the synchrotron emission which we observe in the halo. If on the other hand the halo is a "true" halo, then these electrons have very much to do with it.

Another important point I should mention here is the question of the rate of ambipolar diffusion. That is essentially the question of how well coupled the magnetic fields are to the neutral gas. The reason I include it today is that Dr. Osterbrock has made some calculations during the last few days on the cross section for elastic collisions between heavy ions and hydrogen atoms. These calculations indicate that this cross section is about 10^{-14} cm^2 at $T = 100°$, between 10 and 100 times larger than the values that have been adopted in some of the discussions.

A point that could also be discussed in a more satisfactory manner is the question of the equilibrium and the formation of the clouds, which may give us information on the nature of the magnetic field.

Mass and Energy Balance

The second point on which there has been some discussion and which I think in the present connection is quite important is the question of the mass and energy balance of the interstellar medium.

In the first place there is the question of what I would call the "useful" turnover rate, that is, the "useful" rate at which stars are converted into gas and back again. The reason I say "useful" is that, as evident from Dr. Schwarzschild's discussion, in the turnover rate there may be included an appreciable amount of gas which spends only a very short time in a star; that fraction would not be very important in questions like how much the gas can move through a spiral-arm field. There the only significant part of the turnover rate is the gas that is released rather far from the place where it condensed into stars. But I think it was especially interesting to hear that the turnover rate we usually have assumed may very well have been estimated much too low.

The second related question is what fraction of the magnetic field goes into the stars, and what kinds of magnetic fields, perhaps tangled fields, come out of the stars again during star formation and stellar mass loss. This, of course, is quite an important thing in connection with the structure of interstellar gas clouds and various other problems. A large turnover rate could have a quite profound influence on the magnetic field in interstellar space.

In connection with the energy balance I would think that at the moment our main uncertainty is the question of whether the cosmic rays participate heavily in the energy balance or not. If cosmic rays are accelerated in interstellar space, they are quite an important sink of energy. If on the other hand most of the cosmic rays are produced in other sources, their effect on the energy balance of the interstellar medium may not be important. There is a possibility that this problem could be settled; if it is true that the cosmic rays are accelerated in interstellar space, there should be quite a difference between the energy spectra of the very heavy ions and those of the protons in the cosmic radiation. I have the impression that some recent measurements, including some satellite measurements, tend to show that the differences in the energy spectra of the protons and the heavy particles are by no means as large as has sometimes been supposed.

Finally there is the question of how much the supernovae contribute to the energy balance of the interstellar medium. I do not think that we have at the moment the data to discuss this properly. We really do not know well enough the masses of the supernovae and the velocity with which the main part of the mass comes out.

Spiral Structure

A third group of problems that have been discussed I have included here under the heading of spiral structure. One problem that has come out a few times in the discussion is that it would be very valuable if we had a clearer picture of the contents of a spiral arm. Before one starts to explain how the spiral arms come about it is good to know what one wants to explain. At the moment we do not have, for example, a clear picture of what the stellar content of the spiral arms is.

A related question is whether the spiral arms one observes in a galaxy keep the same appearance all the time, or whether the same galaxy sometimes has very regular features but at other times quite irregular arms.

As indicated by Dr. Oort these problems may be solved by correlating the general appearance of the spiral arms with the more permanent features in the body of the galaxy. In the same category we can also include a study of the past spiral structure in our own galaxy, a study which appears now possible, by making use of the very accurate ages and distances which can be determined on the basis of the photometry by Dr. Strömgren.

With regard to the theory of spiral structure, I think we have rather clearly to distinguish between the barred spirals and the more axisymmetric systems. I would take the results presented by Dr. Prendergast and by Dr. Lindblad to indicate that if there is a suitable deviation from axial symmetry in the gravitational field of a galaxy, the motion of particles or perhaps of gas clouds in that field tends to produce structures which are very suggestive and which can look very much like spiral structures. Dr. Prendergast started with a very strongly nonaxisymmetric gravitational field. In the discussion of Dr. Lindblad these deviations from axial symmetry are much less, and it is interesting to see that even then one can still get features that resemble spiral arms.

On the other hand I would be somewhat doubtful whether in the axisymmetric systems (which the ordinary spirals seem to be) these phenomena would suffice for the explanation of spiral structure. Presumably we shall have to find an explanation which is also based on gas dynamical and hydromagnetic phenomena. It is frequently assumed that there is some kind of circulation in the spiral arms. I think that one of the points which deserves (presumably) much more consideration than it has been given in the past, and perhaps also during this conference, is the question of the transfer of angular momentum and energy, which seem to produce insurmountable difficulties in many models.

Finally, one of the very important things one would like to settle is whether the expanding arms near the galactic center represent a stationary phenomenon or whether they are rather transient.

In the first case, we really have to find some way to produce large-scale circulation throughout the galactic system; in the second case, we presumably can do without such circulation. The only way to settle this question may be to look at fairly nearby spiral systems and see whether features like these expanding regions are the rule or the exception.

General Discussion (*Prof. J. H. Oort presiding*)

Dr. Oort: Perhaps I might follow the invitation given by Dr. Woltjer and add a few words on the problem of the structure and size of the halo. Let me just remind you of the two main features of the halo. A striking characteristic is that it is so little flattened, but it is perhaps still more striking that it has so little concentration toward the center of the system. If you look at the radiofrequency radiation one can differ about the actual size one wants to give the halo. That depends largely on how much extragalactic continuum radiation you subtract; so whether this has a radius of 9 or 12 kpc is difficult to say at the moment. But the point that I want to make now is that over this whole volume of 9 or 12 kpc radius the density of the radiation coming from a certain element of volume varies so remarkably little. There is some concentration near the center, but it is relatively small. And that is in striking contrast to all that we know about stellar populations. Not only are cluster-type variables, globular clusters, and all these halo population II objects extremely concentrated toward the center, but there is also always a very high density gradient in the outer parts. This divergence between the density distribution of radio emission and of stars has been known from the earliest times when we studied this continuous radiation. In the early paper that Dr. Westerhout and I wrote about it, we worried a great deal that there was no population that in any way resembled what one found in the radiofrequency radiation. If one would take the point of view that the radiation in the halo comes from local sources, say supernovae of some type, then one is confronted with a very severe difficulty, I think, to account for the fact that these sources would show no resemblance whatever in their distribution to anything we know about populations in our own galaxy or in any of the other galaxies. That in my mind is a very strong argument for the idea that the halo field should be a large-scale field connected with the galaxy as a whole. In this connection the existence of quite-large-scale irregularities in the halo is relevant. The big spur near 30° (new) galactic longitude is a major feature of the halo. Now one can of course take the point of view, proposed by Hanbury Brown and Davis, that this would represent the outburst of a supernova very close to the sun. The sun would then be situated just at the rim, so to say, of the supernova shell. I must confess that I find that notion a little bit too much to believe. For one thing, one sees that spur only on one side. One would expect to find that it also continues over the galactic pole on the other side. There may be weak signs of that, but nothing very striking. Moreover, one would also expect to find some optical features connected with it. No such features are known. But this is a point one should investigate, especially in the galactic plane, where you might perhaps expect the most striking optical phenomena. Unless one is willing to accept that hypothesis, one would have to conclude that it is a large-scale feature of the halo. In that case one gets again the impression that the halo field must be a large-scale field connected with the galaxy as a whole. By the way, the contribution of this spur to the halo radiation is quite considerable, about one-half of the total intensity one receives from that region of the halo. It would be difficult to find a way out of the conclusion that this is tied up with a field in the disk, and that the fields in the halo would have to be as strong as has been proposed by Dr. Biermann and Dr. Woltjer, in order to get the amount of radiofrequency radiation with as small an amount of cosmic-ray electrons as you find near the sun.

Dr. Spitzer: If you assume more electrons?

Dr. Oppenheimer: Why aren't they here?

Dr. Oort: That is the difficulty. Could you keep them out?

Dr. Spitzer: Perhaps. With either of these two theories, additional complexities must be introduced to protect the theory. It isn't at all clear what the nature of those complexities can be. For example, with a high field picture you have to introduce complexities to explain why the Zeeman effect is so low; you have to introduce complexities to explain why the various filaments and the collapsing protostars and so on don't look as though they are being formed in a strong field, and why the bright rims look as though they are being formed in a weak field. Similarly, if you take the low field picture you have to introduce complexities to explain why the observed density of relativistic electrons is less than the density of these electrons in the halo, if the halo density found from the observed radio intensity is accepted.

Dr. Oort: You would also have to explain the expanding arms in the central region. That is really very difficult, I think.

Dr. Spitzer: Yes, but we don't really know. Ten years ago if we had been asked to explain the expanding arm we would have blamed it on turbulence, because that was the great uncertainty that we didn't understand; so at the first conference on interstellar gas dynamics in Paris we blamed everything on turbulence.

Dr. Oort: But that was before one had outlined the spiral structure of the gas, and one still thought that the interstellar medium filled the whole galactic disk. The data were not sufficient at that time.

Dr. Field: If there is a fairly powerful magnetic field in the arm at 3 kpc, wouldn't you expect it to be a strong continuum emitter?

Dr. Oort: The field wouldn't be any stronger than the general field in this whole central region. There is some concentration of radiofrequency radiation in the central region, but it is not very strong. I don't think there would be a difficulty there.

Dr. Spitzer: I have the feeling that we still don't understand the behavior of gaseous clouds in the gravitational field of the galaxy. This same conclusion was indicated by those very interesting movies that Dr. Lindblad showed, which suggest that if one made similar computations for actual gas motions one might find similar surprises.

Dr. Oort: That would seem very difficult in the galactic system, because there you know the gravitational fields to a considerable extent, and you know that the masses contained in these particular arms are quite negligible compared with the total mass in the central region.

Dr. Lindblad: Perhaps I could point out in this connection that if you would happen to observe this fairly elongated innermost ring, that I had in one of those cases, from just the right direction, you would observe exactly the kind of phenomenon as you do when you see this expanding arm.

Dr. Oort: Also with velocities of that order?

Dr. Lindblad: No. In this case the velocity of expansion you would observe would be only 15 km/sec instead of 53. But of course I have a force field in the center of the galaxy which deviates probably quite appreciably from the actual force field.

Dr. Oort: You have already had to put a lot of mass into the arms, a lot more than I would admit could be possible in the gaseous arms in the galaxy.

Dr. Lindblad: Yes, but you have a very much bigger concentration toward the center in the galaxy than in the Schmidt model; this might give higher velocities. But these things have to be computed.

Dr. Oort: It is not perhaps entirely excluded, but the fact that one also finds other features with very high velocity near the center makes one think that it is a different phenomenon.

Dr. Lüst: Is it not difficult with these magnetic fields to explain the high degree of symmetry of the galaxy—for instance, why it has only two arms? Wouldn't one have the feeling that something has to be added to explain this? At least I was quite impressed by Dr. Lindblad's pictures, where some kind of instability finally leads to just two arms and not more. If one has just general magnetic fields, why should we have this kind of symmetry?

Dr. Woltjer: In the calculations Dr. Lindblad presented, I think the symmetry was already guaranteed at the outset. With the magnetic field, you can start out from an original galaxy, as some people like to draw it, with one long flux tube. If you wind this up you have two spiral arms, not three or one. Also there are in fact galaxies that appear to have more than two arms.

Dr. Spitzer: How do you then get the expanding arm near the center?

Dr. Woltjer: One has to suppose that the central region does not participate in the spiral structure, so that essentially the magnetic field lines would have to run around the central region. This is also apparent from the inner disk, with the very rapid differential rotation. There can't be much spiral structure in that disk.

Dr. Lüst: Just to clarify my position: I was not thinking that this was the true picture. But if, for instance, it could be shown that the instability postulated by Dr. Lindblad is the most severe one for the gravitational instability, then one would get such a structure.

Dr. Prendergast: I would like to make a comment on Dr. Spitzer's remark that we are probably in for some surprises if we do gas dynamics for the galaxy. We almost certainly are, because as far as I am aware no single problem, not even a stability problem, has been solved in a differentially rotating self-gravitating medium. Even without magnetic fields, and even linearizing the equations, it is very hard to make progress. I am certain that if one ever did one would be in for surprises.

Dr. Field: The difficulty that seems to be running through this discussion is: Is the system a self-gravitating one in the sense that the gas acts on the gas, or is it not?

Dr. Oort: The question is whether in the galaxy, with only 2 or 3 per cent gaseous material—and in the central region even much less—the gas could suffi-ciently disturb the general strong gravitational field of population II.

Dr. Prendergast: If you take figures that were acceptable a year or so ago for the magnetic field, the mean turbulent velocity, and the mean density of the gas in the neighborhood of the sun, and estimate the importance of these terms in the equation of motion of the gas, then it seems that for small-scale irregularities, let's say 500 pc or so, you can forget the self-gravitation of the gas. But for a scale of a few kiloparsec you have to consider the self-gravitation of the gas even if the density is only 1 atom/cm^3.

Dr. Lindblad: Do you not think that the population II or part of the popula-tion II could form some kind of a barred elongated structure in the center which will give perturbations? You can gain some perturbing mass from this.

Dr. Oort: There is so much differential rotation there that I don't see how you could very well maintain a bar in these regions. But perhaps Dr. Prendergast would like to answer.

Dr. Prendergast: I agree completely with Woltjer that it is not at all obvious that the barred spirals have anything whatever to do with the spiral arms in what we call ordinary spirals. The mechanisms might be completely different.

Dr. Oort: Yes, although the two groups merge into one another.

Dr. Spitzer: What would be the velocity of escape from the expanding arm if you considered it just by itself? This is only a way of asking how much mass there is from the gravitational standpoint.

Dr. Oort: At most it would be something of the order of 10 km/sec for the gaseous arm.

Dr. Spitzer: That may very well be the order of magnitude of the random velocities inside the arm. So it is conceivable that, as Dr. Prendergast was saying, the excess gravitational force might have effects on a gas whose random velocity distribution was of that order. I don't think it is fair just to take the excess mass of the gas and say it is very small and therefore that it can't have any effect. You have to look at the gravitational force produced by that excess mass and see if it can have an effect on the gas that is there.

Dr. Oort: Yes, but I don't see that it could have a large-scale effect.

Dr. Osterbrock: With respect to the early phase of the galaxy, Dr. Schwarzschild asked yesterday how big the differences could be if the metal content of the interstellar gas were down by a factor of 100. There are calculations by Savedoff, and also by Daub at Wisconsin, which show that in H II regions the temperature could be up to 3 or 4 times higher than it is now. That is, to 30,000 or 40,000°. So that the velocities of expansion of H II regions could be higher by, say, a factor of 2. In the H I regions if you suppose there is no dust at all—if you have that small a percentage of metals you could presumably think there is no dust, and thus no molecular hydrogen—the only cooling mechanism would be the collisions of electrons with heavy elements; and with a low abundance of those I believe that the cooling times could be quite a bit longer than they are in the H I regions today, say of the order of 10^9 years. So that the dissipation time for collisions between clouds could be quite a bit longer.

Dr. Kahn: Wouldn't you rather think that the dissipation time for the organized energy would be much the same but that the clouds would get warmer as a result of the collisions? In present-day conditions the clouds can radiate away the energy that they gain in collisions, but in the early days of the galaxy they could not. The gas would then have got so hot that the motion would be subsonic.

Dr. Strömgren: Since we are now discussing the early phase I would like to bring up the question of the time scale for the flattening of the system as you find it in the early phase. In his discussion of this question, von Weiszäcker found that to maintain this stage you would have to have a high degree of turbulence and that the turbulence would die down in a relatively short span of time. I think we have to reconsider the question and see if there are possibilities of slowing down the process. The difficulty I have in mind is connected with the formation of the extreme population II stars in an interstellar medium of relatively low average density in a relatively very short time.

Dr. Oort: Have you looked into the difficulties that Hoyle considered when he discussed contraction of the mass of gas in the early stages?

Dr. G. R. Burbidge: I have looked at this problem, but the early phases are extremely difficult. One has this fragmentation process which Hoyle suggests.

But it looks as though this might be stopped and the condensation may in fact lead in some cases to a re-expansion of the system. Again it is not clear exactly how that phase goes.

I would say in connection with what Dr. Strömgren just mentioned that in the work done by Salpeter, Schmidt, and other people on the rate of star formation, it has been assumed that the rate of star formation is a function of density alone, simply because it is very difficult to do anything else. But for example, the temperature is also important in this connection. If one considers that one has a very hot gas in the early stages and a lack of cooling mechanisms, I think the whole picture is perhaps quite different.

Dr. Oort: But you do think that Hoyle's first difficulty, that the contraction was not sufficiently rapid, has been sufficiently resolved? It was the opposite from the difficulty that von Weiszäcker had.

Dr. G. R. Burbidge: I don't think it has been resolved properly.

Dr. Schwarzschild: Might it be useful if we would think a little bit about in which direction observational work (other than what we know is going on) might need to be pressed? There seem to me to be at least three points.

First, statistical theories like turbulence are very much in fashion, but I still think it is nice if you happen to have one particularly neat eddy to study in detail. In this connection it seems to me that Dr. Blaauw's little eddy around h and chi Persei (for which he has given good arguments to believe that it is the most powerful recent producer of bright stars that we have close by) is terribly much worthwhile. If I understand, practically no optical studies have been made parallel to the 21-cm studies of this double cloud. I don't mean that as a criticism. But it seems to me that that is one example where one can go fairly neatly after a separate event of a type that we have often discussed here in a variety of ways.

Next, as to the detailed structure of the interstellar matter, we haven't mentioned at this conference possible opportunities in the infrared. If I understand correctly, the infrared does perhaps not give anything new—although I feel very uneasy in making these statements—compared to the 21-cm radiation, except that the angular resolution is much better.

Dr. Oort: What exactly would you propose to study in the infrared?

Dr. Schwarzschild: Just to look at the intensity in the infrared in those wavelengths at which cooling is supposed to take place, and to see the clouds.

Dr. Kahn: An estimate has been made for a proposed experiment. The idea was to look at the emission from molecular hydrogen, in one of the lines Dr. Spitzer described in his paper. I think it turns out that our present apparatus isn't quite good enough to observe it; but expected intensity is about a factor of 10 too low. Perhaps one might be able to look at molecular hydrogen in absorption against the galactic center.

Dr. Spitzer: Maybe one could look directly at the radiation from the grains.

Dr. Schwarzschild: Finally, my third item—again on the observational side. My impression was that radial motions, although not very large, but also not trivially small, were a very important point, at least in one of the possible pictures for spiral arms. Isn't that a field in which, in extragalactic nebulae, measurements along minor axes could give one much more than has been obtained thus far?

Dr. Oort: Yes, that is certainly one of the most important things. I think it would be extremely interesting to take a galaxy like M 81 and really study it well; I mean measure a lot of emission nebulosities on the minor axis as well as on the major axis and get the whole dynamics properly established. But that is a very large job, and these radial components are small.

Dr. G. R. Burbidge: Yes, and there is a lot of difficulty in sorting out the radial motions. One may get velocity disturbances of other kinds which we showed may very well be interpreted as radial motions unless you are prepared for them. You have to put a number of terms in the assumed rotations.

Dr. Oort: It would be a marginal observational program. But still I think it would be very much worthwhile to take a good spiral galaxy and investigate it in detail.

Dr. Schwarzschild: One would like to choose one with strong, reasonably symmetrical spiral arms with steep angles.

Dr. G. R. Burbidge: All of this. But the primary observational criterion is that there should be plenty of emission.

Dr. Oort: M 81 is good in this respect.

Dr. G. R. Burbidge: Then one has to ask oneself the question of whether one is looking at motions that are essentially above the galactic plane. All I want to say is that it is not yet obvious that when one does a detailed analysis one can make a conclusive statement that we have found radial motion in the plane in the way it is observed in our galaxy.

Dr. Oort: M 33 might be another possibility. But that is so irregular that it would be still more difficult to get an over-all picture that would be meaningful and that would convince you.

Dr. Kahn: What kind of object would you look at for these radial motions?

Dr. Oort: Emission nebulae.

Dr. Kahn: Do they move like normal interstellar matter, or are they affected by the stars?

Dr. G. R. Burbidge: Are they not part of the normal interstellar matter?

Dr. Pottasch: Yes, I think there is evidence that in the H II regions the radial velocity isn't as great as was expected. If you look at the profiles of H_α that Courtès has, they just correspond to a temperature of about 7500°, and this doesn't leave so much room for motion. If the gas temperature is 6000°, you may have motions in the H II region of the order of 5 km/sec at most.

Dr. Oort: So much the better, for our purpose. Speaking of Courtès, he has observed little wisps of nebulosity with high velocities near the center of our galaxy. If they really belonged to the central part of the galaxy one would wonder whether they could give us some information on the chemical composition there. That would be an interesting observation by itself, because it would bring up again the problem of the mixing from the central to the outer regions. These nebulae are very faint, so I don't know whether it would be observationally possible to do this.

Dr. Pottasch: It is very difficult to determine the chemical composition from these things, because it is impossible to get an electron temperature.

Dr. Woltjer: Do the low expansion rates that Dr. Pottasch mentioned indicate that one has to confine them by a magnetic field?

Dr. Kahn: No. Goldsworthy gives cases with velocities of that order and he did not include magnetic fields.

Dr. Oort: Returning to Professor Schwarzschild's last question—that one should really go after observations that would be planned so as to give a little more information on the really essential problems—I am very much in agreement with him. One of the evident difficulties is the enormous irregularity in the spiral structure in any system, and in particular in our own. So one should certainly try this kind of work in a good spiral system where one can see the structure as a whole.

One would like to have an idea of how much mass, or how much light, is concentrated in the arms, and how the light concentration is situated with respect to the emission nebulae, for instance. And one would like to do this in various colors. The observations are complicated by the irregularity characteristic of all spiral structure and by the absorbing material. I wonder how definite the conclusions would be that one could draw. Yet I feel that one should certainly try to make a good attack on this problem.

Dr. E. M. Burbidge: I agree with you, it is very important. I think an attack should be made, and I think one should try a program such as the one you have suggested. I might just mention that observations have been obtained last fall on NGC 253 for the purpose of checking on radial flow, but the spectra have not yet been measured.

Dr. Kahn: May I come back to the last thing Dr. Burbidge mentioned in his talk, namely, the hypothesis that radio galaxies are caused by supernovae within these galaxies. Would one not expect a large amount of luminosity from the supernovae?

Dr. G. R. Burbidge: At the time that this occurs, yes. Perhaps a source like Cygnus A is such an object today. I mean if one supposed such a thing, one has to ask is Cygnus A in fact something like M 32, which is in the process of going through such a stage. A tremendous amount of the light we see in an object like Cygnus A, and in this very distant source (3 C 295)—which Minkowski has assumed is similar to Cygnus A—is in the emission lines. I think in the distant one he estimates that something like 30 per cent of the output is in $\lambda 3727$. So one would think that there would be a tremendous increase in light. One doesn't know what fraction of that would get into the emission lines, into the forbidden lines, and in the Lyman region, of course.

Dr. Oort: It should have happened some time ago in Cygnus A because it is so large.

Dr. G. R. Burbidge: It depends on what you want to assume about the rate at which it has been propagated.

Dr. Oort: I quite agree with the tendency of the remarks that Dr. Burbidge made on the collisional processes for radio sources, but at the same time one must add, I think, that there is this Perseus source, NGC 1275, in which one has all the evidence, so to say before one's eyes, that a collision is going on. That is not an exceedingly strong radio source, but still it is one.

Dr. G. R. Burbidge: The evidence one has is that there is a large velocity of one region relative to another. I think that it is hard to distinguish two interacting galaxies there. If one says that the velocity difference is the important point, all I would argue is that whatever mechanism gives rise to a large flux of very high energy particles in the radio source might also give rise to this large velocity.

Dr. Strömgren: I would like to return to the question of possible future observations, in particular the very difficult ones. We have, of course, come to rely on the 21-cm work for information of the distant parts of the spiral structure. But I wonder if one might perhaps try to supplement this with observations, in the optical range, of quite distant and extremely reddened B stars. This problem has more of a future now that the work of Westerhout indicates the location of very large H II regions at great distances, where we see nothing optically. If one asks the question of the exciting stars in such regions, unobserved until now in the optical region, but inferred from the 5- or 10-cm work, the first conclusion is that the exciting stars which must be there must presumably look to us as extremely red stars, stars seen through perhaps 10 or 12 magnitudes of absorption. In the case of one of the strong Westerhout regions (No. 43) a search was actually made for these stars, and the brightest of the possible candidates was measured by Kron and Mayall, who found it to be the reddest star they have measured. I have since had an opportunity to take a 48-inch plate of the region and have found a nest of red stars. This doesn't prove the point, of course, but if one could go further and compare this phenomenon with other Westerhout regions, or, even better, obtain UBV photometry, one could perhaps decide whether or not such a search is worthwhile. The best of all would be to get a good spectrum of some of the very red stars in question. The star that I referred to is 15^m visual, and a perfectly feasible object with the 200-inch telescope. One would then have, in a number of distant H II regions, the stellar radial velocities, and also spectroscopic distances with admittedly large linear uncertainties. One would further obtain a kind of a mapping of the interstellar reddening at large distances.

Dr. Pottasch: You should easily be able to recognize stars with H II regions between them and us by looking for the λ10830 line of helium. If in an H II region we should have enough helium in the 2 triplet S state, you should see a sharp interstellar absorption line.

Dr. Strömgren: Yes, I think that might be a very nice feature to look for. One would also expect the λ4430 line, or, better, the corresponding diffuse feature in the red, to be very much strengthened.

Dr. Oort: There is no doubt, I think, that with proper radio equipment one will be able to locate accurately H II regions over the whole galactic system and get a more or less complete catalogue of all H II regions, of the order of the Orion nebula and larger, out to the farthest distances in the galactic system.

Dr. Strömgren: This changes the whole outlook. If you know a small region in which to look it is of course much easier to find the early type of stars in question.

Dr. Pottasch: The λ10830 line would also give you the possibility of obtaining the velocity.

Dr. Biermann: I would like to return to the difficulty of accounting for the change of angular momentum in a stationary theory of the spiral arms. I tried to make an estimate on the basis of the figures given by Professor Oort. If we say that we have for stationary conditions a streaming motion along the arm with, say, 10 or 20 km/sec, and an angle of inclination of, say, 5° or 10° or so, then that means that the radial displacement is something of the order of only, say, 2 km/sec, and thus very slow. Then, combining the radial displacement with the tangential velocity and with the density, we get something of the order of 10^{-11} dyne/cm². If I take for the density 10^{-23} g/cm³ for the whole spiral arm I get a third or so of 10^{-10} dyne/cm². So it would appear that in the disk itself a magnetic field of the stronger variety would indeed be sufficient to transmit the angular momentum and to guarantee a stationary character of the observed features. The same would be true of the halo.

We should now complete the picture of this circulation. The circulation velocity will also be small in the halo, where the density is smaller but the cross section larger. The resulting circulation pattern is in some respects reminding us of that which the sun might have, if we accept one of the current pictures of the cycle of solar activity. We get for the whole period of circulation a time that is very long, of the order of some billion years (10^{17} sec), which I think is reasonable. It is really quite large compared with a period of rotation, so large that we might have a not strictly stationary state. I will not go into further details. I just wanted to say that in this framework it doesn't seem quite impossible to account for the change of angular momentum of rotation.

Dr. Spitzer: In this glass-tube theory of spiral arms the gas has to give up energy as it goes in, in addition to giving up angular momentum. How does one do that either with or without magnetic fields?

Dr. Oort: This is again a very slow process, of course.

Dr. Biermann: I haven't tried to estimate this particular point because I thought the angular momentum was somewhat more difficult.

Dr. Spitzer: Isn't that much easier in a way, because if you have rigid lines of force, the material as it comes in keeps pushing against those lines of force and will deform them, and so it is quite easy to transfer the angular momentum to the magnetic field. How do you contrive so that at each point along the flow the gas is moving at circular velocity?

Dr. Biermann: That will come almost automatically by the dynamics, the magnetic fields tending to make the rotation of the figure, that is to say the angular velocity of rotation, rather uniform.

Dr. Spitzer: How does it give up its energy as it comes in? Are the lines of force linked to it or, if it is just moving along the lines of force, how does the magnetic field affect it?

Dr. Biermann: As pointed out, the energy moves so slowly that I wouldn't imagine you would have insurmountable difficulties on that account (10^{14} ergs/g divided by 10^{17} sec $\to 10^{-3}$ erg/g/sec).

Dr. Woltjer: I was somewhat doubtful about the parallelism Dr. Biermann drew between the circulation in the star and in the interstellar medium. Isn't one of the basic features in the star that the material is able to withstand an appreciable pressure gradient, while in the interstellar case you have no pressure that can push matter out of the plane or decelerate it when it moves inward? You don't have a continuous fluid of the kind you have in a star.

Dr. Biermann: I was referring to the sun only as far as the kinematic features are concerned. I fully recognize that when you fix attention to the dynamics there are very important differences.

Dr. Oort: And the pressure would be put in in some unknown way. If you want to put the matter back into the halo, you have to put in some processes that would act like a pressure.

Dr. Woltjer: Then you invoke a quite different mechanism from the one that you have in rotating systems normally.

Dr. Oort: I wouldn't exclude the possibility that the supernovae could do this.

Dr. Woltjer: I would indeed agree with Professor Spitzer that this is an essential difficulty of the glass-tube model. Why should the gas remain at the circular velocity? It is not at all obvious that this can be done.

Dr. Biermann: One might consider that you can get the circulation going only in those places in which the magnetic field is able to transfer the angular momentum. That is to say, where the magnetic field is not acting you simply can't do it. And that, therefore, might explain the not really regular character of the whole feature.

Dr. Prendergast: One can look into the question of transfer of angular momentum with the aid of Woltjer's exact integrals for the axisymmetric hydromagnetic problem. It seemed to me that the magnetic field needed was much larger than one would like to think, even larger than Woltjer would like to think.

Dr. Lüst: May we come back to the magnetic fields. As a reason for a high magnetic field you gave the cosmic rays. I think that they lead only to fields of the order of 5×10^{-6}.

Dr. Woltjer: In the halo. On my model you have 7×10^{-6} in the halo but four times as much in the disk. This ratio of four which Dr. Biermann, Dr. Davis, and I determined is a consequence of the difference of a factor of 10 in the radio-frequency emission per unit of volume between the spiral arms and the halo.

Dr. Field: Is it certain that the electron density based on the 11 electrons that have been observed at the earth's surface is everywhere the same throughout the galaxy?

Dr. Woltjer: From the evidence on the chemical composition of the cosmic rays it follows that at least the ions have a certain ability to travel around through the galactic system. They cannot remain very long in the spiral arm because after more than 10^6 years you would already get in trouble with the composition. I would think that if the comic rays can travel fairly well from region to region, then the electrons of the same rigidity should be able to do so, too.

Dr. Field: Is it ruled out that one couldn't have, say, five times as many electrons in the disk as in the halo?

Dr. Woltjer: I think that would be very difficult.

Dr. Field: Certainly the assumption of uniform density is the simplest one. I am not sure it leads unambiguously to the magnetic field strength that you assume.

Dr. Woltjer: The assumption of uniform density is a thing which you know to be strictly true if there is free communication between different parts of the field and sufficient randomization of the moments of the particles in the region of low field.

Dr. Field: This free communication is the question at issue, it seems to me.

Dr. Biermann: But you see a very high degree of isotropy. I think that is quite a strong argument in favor of our picture.

Dr. Field: I would like to point out that the Van Allen particles in the magnetic field of the earth have a high degree of isotropy. But if you move over one field line there are no particles at all. The argument depends very critically on the various lines in question being connected, it seems to me.

Dr. Woltjer: Right. There is, for example, evidence that in the central region of the galaxy you have a region—the radio source Sgr A—which does not freely communicate with the rest of the galaxy. You can show that the density of relativistic electrons there has to be higher than it is near the sun.

Dr. G. R. Burbidge: Doesn't this depend on what you assume for the magnetic field in the center?

Dr. Woltjer: You can't assume too high a field there because you are limited by dynamical considerations.

Dr. Spitzer: You could assume that there are magnetic mirrors between one region and another, and that you get a lot of trapped particles in one region.

Dr. Woltjer: The isotropy tends to be destroyed fairly easily.

Dr. Spitzer: There could be a small "forbidden cone"; particles with velocity vectors in directions outside this cone would be confined.

Dr. Woltjer: Shouldn't you see that on earth?

Dr. Spitzer: I don't know. There would be two directions in which no relativistic electrons were moving, but the radiation emitted should not be much affected.

Dr. Biermann: You have to assume some scattering in any case, as would be done by magnetic shock fronts, for instance. These are known to be very narrow, so they can really do it.

Dr. Spitzer: You wouldn't expect shock fronts on a strong field theory, because all the velocities are so subsonic.

Dr. Oppenheimer: I think there are weaknesses in the electron argument. But that is really because so few have been seen that one doesn't know whether they have anything to do with cosmic rays or not. I think it is a little harder to imagine that there are many more electrons in the halo than there are around the sun. But that there should be many fewer would not seem to me surprising.

Index

Index

Page numbers in italics refer to the discussions.